New Linear Polymers

HENRY LEE
Technical Director

DONALD STOFFEY
Director of Chemical Research

KRIS NEVILLE
Program Manager

Research & Development Center
The Epoxylite Corporation, South El Monte, Calif.

New Linear Polymers

McGRAW – HILL
BOOK COMPANY

New York
San Francisco
Toronto
London
Sydney

New Linear Polymers

Preface

The middle 1960s has marked a sudden upsurge in the development and commercial introduction of new linear polymers. Within a single year, a dazzling array of new materials is being offered American industry with the promise of more to come.

The new materials, molding compounds, coatings, laminating matrices, adhesives, foams, are both like and unlike the familiar ones. Their introduction over a very short period has resulted in understandable confusion: What, chemically are the new polymers; what can be expected of them; what are they best suited for?

Few workers have time to keep abreast of all the plastics development; and the widely scattered, and in some cases, virtually inaccessible literature of the new technology poses particularly difficult problems for those who must remain conversant with new developments. The absence of a readily available, single source describing the features of these new engineering materials has prompted the writing of this book.

This is an introduction to the chemistry and technology of ten new commercial plastics: polyimides, polyamide-imides, polyester-imides, aromatic polyamides, polycyclamides, polybenzimidazoles, polyphenylene oxides, polysulfones, poly(p-xylylenes), and phenoxies.

The new linear polymers are described, and extensive property data on the commercial materials are listed. Existing and potential uses for the new materials are enumerated, and they are compared with themselves and with other plastics.

The information, thus, is both timely, as timely as the requirements of the book publication permit, and yet hopefully, in the broader sense, of more lasting interest.

In the preparation of this volume, we are indebted to a number of people for their kind comments and criticisms of individual chapters. Although, for these reviews, we have sought out acknowledged experts in each particular field, we cannot absolve ourselves for any errors of fact or opinion: these are ours, and not those of the reviewers.

We wish, therefore, to thank the following:

Dr. Harold H. Chen of Aerospace Corporation

Elliott N. Dorman of Ciba Products Company

James E. Freeman of Westinghouse Electric Corporation

Dr. William F. Gorham of Union Carbide Corporation

H. P. Henriques of Union Carbide Corporation

Dr. James E. Horan of Amoco Chemical Company

Ralph Huff of Calitone Chemical Company

Dr. J. Idris Jones of National Physical Laboratories, England

H. H. Levine, Narmco Research & Development, a Division of
    Whittaker Corporation

D. L. McClenahan of Schenectady Chemicals, Inc.

John T. Milek of Hughes Aircraft Corporation

T. G. Nock of Shell Chemical Company

M. N. Paul of Union Carbide Corporation

R. T. Schwartz, Air Force Materials Laboratory, WPAFB

Charles Segal of Rocketdyne

Donald F. Smith of Hughes Aircraft Corporation

Robert C. Witt of The Dow Chemical Company

J. M. Witzel of General Electric Company

We are particularly indebted to Mr. John Milek of Hughes Aircraft
Corporation for making available to us, in advance of publication, a copy
of his excellent State-of-the-Art Survey on the Aromatic Polyimides.
Additionally, we wish to thank Mr. Reginal Talley of UCLA. For typing
the manuscript, with all its vexing chemical structures and tables, we
are indebted to the irreplaceable Mrs. Marion Stocker of The Epoxylite
Corporation. And finally, we owe a large debt of gratitude to our
publishers, who have been unfailingly considerate and helpful.

Henry Lee
Donald Stoffey
Kris Neville

Contents

1

Introduction

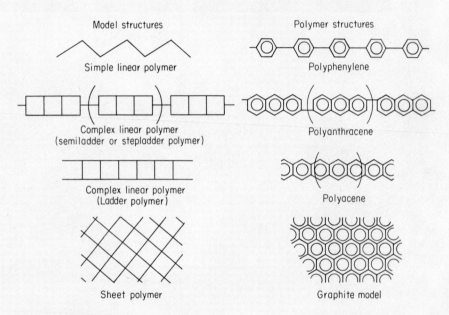

Model structures   Polymer structures

Simple linear polymer   Polyphenylene

Complex linear polymer   Polyanthracene
(semiladder or stepladder polymer)

Complex linear polymer   Polyacene
(Ladder polymer)

Sheet polymer   Graphite model

FIG 1.1 *Definition of linear and ladder polymers. Note that these terms supplement to some degree and replace the older terms "thermoplastics" and "thermosetting."* (**G. F. Pezdirtz** [10-37]).

*T*his book is concerned with 10 new, commercially available polymers or polymer classes which we designate as belonging to the linear polymer class. By *linear polymers* we are referring to resins or polymers which are linear in structure, and which contain no crosslinking, as shown in Fig. 1.1. In using the term linear polymer, we are bypassing the term thermoplastic, since, in the conventional sense, thermoplastic polymers are meltable or fusible. The polymers we describe in this book are, in only a few cases, thermoplastic in the conventional sense. Most of the new complex linear polymers, once formed or applied, are essentially infusible, because of their ring structures.

The 10 new linear polymers share a number of features. (1) They have all become commercially available only in the mid-1960s. (2) They are linear polymers which contain hetero atoms (e.g., noncarbon atoms) as well as carbon atoms in the polymer chain, except for the xylylenes which have an all-carbon back-bone. (3) They all contain cyclic structures, either cyclohexanes, aromatic groups, or heterocyclic structures, in the polymer chain, making them complex linear polymers.

Some of the polymers could be further defined as semiladder or stepladder polymers. In a few instances, evidence indicates that some crosslinking does incidentally occur. This, as such, is treated in the appropriate sections of the book, but, in the main, we believe that the concept of linear polymers is the valid underlying concept which relates to the 10 polymer types in this book.

The molecular structure of the 52 principal types of linear polymers or resins commercially available today are outlined in Tables 1.1 through 1.4. Table 1.1 presents the structure of those having only aliphatic carbon atoms in the polymer chain. Table 1.2 presents the structure of those polymers having aliphatic carbon atoms and hetero atoms (oxygen, nitrogen, and silicon) in the polymer chain. Table 1.3 presents the structure of those polymers having hetero atoms and aromatic carbon atoms in their backbone, in addition to aliphatic carbons. Table 1.4 presents the structure of the 10 new linear polymers discussed in this book.

In these tables, we have presented the polymers in expanded form showing more than one repeating unit, generally, so that the reader obtains a better view of the spatial and linear nature of these polymers.

These tables are presented as a reference at this point so that the reader may compare the structures of all these polymers, and draw various generalizations. The chief generalizations to be drawn from Tables 1.1 to

3

TABLE 1.1 Commercially Available Linear Polymers Having Only Carbon-to-Carbon Bonds in the Main Chain

Polyethylene (T_g $-120°$C)	
Polypropylene (T_g $-18°$C)	
Poly(ethylene–vinyl acetate)	
Natural rubber (*cis*-1,4-Polyisoprene) (T_g $-73°$C)	
Gutta-percha (*trans*-1,4-Polyisoprene)	
Orlon (Polyacrylonitrile) (T_g 104, 130°C)	
Poly(vinyl fluoride)	
Saran (Polyvinylidene chloride) (T_g $-17°$C)	

TABLE 1.1 (*continued*)

Polyvinylidene fluoride (T_g −35°C)	structure
Kel-F, Fluorothene (Polymonochlorotrifluoroethylene) (T_g 45°C)	structure
Teflon (Polytetrafluoroethylene) (T_g 126°C)	structure
Viton (Copolymers of vinylidene fluoride and hexafluoropropylene)	structure
Neoprene [Polychloroprene or poly(2-chloro-1,3-butadiene)] (T_g −50°C)	structure
ABS (Acrylonitrile-butadiene-styrene)	structure
Polyvinylbutyral (T_g 49°C)	structure

TABLE 1.1 (*continued*) **Commercially Available Linear Polymers Having Only Carbon-to-Carbon Bonds in the Main Chain**

TPX [Poly(4-methylpentene-1)] (T_g 29°C)	
Polystyrene	
Poly(vinyl chloride) (T_g 87°C)	
Poly(vinyl acetate) (T_g 29°C)	
Poly(vinyl alcohol) (T_g 85°C)	
Poly-α-methylstyrene	

TABLE 1.1 (*continued*)

Buna S (Butadiene-styrene copolymer)	$\begin{array}{ccccc} & \overset{H}{C} & \overset{H_2}{C} & & \overset{H_2}{C} \\ & & & \overset{H}{C} & \\ \diagdown\;C & C & & \overset{}{C} & \diagup \\ H_2 & H & & \bigcirc & \end{array}$
Lucite, Plexiglas (Polymethylmethacrylate)	$\begin{array}{cccc} CH_3\;\overset{H_2}{C} & CH_3\;\overset{H_2}{C} & CH_3\;\overset{H_2}{C} & CH_3 \\ \diagdown C & C & C & C \diagup \\ C{=}O & C{=}O & C{=}O & C{=}O \\ O & O & O & O \\ CH_3 & CH_3 & CH_3 & CH_3 \end{array}$
Polymethacrylate	$\begin{array}{cccc} \overset{H_2}{C} & \overset{H_2}{C} & \overset{H_2}{C} & \\ H\;\overset{}{C} & H\;\overset{}{C} & H\;\overset{}{C} & H \\ \diagdown C\diagup & C\diagup & C\diagup & C \\ C{=}O & C{=}O & C{=}O & C{=}O \\ O & O & O & O \\ CH_3 & CH_3 & CH_3 & CH_3 \end{array}$
Methyl-α-cyanoacrylate (Eastman 910)	$\begin{array}{cccc} \overset{H_2}{C}\;CN & \overset{H_2}{C}\;CN & \overset{H_2}{C}\;CN & \overset{H_2}{C}\;CN \\ C & C & C & C \\ C{=}O & C{=}O & C{=}O & C{=}O \\ O & O & O & O \\ CH_3 & CH_3 & CH_3 & CH_3 \end{array}$
Poly(acrylamide)	$\begin{array}{ccc} \overset{H_2}{C} & \overset{H_2}{C} & \overset{H_2}{C} \\ H\;\overset{}{C} & H\;\overset{}{C} & H \\ \diagdown C\diagup & C\diagup & C \\ C{=}O & C{=}O & C{=}O \\ NH_2 & NH_2 & NH_2 \end{array}$
Copolymer of styrene and maleic anhydride	$\begin{array}{ccc} & \overset{H_2}{C} & \overset{H}{C} \\ H\;\overset{}{C} & H\;\overset{}{C} & \\ \diagdown C & C & \diagup \\ \bigcirc & \underset{O}{C}\;{-}O{-}\;\underset{O}{C} & \end{array}$

TABLE 1.1 (*continued*) **Commercially Available Linear Polymers Having Only Carbon-to-Carbon Bonds in the Main Chain**

Copolymer of methyl vinyl ether and maleic anhydride	
Poly(methyl vinyl ether)	

TABLE 1.2 **Commercially Available Linear Aliphatic Heterochain Polymers**

Delrin (Polyformaldehyde)	
Penton (Chlorinated polyether)	
Polyethylene glycol	

TABLE 1.2 (*continued*)

Polypropylene glycol	(structure)
Perlon U (1,4-Butanediol and hexamethylene diisocyanate)	(structure)
Nylon 66 (T_g 50°C)	(structure)
Nylon 6	(structure)
Polydimethylsiloxane (T_g −123°C)	(structure)
Poly(methylphenyl-siloxane)	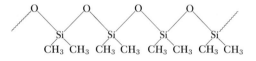
Poly(methylvinyl-siloxane)	(structure)

TABLE 1.3 Commercially Available Aromatic Linear Polymers

Mylar, Dacron (Polyethylene terephthalate) (T_g 69°C)	(chemical structure)
Lectra (Polycarbonate) (T_g 150°C)	(chemical structure)
Spandex polyurethane fibers (Lycra)	(chemical structure)
Nitroso rubber	(chemical structure)

1.4, of course, are that divalent atoms, such as oxygen, which provide a high degree of freedom of rotation to polymer chain segments, produce a marked decrease in glass transition temperature (T_g, i.e., second-order transition temperature). On the other hand, rigid, ringlike structures, as present in linear polymers and ladder polymers, shown in Fig. 1.1, resist chain rotation—and bending—and thus produce polymers with very high glass points and still higher melting points.

In addition to the evidence of this fact, shown by the glass points reported in Tables 1.1 to 1.4 for commercial polymers, the melting-point-range data shown in Fig. 1.2 and in Tables 1.5 and 1.6 for a variety of chiefly experimental polymer types present evidence of the wide variation in glass point or melting point that can be achieved in even minor structural changes which prohibit free-chain segment rotation.

In general, it is easy to visualize that polymers with more and more cyclic structure in their chains tend to be stiffer and more resistant to deformation. Chain segments which permit segmental rotation become

TABLE 1.4   New Linear Polymers

Phenoxy	
Polyphenylene oxide (Poly-2,6-dimethylphenylene oxide)	
Poly(p-xylylene)	
Aromatic polysulfone	
Alicyclic polyamide	
Aromatic polyamide (Nomex)	
Aromatic polyamide-imide	
Aromatic polyimide	
Polybenzimidazole	

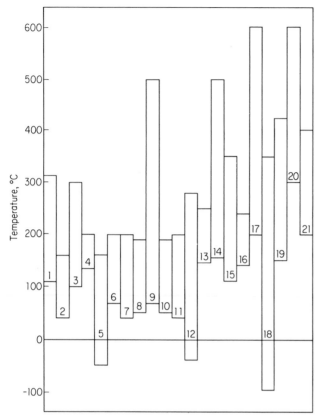

FIG 1.2 *Intervals of melting or softening points of different polymer classes* [1]. *(1) Polymeric hydrocarbons; (2) polymeric chloroderivatives; (3) polymeric fluoroderivatives; (4) polymeric alcohols; (5) polymeric vinyl esters (simple); (6) polymeric vinyl esters (complex); (7) polymeric acrylic esters; (8) polymeric dienes; (9) polyphenylenes; (10) polyesters, simple; (11) polyacetals; (12) complex polyesters; (13) polycarbonates; (14) polyarylates; (15) polyamides; (16) polyurethanes; (17) polybenzimidazoles; (18) polysiloxanes; (19) polychelates; (20) polypyrromellitimides; (21) polypyrazoles.*

fewer and fewer as the cyclic back-bone is increased and as flexibilizing divalent atoms such as oxygen are eliminated. Hence, the melting points go up higher and higher than those of older resins, and the glass transition temperatures go up also (Fig. 1.3). Solubility decreases. Deformation under load at elevated temperature decreases. Because there are no cross-linking primary valence bonds, the polymer chain usually can slide and slip so as to absorb stresses, with toughness then becoming a characteristic.

The aromatic and heterocyclic rings contribute to high resonance energies and thus high heat resistance, and in the polyimides and polybenzimidazoles,

TABLE 1.5   Effect of Rings in Chains on Polymer Melting Point [1]

Structure	Melting or softening point
$-CH_2-CH_2-CH_2-CH_2-CH_2-CH_2-$	115
$-\!\langle\bigcirc\rangle\!-$	530
$-\!\langle\bigcirc\rangle\!-CH_2-CH_2-$	380
$-O(CH_2)_2OCO(CH_2)_6CO-$	45
$-O(CH_2)_3OCO-\!\langle\bigcirc\rangle\!-CO-$	264
$-O-\!\langle\bigcirc\rangle\!-OCO(CH_2)_6CO-$	225
$-O-\!\langle\bigcirc\rangle\!-OCO-\!\langle\bigcirc\rangle\!-CO-$	500
$-O-\!\langle\bigcirc\rangle\!-OCO(CH_2)_3CO-$	172
$-NH(CH_2)_6NHCO(CH_2)_6CO-$	235
$-NH(CH_2)_6NHCO-\!\langle\bigcirc\rangle\!-CO-$	350 decomposes
$-O(CH_2)_2OCO(CH_2)_{12}CO-$	80
$-O(CH_2)_2OCO-\!\langle\bigcirc\rangle\!\langle\bigcirc\rangle\!-CO-$	330
$-OCH_2-\!\langle\bigcirc\rangle\!-CH_2-OCO-\!\langle\bigcirc\rangle\!-CO-$ (cyclohexane ring)	238
$-OCH_2-\!\langle\bigcirc\rangle\!-CH_2-OCO-\!\langle\bigcirc\rangle\!-CO-$ (benzene ring)	290
$-HN-\!\langle\bigcirc\rangle\!-NHCO(CH_2)_4CO-$ (aromatic)	258
$-HN-\!\langle\bigcirc\rangle\!-NHCO(CH_2)_4CO-$ (trans)	300
$-HN-\!\langle\bigcirc\rangle\!-NHCO(CH_2)_4CO-$ (cis)	165

TABLE 1.5   (continued)

Structure	Melting or softening point
—NH(CH$_2$)$_6$NHCO(CH$_2$)$_4$CO—	250

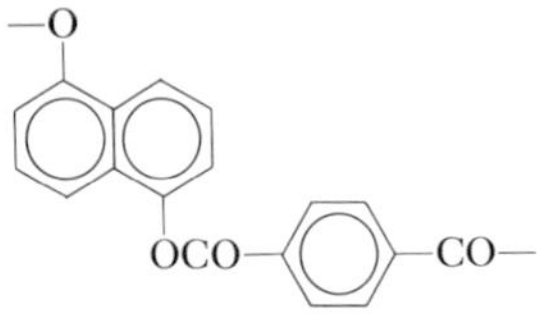

630 decomposes

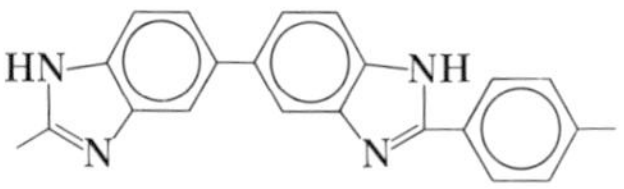

600

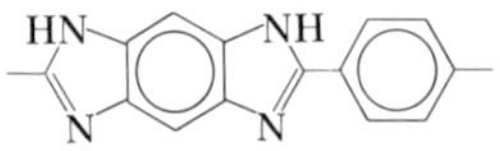

500

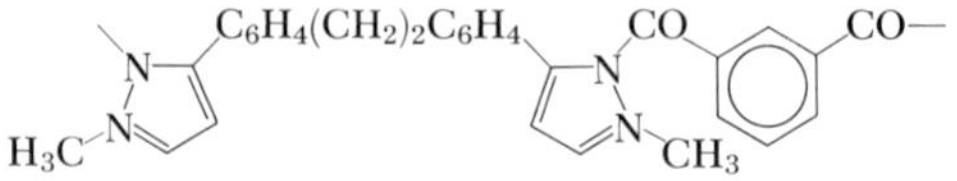

280

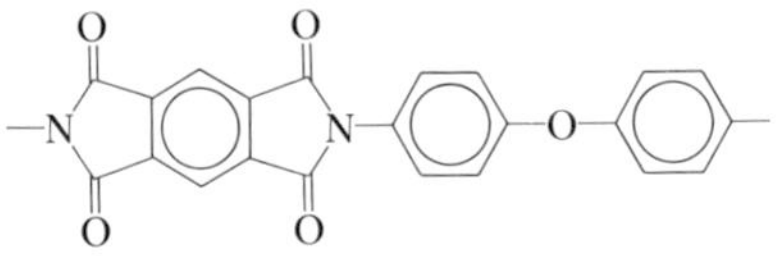

400

where no atoms are present that are not part of an aromatic or heterocyclic ring, or are otherwise stabilized by resonance considerations, extreme thermal stability is realized.

The properties and description of each of these new polymers is the subject of a separate chapter, such that each chapter is a complete, self-contained, and independent review of a particular new polymer or polymer type.

We have arranged the chapters on the basis of a logic which appeals to us—we took what was essentially a very high molecular-weight epoxy resin (i.e., phenoxy, see Table 1.4) and then started substituting into the chain in a stepwise manner to see which resin type seemed to follow next on a structural basis.

Thus, phenoxy gives us a polymer with some of the properties of an epoxy resin, wherein we trade thermoplastics processability for an upper service temperature of 100°C, instead of the 250°C we have come to expect for crosslinked epoxy resins.

TABLE 1.6 Effect of Isomerism of Substitution in Rings on the Polymer Melting Point [1]

Structure	Melting or softening point
—CO—⬡—CONH(CH$_2$)$_6$NH—	350
—CO—⬡ CONH(CH$_2$)$_6$NH—	150
—CO CONH(CH$_2$)$_6$NH— ⬡	50
—CO—⬡—COO(CH$_2$)$_2$—O—	256
—CO—⬡ COO(CH$_2$)$_2$O—	103
—CO COO(CH$_2$)$_2$O— ⬡	63
—CO—⬡—⬡—CONH(CH$_2$)$_6$NH—	360
—CO—⬡—⬡ CONH(CH$_2$)$_6$NH—	140
⬡—⬡ —CO CONH(CH$_2$)$_6$NH—	142

By removing the aliphatic glyceryl portion of the epoxy resin, one arrives at aromatic polysulfone and polyphenylene oxide. Or by eliminating the ether oxygen atoms in favor of an aliphatic chain between the aromatic rings, one arrives at poly-*p*-xylylene.

Substituting nitrogen for oxygen in the polymer chain, one arrives at the aromatic and alicyclic polyamides.

Once into the nitrogen class, the door is opened to the heterocyclics; and

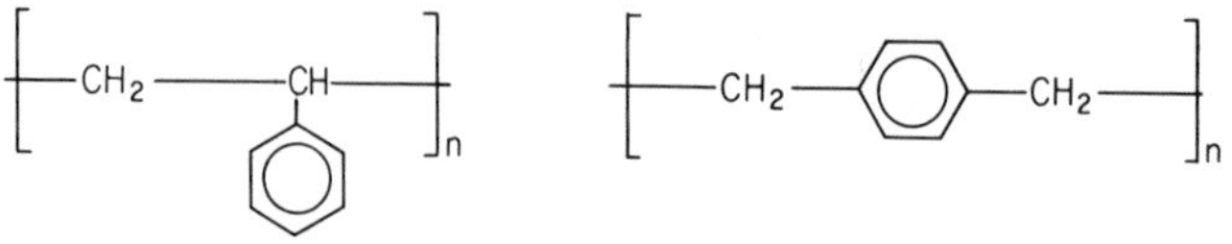

Isotactic poly(styrene)
m.p. 240°C

Poly(*p*-xylylene)
m.p. > 400°C

FIG 1.3 *Comparison of melting points of two polymers having same ratio of aliphatic to aromatic carbon atoms showing effect of locating aromatic ring in the polymer chain.*

the poly(amide-imides), poly(ester-imides), polyimides, and polybenzimidazoles become logical steps.

In conclusion, we have added a survey of research polymers to illustrate the wide range of possibilities which are undergoing study at the frontiers of polymer chemistry and physics, and to outline what may still lie ahead.

REFERENCES

1964

1. V. V. Korshak and Ye. S. Krongauz, Advances in the Synthesis of Heat-resistant Polymers, *Usp. Khim.* **33**(12):1409. (English translation: AD 482 302.)

2

Phenoxy Resins

The commercial phenoxy resins are produced from the reaction product of epichlorohydrin and bisphenol A. They are supplied in molecular weights ranging from 15,000 to 40,000. The lower-molecular-weight species are available as 100 percent solids and are suitable for use as molding compounds and adhesive films, and in solution coatings. The higher-molecular-weight species are available in solution only and are primarily used in coatings applications.

In coatings, the phenoxy resins may be used in the unmodified form to provide thermoplastic coatings with excellent adhesion and good ambient temperature resistance to chemical environments. The coatings may be modified through esterification to obtain other air-drying systems or may be crosslinked with a variety of other resinous compounds to obtain films of overall improved properties.

The largest present application for the phenoxy coatings is as primers for automotive, marine, and heavy industrial applications.

*P*henoxy resins, an outgrowth of the epoxy resin technology, are developed from the reaction of epichlorohydrin and dihydric phenols.

Like the epoxy resins, the first phenoxies were synthesized in the early 1930s, but their importance was not appreciated until after World War II.

Production of phenoxy resins for films and fibers was reported as early as 1949 [1]. These were obtained by either a one- or a two-step synthesis route. Concurrently, in the late 1940s, research was being conducted by several workers to produce higher-molecular-weight epoxy resins by a two-step synthesis, the extension of which logically resulted in the development of the commercial phenoxy resins.

In 1961, phenoxy resin solutions were introduced in the United States for coatings applications by Shell Chemical Company. Subsequently, Union Carbide Plastics Company offered solutions, films, and granular molding compounds. By 1965, nearly all the major United States epoxy resin producers were supplying phenoxy resin solutions in various molecular-weight grades. Union Carbide Plastics Company, although discontinuing its production of film, remained the sole supplier of the molding compounds.

The phenoxy resins offer an interesting introduction to the new linear polymers. They bridge the gap between the thermosetting and the thermoplastic fields, being used commercially in both forms. Their technology serves to suggest the technology of the remaining polymers described in this volume.

SYNTHESIS

The phenoxy resins, as a class, may be represented by the following idealized structure

Phenoxy resin from epichlorohydrin and bisphenol A

The synthesis is accomplished by reacting the dihydric phenol and the epichlorohydrin in the presence of a caustic. In theory, any dihydric phenol, or any combination of dihydric phenols, may be employed. In practice, the most commonly used precursor is bisphenol A.

19

Atom model of phenoxy resin from epichlorohydrin and bisphenol A. (The Epoxylite Corporation.)

The properties of the phenoxy will, of course, be determined in part by the precursor diphenol employed. Additionally, the resins manufactured from the same parent phenol or phenols will vary in terms of molecular weight and molecular-weight distribution depending on the conditions of synthesis and the combining ratio of reactants.

Chemistry

In theory, the phenoxy resin may be obtained by reacting a bisphenol and epichlorohydrin in a 1/1 mole ratio. The reaction, in the presence of a dehydrohalogenating agent such as sodium hydroxide, would progress as follows:

Bisphenol A   Epichlorohydrin

Chlorohydrin intermediate

$$HO-\bigcirc-\underset{\underset{CH_3}{|}}{\overset{\overset{CH_3}{|}}{C}}-\bigcirc-OCH_2\overset{\overset{OH}{|}}{C}HCH_2Cl + NaOH \longrightarrow$$

Chlorohydrin intermediate   Sodium hydroxide

$$HO-\bigcirc-\underset{\underset{CH_3}{|}}{\overset{\overset{CH_3}{|}}{C}}-\bigcirc-OCH_2CH\overset{O}{\diagup\diagdown}CH_2 + NaCl + H_2O$$

Monoepoxy intermediate
Salt   Water

$$X\; HO-\bigcirc-\underset{\underset{CH_3}{|}}{\overset{\overset{CH_3}{|}}{C}}-\bigcirc-OCH_2CH\overset{O}{\diagup\diagdown}CH_2 \xrightarrow{catalyst}$$

$$\left[-O-\bigcirc-\underset{\underset{CH_3}{|}}{\overset{\overset{CH_3}{|}}{C}}-\bigcirc-O-CH_2\overset{\overset{OH}{|}}{C}HCH_2-\right]_x$$

The actual ionic reactions, including the side reactions, are:

(1) $OH^- + \bigcirc-OH \rightleftharpoons \bigcirc-O^- + HOH$

(2) $\bigcirc-O^- + CH_2\overset{O}{\diagup\diagdown}CHCH_2Cl \longrightarrow \bigcirc-OCH_2\overset{\overset{O^-}{|}}{C}HCH_2Cl$

(3) $\bigcirc-OCH_2\overset{\overset{O^-}{|}}{C}HCH_2Cl + Na^+ \longrightarrow$

$$\bigcirc-OCH_2CH\overset{O}{\diagup\diagdown}CH_2 + NaCl$$

or

(a) $\bigcirc-OCH_2\overset{\overset{O^-}{|}}{C}HCH_2Cl + \bigcirc-OH \longrightarrow$

$$\bigcirc-OCH_2\overset{\overset{OH}{|}}{C}HCH_2Cl + \bigcirc-O^-$$

(b) $\langle\bigcirc\rangle$—OCH$_2$CHCH$_2$Cl + Na$^+$ + OH$^-$ $\longrightarrow$ (with OH on the CH)

$\langle\bigcirc\rangle$—OCH$_2$CH—CH$_2$ (epoxide) + NaCl + HOH

(4) $\langle\bigcirc\rangle$—OCH$_2$CH—CH$_2$ (epoxide) + $\langle\bigcirc\rangle$—O$^-$ $\longrightarrow$

$\langle\bigcirc\rangle$—OCH$_2$CHCH$_2$O—$\langle\bigcirc\rangle$ (with O$^-$ on the CH)

(5) $\langle\bigcirc\rangle$—OCH$_2$CHCH$_2$O—$\langle\bigcirc\rangle$ (with O$^-$ on the CH) + $\langle\bigcirc\rangle$—OH $\longrightarrow$

$\langle\bigcirc\rangle$—OCH$_2$CHCH$_2$O—$\langle\bigcirc\rangle$ (with OH on the CH) + $\langle\bigcirc\rangle$—O$^-$

When producing lower-molecular-weight species, side reactions can be overcome in a variety of ways. For example, when producing lower-molecular-weight epoxy resins, epichlorohydrin is used in substantial excess of the stoichiometric requirement for a given molecular weight. With excess epichlorohydrin, mild reaction conditions can be employed which operate against the possibility of ring opening by water and the subsequent epoxy–aliphatic hydroxyl reaction.

With slightly higher molecular-weight species, as the reaction nears completion, the possibility of reaction with secondary alcohols on the resin chain becomes more probable. This can be minimized by use of a mono-hydric primary alcohol, which will react in preference to the secondary alcohols and will thereby prevent branch chain formation and crosslinking.

However, as one attempts to synthesize higher and higher molecular-weight species from ratios of bisphenol to epichlorohydrin approaching 1/1, the possibility of undesirable side reactions is sharply increased. Because the sodium hydroxide is consumed in the ring-closure operation, it must be present in a sufficient amount to initiate the reaction plus the larger amount equal to the phenolic hydroxyls initially present. The concentration of any monofunctional reactant will impose a natural limit to the average size of the polymer molecules. Further, as the reaction builds higher and higher weights, higher temperatures will be required to continue the polymerization and the likelihood of branch-chain formation is increased.

These difficulties may be overcome by a two-step synthesis process. In the first step, using excess epichlorohydrin, a relatively low molecular-weight epoxy resin is produced and excess reactants removed.   The low-molecular-weight epoxy resin is then reacted with an additional charge of diphenol in the presence of a suitable catalyst.   The catalyst is not required to function as a dehydrohalogenating agent and can therefore be employed in true catalytic amounts, thereby minimizing formation of monofunctional species.   Highest molecular weights are obtained by employing one mole of the diphenol for each mole of the diepoxy resin.   The reaction is usually carried out in the presence of a solvent, typical of which is methyl ethyl ketone, although lower-molecular-weight phenoxy resins may be produced without solvent.   It has been found that it is necessary to employ an epoxy resin low in saponifiable chlorine as the starting resin for the second step of the synthesis.   Otherwise, this chlorine will react with the basic catalyst, necessitating higher concentrations of catalyst than are desirable.

Preparative Procedure

Two examples from the literature will illustrate the actual synthesis of phenoxy resins.

SYNTHESIS OF PHENOXY RESIN, MOL. WT. APPROX. 4,000–5,000

To 2,255 parts of (an epoxy resin from bisphenol A and epichlorohydrin having a molecular weight of approximately 385) were added 1,175 parts of bisphenol A and 0.052 part of lithium hydroxide monohydrate.   The temperature was maintained at 190 to 195°C for 2 hours and then lowered in 20 minutes to 150 to 155°C and held at this temperature for 1 hour.   The resin was then poured into trays and allowed to cool.   The resulting resin had the following properties:

Molecular weight	4,000–5,000
Melting point (Durran)	126°C
Epoxide content	0.55 epoxide equivalents/kg
Color Gardner	1–2 [2]

SYNTHESIS OF PHENOXY RESIN, MOL. WT. APPROX. 40,000

To a vessel containing methyl ethyl ketone are added substantially 100 percent pure p,p'-bisphenol A, substantially 100 percent pure diglycidyl ether of p,p'-bisphenol A, and 60 percent aqueous solution of benzyltrimethylammonium hydroxide in a molar ratio of 1.0/1.0/0.02.   The mixture is made up to contain 67 percent by weight of active reactants.   The solution is heated to reflux temperature, with stirring, and maintained at that temperature, about 80°C, for 13 hours.   Chloroform is then added in an amount which decreases the concentration of reactants (including product) to 57 percent by weight.   After 28 hours total time, additional chloroform is added in an amount which decreases the concentration of reactants to 50 percent by weight.

After a total reaction time of 57 hours the solution is cooled, an equal volume of chloroform added thereto, and the resultant solution washed twice with volumes of water equal to the volume of resin solution. The resin-rich phase is then stabilized in a vacuum oven at a temperature of 160°C and 50 mm mercury for 6 hours.

The stabilized resin is dissolved in dioxane to produce a solution of about 15 percent resin content and the solution poured as a fine stream into 10 times its volume of cold water (1 to 15°C) with vigorous agitation. This results in dissolving dioxane out of the resin solution into the aqueous phase and leaves the substantially solvent-free resin as a suspension of shred or fibers. . . .

Shredded resin prepared in this manner has a softening range of 145 to 185°C and an intrinsic viscosity of 0.35 to 0.45 dl per gram at 25°C in dimethoxyethane [19].

SYNTHESIS OF PHENOXY RESINS FROM COPOLYMER SYSTEMS

In addition to the synthesis of phenoxy resins from one specific bisphenol, it is also possible to employ two or more bisphenols during the synthesis. Typical of the polymers that have been produced by this method are those shown in Table 2.1. The structures of the bisphenols employed are displayed in Table 2.2.

When mixed phenols are used during the course of the one-step synthesis (i.e., the direct reaction of epichlorohydrin with the phenols), the sequence of the units in the polymer chain (unless there is a significant difference in the reaction rates of the phenols) will be irregular.

If the two-step synthesis is employed, using a resin from one of the

TABLE 2.1   Random Hydroxy-ether Copolymers [9]

$$+R_1OCH_2\overset{\overset{\displaystyle OH}{|}}{C}HCH_2O+_m-ir+R_2OCH_2\overset{\overset{\displaystyle OH}{|}}{C}HCH_2O+_n$$

Source of R_1	Source of R_2	Mole ratio of R_1/R_2 in monomer feed	Reduced viscosity[*]
Bisphenol A	Tetrachlorobisphenol A	9/1	0.30
		4/1	0.22
		2/3	0.15
Bisphenol A	Bisphenol V	1/3	0.54
		1/1	0.55
		3/1	0.60
Bisphenol A	Bisphenol L	1/1	0.64
Bisphenol A	Dichlorobisphenol A	1/1	0.52
Bisphenol S	Tetrachlorobisphenol A	1/1	0.10
Bisphenol V	Tetrachlorobisphenol A	1/1	0.29
Bisphenol V	Bisphenol ACP	1/1	0.33
Bisphenol V	Dichlorobisphenol A	1/1	0.40

[*] Measured in tetrahydrofuran, 0.2 g of polymer/100 ml of solution at 25°C.

TABLE 2.2   Names and Structures of Various Bisphenols [9]

Bisphenol	Structure
Bisphenol A	HO—⟨⟩—C(CH₃)₂—⟨⟩—OH
Dichlorobisphenol A	HO—⟨Cl⟩—C(CH₃)₂—⟨Cl⟩—OH
Tetrachlorobisphenol A	HO—⟨Cl,Cl⟩—C(CH₃)₂—⟨Cl,Cl⟩—OH
Tetrabromobisphenol A	HO—⟨Br,Br⟩—C(CH₃)₂—⟨Br,Br⟩—OH
Bisphenol F	HO—⟨⟩—CH₂—⟨⟩—OH
Bisphenol ACP	HO—⟨⟩—C(CH₃)(C₆H₅)—⟨⟩—OH
Bisphenol L	HO—⟨⟩— (ring S, CH₃, CH(CH₃)₂) —⟨⟩—OH
Bisphenol V	HO—⟨⟩— (ring S, CH₃, CH₂) —⟨⟩—OH
Bisphenol S	HO—⟨⟩—SO₂—⟨⟩—OH

bisphenols with the second diphenol employed for the final reaction, then an alternating copolymer will result. Typical of the alternating copolymers which have been prepared are those indicated in Table 2.3; for structures, see Table 2.2.

TABLE 2.3　Alternating Hydroxy-Ether Copolymers [9]

$$-(R_1OCH_2\overset{\underset{\displaystyle |}{OH}}{C}HCH_2OR_2OCH_2\overset{\underset{\displaystyle |}{OH}}{C}HCH_2O)_{\overline{n}}$$

Source of R_1	Source of R_2	Reduced viscosity°
Tetrachlorobisphenol A	Hydroquinone	0.45
Bisphenol V	Tetrachlorobisphenol A	0.21
Bisphenol A	Tetrachlorobisphenol A	0.67
Bisphenol F	Tetrachlorobisphenol A	0.65
Dichlorobisphenol A	Bisphenol A	0.43
Tetrabromobisphenol A	Bisphenol A	0.30

° Measured in tetrahydrofuran, 0.2 g of polymer/100 ml of solution at 25°C.

It is evident, therefore, that the term phenoxy is not restricted to the materials based on bisphenol A but potentially embraces a large number of related polymers which possess properties differing in accordance with their structural makeup.

Final Processing

When the phenoxy resin is to be supplied in solution form, it is not necessary to complete the removal of the solvents used during synthesis. After the washing operation, additional solvents may be added to provide the required flow properties and evaporation rates.

When the phenoxy is produced by solventless technique, the cooled material may be broken up and dissolved in the selected solvents.

When the 100 percent solids material is required, the phenoxy may be processed by use of water-soluble solvents during synthesis. After synthesis, these sheets are dissolved into water, in which the resin is insoluble, and the resulting solid shreds and fibers of phenoxy resin are removed by filtration and dried. Subsequently, they may be powdered and pelletized.

Films from the solvent phase may be produced by pouring the resin solution onto the top roll of a two-roll mill. As the solution passes between the rolls, the solvent is evaporated and the solid resin then sheeted off.

MODIFICATION AND FORMULATION

With the thermoplastic materials, generally, only a minimum amount of formulation and modification is practical. Such modifications as are required are most often accomplished by the manufacturer in the course of his processing, for example, through the addition of pigments, plasticizers, and chemical additives. Thus, the materials are most commonly used in the as-delivered form from the basic supplier.

The 100 percent solids phenoxy resins are normally used as supplied. In theory, they may be reinforced with various types of fibers when used as molding compounds, but performance data on such systems are lacking. Solution coatings, on the other hand, are normally modified before use.

Modification of Solution Coatings

One of the most simple apparent methods for modifying the phenoxy resin is through esterification, which can be accomplished by the reaction of the secondary alcohols along the chain with acid halides, acid anhydrides, or free acids. Esterification may also be accomplished by ester interchange.

Provided monofunctional reactants are employed for esterification, the thermoplastic, soluble nature of the phenoxy may be preserved. These branched-chain thermoplastic phenoxy compounds may be substituted variously to improve flexibility and flame resistance, to lower cost, etc. When drying oils are used, thermosetting films may be developed which cure under the influence of oxygen and catalysts.

Thermosetting films, likewise, may be developed through the use of polyfunctional coreactants capable of reacting with the alcoholic hydroxyls on the phenoxy resin. Typical of these compounds are urethanes, methylol-containing resins, epoxy resins, and anhydrides [14].

Formulation of Solution Coatings

In the development of coating formulations, viscosity and flow properties are adjusted primarily through the selection of solvents. The effect of typical solvents on viscosity is shown in Table 2.4. The effect of solvent concentration on viscosity is shown in Fig. 2.1.

With the coating formulations, pigments and extenders are frequently employed. A typical formulation is indicated in Table 2.5. When the phenoxy solution is used as a wash primer, phosphoric acid may be added (Table 2.6), in addition to fillers. Crosslinking agents may be added as indicated in Table 2.7, where a melamine-formaldehyde resin is used in low concentrations.

Other resinous materials may be used in combination with the phenoxy resin for the formulation of more sophisticated coatings. Typical compatibility data are given in Table 2.8.

PHYSICAL PROPERTIES

Typical of the commercially available phenoxy resins are those indicated in Table 2.9. An infrared curve of a typical phenoxy is shown in Fig. 2.2.

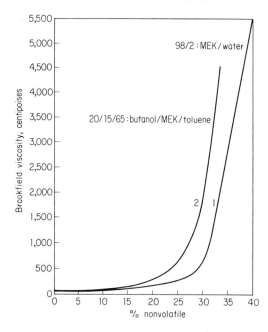

FIG 2.1 *Viscosity vs. percent nonvolatile of phenoxy resin PKHH solutions* [12].

The materials are available in a variety of solvents and solution solids. The average molecular weight for the commercial phenoxies ranges from 15,000 to 40,000. Typical of the molecular-weight distribution that may be expected are the values indicated in Figs. 2.3 and 2.4. The resins contain about 6 percent secondary hydroxyl groups.

In view of the wide range of molecular weights and molecular-weight distributions that are offered commercially, properties cited in this chapter are given in terms of specific commercial compounds, rather than more generally.

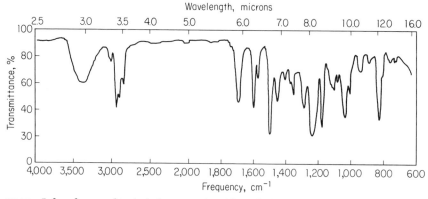

FIG 2.2 *Infrared curve of typical phenoxy resin with residual MEK solvent.*

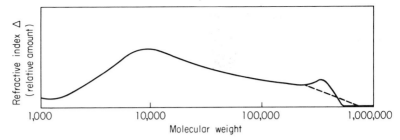

FIG 2.3 *Chromatogram of low-molecular-weight phenoxy resin, showing molecular-weight distribution* [20].

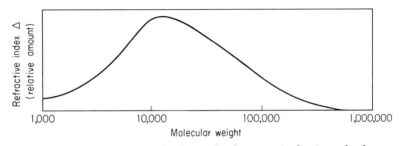

FIG 2.4 *Chromatogram of high-molecular-weight phenoxy resin showing molecular-weight distribution* [20].

TABLE 2.4 Solution Viscosity Data (25% nonvolatiles at 25°C) [12]

Solvent	Brookfield viscosity, centipoises	Gardner-Holdt viscosity
Butyl Carbitol	6,630	Z4−
Butyl Carbitol acetate	4,670	Z2+
Butyl Cellosolve	4,550	Z2–Z3
Carbitol solvent	14,000	Z5+
Cellosolve solvent	2,648	Z
Cellosolve acetate	1,708	X+
Diacetone alcohol	6,250	Z3+
Diethyl Carbitol	1,370	W–X
Dimethylformamide	534	S
Dimethyl sulfoxide	2,860	Z–Z1
Dioxane	1,236	W−
Ethoxytriglycol	9,160	Z4–Z5
Mesityl oxide	392	O–P
Methyl Cellosolve acetate	1,400	X
Methyl ethyl ketone (MEK)	252	I+
Methyl ethyl ketone (MEK) (40% nonvolatile at 25°C)	3,350	Z1–Z2
MEK/Cellosolve acetate/toluene, 38/47/15	548	R–S
MEK/toluene, 1/1	358	M–N
Pent-Oxol	3,330	Z1–Z2
Pent-Oxone	1,810	Y
Tetrahydrofuran	398	J+
Toluene/butanol, 60/40	1,058	V–W

TABLE 2.5   White Decorative Paint Based on Phenoxy Resin [12]

Formula	Pounds	Weight %	Gallons
Rutile TiO$_2$........	83.25	2.42	9.63
Antimony oxide	20.90	0.44	2.42
Barytes	18.55	0.50	2.15
UCC PKHH.......	102.33	10.41	11.84
MEK............	285.58	42.56	33.04
Cellosolve acetate...	353.73	43.67	40.92
Total.........	864.34	100.00	100.00

Properties: PVC 24.4%.   Nonvolatile 26.0%.   Diluent: dilute to desired spray viscosity (approximately 23% nonvolatile) with toluene. Add toluene slowly with good agitation.

Properties of Molding-grade Compounds

The commercially available phenoxy molding compounds give mechanical properties as indicated in Table 2.10.   Here, the properties are compared with those obtained with the older linear polymers.   These values are typical of the properties offered by PRDA-8030 and PRDA-8060.   PRDA-8160, containing a chlorinated hydrocarbon and antimony trioxide, gives

TABLE 2.6   Wash Primer Formulations [3]

Ingredients	Formulations						Conventional primer		
	Without acid			With acid					
	Wt. %	lb	gal	Wt. %	lb	gal	Wt. %	lb	gal
Zinc chromate Y563D[a]....	8.67	67.0	2.14	6.98	53.7	1.71	5.45	42.4	1.35
Magnesium silicate #399[b]..	1.28	9.9	0.044	1.03	8.0	0.35	3.50	27.0	1.20
Lampblack BTA[c].........	0.10	0.7	0.05	0.08	0.6	0.04			
Celite 266[d].............	....	....	....	....	....	....	1.94	15.1	0.90
Nuosperse 657[e]..........	....	....	....	....	....	....	0.16	1.3	0.16
Eponol 55-B-40.........	22.52	174.0	22.46	18.11	139.5	18.00	27.44	213.4	27.54
Acetone...............	30.34	234.5	35.58	24.42	187.6	28.46	27.85	216.6	32.87
Toluene...............	30.34	234.5	32.39	24.42	187.6	25.91	29.27	227.6	31.44
Pent-Oxone[f]...........	6.75	52.2	6.94	5.44	41.8	5.57	4.39	34.2	4.54
H$_3$PO$_4$.............	....	....	....	3.62	27.8	2.32			
Cellosolve acetate........	....	....	....	2.42	18.6	2.29			
Neosol proprietary solvent[f].	....	....	....	13.48	103.6	15.35			
Totals..............	100.00	772.8	100.00	100.00	768.8	100.00	100.00	777.6	100.00
Solids, wt. %...........	19.05			15.36			22.05		

[a] E. I. duPont de Nemours & Co.   [c] Monsanto Chemical Co.   [e] Nuodex Products Co.
[b] Whittaker, Clark & Daniels Co.   [d] Johns-Manville Co.   [f] Shell Chemical Co.

TABLE 2.7 Clear Coating Formulation [3]

	Formulations	
Ingredients	Pounds	Gallons
Eponol 55-B-40..............	293.2	37.83
Uformite F-240° (as supplied).....	5.0	0.58
Cellosolve acetate.............	398.8	49.17
Toluene.....................	89.9	12.42
Total....................	786.9	100.00

Constants: Total solids 15.28% by weight. Weight per gallon 7.87 lb.
°Rohm & Haas Co.

physical properties in the same range, with some increase in specific gravity and some reduction in impact strength.

The data indicate moderately good impact resistance coupled with relatively high strengths and good elongations. In spite of the elongations, creep resistance is quite good, as shown in Fig. 2.5 and Table 2.11.

Few data are available on the effect of changed bisphenol composition on the properties of the molding-grade compounds. However, the effect of esterification on strength properties has been published, giving data as shown in Table 2.12.

Portable cleaner weighs only 4 lb 2 oz, sucks in more than 4 gal of air per sec. Appliance's one-piece exhaust plate and tunnel is molded of self-extinguishing-grade phenoxy, demonstrates materials' toughness, dimensional stability, and low mold shrinkage. (Union Carbide Corp.)

TABLE 2.8   Dry-film Compatibility [12]

Test material	Ratio of UCC PKHH/test material°		
	1/4	1/1	4/1
Acrylic-Acryloid A-10	I	I	I
Cellolyn 102	I	I	I
Epoxy resin (epoxy assay 450 to 525)	C	C	C
Bakelite epoxy resin ERL-2774	C	C	C
Melamine-formaldehyde resin Cymel 245-8	Sl.I	C	C
Melamine-formaldehyde resin Uformite MM-55	Sl.I	Sl.I	C
Nitrocellulose RS ½ second	I	I	I
Bakelite phenolic resin BKR-2620	Sl.I	Sl.I	Sl.I
Bakelite phenolic resin CKR-1634	I	C	C
Bakelite phenolic resin CKM-2400	Sl.I	I	I
Bakelite phenolic resin CKM-5254	C	C	C
Rosin ester Lewisol 28	I	I	I
Rosin ester Lewisol 33	I	I	I
Rosin ester Pentalyn A	I	I	I
Rosin ester Pentalyn G	I	I	I
Shellac	I	I	I
Urea-formaldehyde Uformite F-240	C	C	C
Bakelite vinyl resin AYAF	I	I	I
Bakelite vinyl resin QYNV	I	I	I
Bakelite vinyl resin VAGH	I	I	I
Bakelite vinyl resin VMCH	I	I	I
Bakelite vinyl resin VYHH	I	I	I
WW-rosin	C	C	C
Triphenyl phosphite	C	C	C
Coumarone-indene resins:			
R-27 Neville	C	C	C
R-13 Neville	Sl.I	Sl.I	Sl.I
R-9 Neville	Sl.I	Sl.I	Sl.I
Paradene no. 1	C	I	I
Phenol-modified coumarone-indene resins:			
Nevillac 10°	C	C	C
Nevillac hard	C	C	C
Ketone-formaldehyde resins:			
Krumbar 1717	C	C	C
Bakelite ZKRA-0252	C	C	C
Bakelite ZKRA-0251	C	C	C

° All films baked 30 minutes at 175°C, except for vinyl chloride and chloride acetate copolymers which were baked only 5 minutes at 175°C.

Key: C   Compatible.
     Sl.I   Slightly incompatible.
     I   Incompatible.

TABLE 2.9   Typical Commercially Available Phenoxy Resins

Solutions

Supplier	Solids, %	Color Gardner	Viscosity, Gardner-Holdt or Brookfield
Ciba Products Co. [13]			
Araldite 488 E-32	32	3	X–Z1
Araldite 488 N-40	40	3	U–W
Dow Chemical Co. [14]			
D.E.R. 686 MK 40	40	3	Z4–Z7
D.E.R. 684 MK 40	40	3	U–Y
Jones-Dabney Co. [18]			
Epi-Rez 2287	29–31	6	W–Z
Shell Chemical Co. [3]			
Eponol 53-L-32	32	3	Z1–Z6
Eponol 53-40	40	3	X–Z3
Eponol 55-L-32	32	3	Z1–Z6
Eponol 55-B-40	40	3	Z4–Z8
Union Carbide Plastics			
PKHS	40	3	5,500–7,700 centipoises
PKHS-1	40	3	3,900–5,500 centipoises
PKHS-2	40	3	3,900 centipoises

Solids

Supplier	Coatings grade	Adhesive	Molding
Union Carbide Plastics Co. [4, 12]			
PAHJ	. . . .	×	
PRDA-8100			×
PKHC	×		
PKHH	×		
PKHA	×		
PRDA-8030			×
PRDA-8060			×
PRDA-8160			× (flame-resistant)

TABLE 2.10 Comparative Properties of Bakelite Phenoxy Molding and Extrusion Materials and Other Plastics

Property	Phenoxy PRDA-8060 and -8030	Phenoxy PRDA-8100	Phenoxy PRDA-8160	Polycarbonate (Lexan)	Acetal (Delrin 500)	ABS (Cyco-lac T)	Bakelite polysulfone	CAB (Tenite butyrate 205 MH)
Price (6/15/65), tankloads, $/lb	0.75	0.78	1.00	1.05	0.65	0.39	1.00	62
Specific gravity	1.18	1.17	1.32	1.20	1.425	1.04	1.24	1.20
Pound volume cost, ¢/in.³	3.2	3.3	4.8	4.6	3.3	1.5	4.6	2.7
A. Mechanical Properties at 25°C								
Tensile yield strength, psi	9,000	8,000	9,000	8,500	10,000	6,400	10,200	4,300
Flexural strength, psi	14,000	12,000	14,500	12,500	14,100	10,000	15,400	6,200
Ultimate elongation, %	50–100	100	50	50–100	15	....	50–100	54
Flexural modulus, psi	400,000	340,000	400,000	375,000	400,000	310,000	390,000	135,000
Izod impact, ⅛-in. bar, ft-lb/in.	2.3	12	1.5	12–16	1.4	3.5	1.3	2.1
Charpy impact at −40°, ft-lb/in.	No break	No break	No break	No break				
Rockwell hardness, R scale	123	118	123	118	120	101	120	104
B. Thermal Properties								
Deflection temperature, °C:								
At 264 psi	87	86	80	137	100	92	175	66
At 66 psi	91	92	86	140	170	100	....	80
Coefficient of thermal expansion, in./(in.)(°F) × 10⁵	3.5	3.4	3	3.9	4.5	5	3.1	8
Flammability	Burns slowly	Burns slowly	Self-ext. nondrip	Self-ext. drips	Burns slowly	Burns slowly	Self-ext. nondrip	Burns slowly

C. Electrical Properties

	Col 1	Col 2	Col 3	Col 4	Col 5	Col 6	Col 7	Col 8
Dielectric constant:								
At 60 cycles	4.1	4.1	4.1	3.2	3.7	2.9	3.14	3.5–6.4
At 1 Mc	3.8	3.8	3.7	....	3.7	2.4	3.14	3.2–6.2
Dissipation factor at 60 cycles	0.0012	0.0012	0.0009	0.0009	0.0034	0.005	0.0008	0.01–0.04
Dielectric strength, volts/mil								
⅛-in. plaque, short time	520	400	505	400	465	.....	425	250–400
D. Chemical Resistance								
To acids	Excellent	Excellent	Excellent	Very good	Fair	Very good	Excellent	Fair
To alkalies	Excellent	Excellent	Excellent	Poor	Fair	Excellent	Excellent	Fair
To solvents	Poor	Poor	Poor	Poor	Very good	Poor-fair	Fair	Poor
E. Miscellaneous								
Mold shrinkage, in./in.	0.004	0.004	0.003	0.006	0.020	0.005	0.0076	0.003
Weatherability	Poor-fair	Poor	Under test	Fair	Poor-fair	OK in black	Fair	Good
Color	Transparent light straw	Translucent straw	Opaque white	Transparent light straw	Opaque white	Opaque	Transparent amber	Transparent clear
Water absorption in 24 hours, %	0.13	0.13	....	0.35	0.12–0.4	0.2–0.3	0.22	1.6
Bearing characteristics	Poor	Poor	Poor	Poor	Good	....	Fair	....
Creep°	8	7	7	9	6	3	10	1
O_2 permeability, cc/(100 in.²)(day)(mil)	5.8	....	....	100–200	12–17	....	High	Over 1,000
MVT, g/(100 in.²)(day)(mil)	3.5	....	....	9	High	....	High	80–100

° 10 = best; 1 = very poor.

35

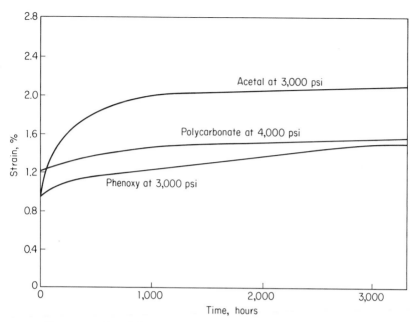

FIG 2.5 *Creep properties of phenoxy resin PRDA* 8060 *vs. other resins at* 23°C [5].

TABLE 2.11 Creep Data of PRDA-1800 vs. Other Molding Resins*
(Performed at room temperature and 50% relative humidity) [21]

Material	Stress, psi	Total strain after 6 Months, %
PRDA-8100	3,000	2.3
Polycarbonate	4,000	1.6
Acetal homopolymer	3,000	2.3
ABS	3,000	3.5
Nylon	2,000	2.0
Impact rigid PVC	2,000	1.4
Impact polystyrene	2,000	4.8
Impact polypropylene	500	1.4
High-density polyethylene	500	1.6
Low-density polyethylene	500	13.7

° Specimens machined from compression-molded samples.

TABLE 2.12 Properties of Esterified Phenoxy Resin PAHJ [4]

| Property | Derivatives | | | |
	Phenoxy	Acetyl	Stearyl	Benzoyl
Tensile modulus, psi	275,000	270,000	960	308,000
Tensile strength, psi	9,500	8,800	960	9,800
Elongation at break, %	100	5.5	370	4

36

Properties of Coating Compounds

In view of the modifications that may be effected in phenoxy coating formulations and in view of the number of crosslinking agents that may be employed, it is not unexpected to find physical properties of the coating systems varying widely.

Typical properties of clear and pigmented coatings are compared in Table 2.13. The abrasion resistance of the clear coatings is compared with other clear coatings in Table 2.14. As would be expected, the mechanical properties of the uncrosslinked phenoxy film will be a function of the molecular weight of the polymer. This is illustrated in Fig. 2.6, where impact resistance, measured on a 0.01-in. film, is shown as a function of average molecular weight of the phenoxy.

Crosslinking generally reduces the film flexibility somewhat while improving other properties, in particular, thermal and chemical resistance. The coatings cured with methylol-bearing resins generally require heat cures. Typical of the properties obtained with a urea-formaldehyde-cured phenoxy are those shown in Table 2.15. This system was cured, after an air dry, for 30 minutes at 175°C. It should be noted that the curing agents can be used successfully over a range of concentrations.

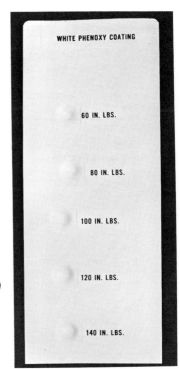

Phenoxy coatings have excellent reverse impact resistance as indicated on test panel shown here. (Union Carbide Corp.)

TABLE 2.13 Properties of Clear and Pigmented Phenoxy Films [11]

Property	Clears		Whites*	
	Eponol 53-B-40, 12% N.V.†	Eponol 55-B-40, 12% N.V.	Eponol 53-B-40, 20% N.V.	Eponol 55-B-40, 20% N.V.
Dry-film thickness, mils	0.4	0.5	1.5	2.0
Impact in.-lb	>160	>160	>160	>160
Flexible conical mandrel	Pass ⅛ in.	Pass ⅛ in.	Pass ⅛ in.	Pass ⅛ in.
Tukon hardness development (Knoop hardness KHN_{25}) after:				
1 day	5.0	3.3	0.9	0.04
2 days	7.4	5.2		
4 days	....	....	2.2	
5 days	11.8	9.2	2.7	
6 days	12.5	10.4	4.1	1.8
7 days	12.5	12.4	5.0	2.0

* Pigment/binder ratio 1/4 pigment used—TiO_2 R-610, E. I. duPont de Nemours & Co., Inc.
† All samples reduced with Pent-Oxone/MEK/toluene, 6/3/1 parts by weight.
N.V. = nonvolatile.

TABLE 2.14 Comparative Tabor Abrasion Resistance of Films [3]

System and cure conditions	*Weight loss, mg/100 rev, 500-g weights, CS-10 wheels*
Eponol 55 (force-dried, lacquer type)	0.4
Epon 1007, urea-converted (20 minutes at 190°C)	0.6
Vinyl resin (force-dried, lacquer-type)	0.7
Epon 1001, amine-cured (room temperature)	1.9
Epon ester, melamine-converted (30 minutes at 150°C)	2.1
Acrylic resin (force-dried, lacquer-type)	3.3

TABLE 2.15 Properties of Phenoxy Films Crosslinked with Urea-Formaldehyde Resin [3]

Beetle 227-8*		Eponol H-53-B-40		Eponol 55-B-40	
Weight %, resin basis	Impact, in.-lb	Flexibility	Tukon hardness	Flexibility	Tukon hardness
0	>160	Pass ⅛ in.	16.0	Pass ⅛ in.	12.2
1	>160	Pass ⅛ in.	15.0	Pass ⅛ in.	13.4
2	>160	Pass ⅛ in.	16.9	Pass ⅛ in.	15.8
5	>160	Pass ⅛ in.	19.8	Pass ⅛ in.	16.9
15	>160	Pass ⅛ in.	22.1	Pass ⅛ in.	19.0
30	44	Pass ⅛ in.	24.3	Pass ⅛ in.	27.9
45	2	9/16 in.	28.9	¾ in.	26.4

* American Cyanamid Co.

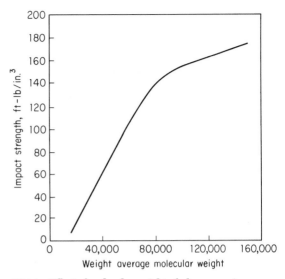

FIG 2.6 *Effect of molecular weight of phenoxy resin on impact strength of film* [8].

When crosslinked systems which cure at room temperature are desired, polyurethanes are the logical choice for coreactant. With these, tank coatings resistant to the microbial action of bacteria in jet fuel have been developed [6]. Typical of the properties of room-temperature-cured phenoxy/polyurethane blends are the data given in Table 2.16. The polyurethane provides cured films of improved temperature resistance, improved

The outstanding chemical resistance of primer coats based on phenoxy resins is shown in this test panel, which was subjected to 8000 hours in 5% salt spray. This panel was top-coated with a standard hydroxyl-containing vinyl resin/red lead coating. (Union Carbide Corp.)

TABLE 2.16   Properties of Phenoxy Resins Crosslinked with Polyurethane
Resins [6]

	Eponol 53-B-40					Eponol 55-B-40				
Ratio, NCO/OH	1.1/1	1.0/1	0.75/1	0.5/1	0.25/1	1.1/1	1.0/1	0.75/1	0.5/1	0.25/1
% weight, Mondur CB-60° . . .	39.1	35.3	30.8	22.2	12.8	39.1	35.3	30.8	22.2	12.8
Dry-film thickness, mils†	0.5	0.5	0.5	0.5	0.6	0.5	0.75	0.7	0.75	1.0
Pencil hardness after:										
1 day	6B	6B	6B	6B	6B	6B	6B	6B	6B	6B
7 days	F	F	F	F	F	F	F	F	F	F
Tukon hardness KHN$_{25}$										
after 8 days	18.9	20.7	20.4	15.6	6.5	22.8	16.9	13.2	12.5	5.2
Flexible conical mandrel after:										
1 day ⎫ 7 days ⎭ . . . . All pass ⅛ in.										
Impact, in.-lb, after:										
1 day . . . . All pass 160 in.-lb										
7 days	150	>160	>160	>160	>160	150	>160	>160	>160	>160

° As received, Mobay Chemical Co.
† Reduction solvent—Pent-Oxone.

resistance to staining and blushing, improved abrasion resistance, improved weathering, higher hardness, and somewhat better chemical resistance than the thermoplastic phenoxy.

As is true with the epoxy resins, the phenoxy resins are generally poor in color retention in exterior environments, and the weathering resistance is unsatisfactory for many applications.

Properties of Adhesive Compounds

The 100 percent solids phenoxy resins have been shown to be excellent thermoplastic adhesives. Properly applied, they provide metal-to-metal bond strengths of better than 3,000 psi in lap shear at room temperature— values equal to those obtained with the better thermosetting adhesive compounds.

The high adhesive strengths may be attributed to the presence of numerous polar hydroxyls, to wettability characteristics at application temperatures, to ductility in the adhesive layer, and to minimized shrinkage.

The 100 percent solids phenoxy resins are good adhesives for ferrous and most nonferrous metals. They bond well to most of the thermosetting plastics and some of the thermoplastic materials.

Properties of Filament-wound Composites

The phenoxy resins appear to be promising candidates for filament winding applications. Unlike most of the thermoplastics, they provide good adhesion to glass, while providing suitably high elongations, which serve to permit stress transfer from the matrix to the glass without internal fractures. The use of thermoplastics generally, and phenoxies specifically, in filament winding is in its infancy. The field is presently dominated by the thermo-setting resins, primarily the epoxies.

Preliminary data on filament-wound structures (NOL rings) are as indicated in Table 2.17.

Advantages obtained with the thermoplastic phenoxies include indefinite shelf life on the prepreg, elimination of the cure time and temperature requirements of thermosetting compounds, unlimited working life, ease of postforming, and high reproducibility of product, insofar as the variables with regard to mixing, pot life, etc., of thermosetting materials are eliminated.

THERMAL PROPERTIES

The thermal strength retention of the thermoplastic phenoxy resins is inferior to that obtained with many of the new linear polymers. However, within the operating range from -60 to about $80°C$, the properties are rather flat with temperature, as indicated in Figs. 2.7 and 2.8.

The point in temperature where physical properties begin rapidly to decline may be considered to be the second-order transition temperature T_g of the polymer. The T_g will vary somewhat depending on the specific property being tested, but only over a fairly narrow range.

With the thermoplastic systems, the nature of the chain elements will affect the T_g. A considerable number of data have been generated on this point, results of which are presented in Tables 2.18 to 2.22. The data were obtained from tensile modulus testing with thin films.

TABLE 2.17 Preliminary NOL Ring Data for Phenoxy Filament Windings [13]

Glass type	Resin, %	NOL burst, psi	Flexural strength, psi	Flexural Modulus, psi $\times 10^{-6}$	Glass fiber stress, psi	Horizontal shear, psi	Void, %
			Phenoxy				
HTS-S	21	221,700	139,000	8.0	324,500	7,200	11
HTS-E	22	156,700	121,960	7.1	256,000	6,500	9
801-E	22	150,880	126,140	6.8	244,000	5,970	10.3
			Epoxy Prepreg				
HTS-S	19	. . . .	210,000	7.5	. . . .	8–11,000 psi	4
HTS-E	15	210,000	200,000	. . . .	290,000	7–11,000	4
801	16	180,000	200,000	. . . .	255,000	7–11,000	4

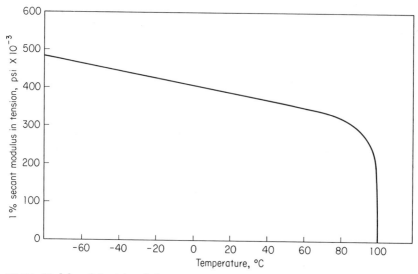

FIG 2.7 *Modulus of elasticity of phenoxy resin PRDA 8030 vs. temperature* [5].

The values obtained for T_g in thin films are in substantial agreement with the values recorded for the deflection temperature of molding compounds and probably represent about the upper limit of load-bearing structural strengths for the phenoxy resins. This is further illustrated by the drop-off in adhesive strengths in the range between 80 and 100°C (Table 2.23). Interestingly, however, from Table 2.23 it can also be seen that creep

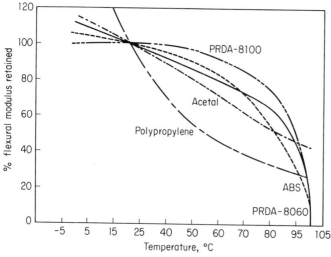

FIG 2.8 *Retention of flexural modulus vs. temperature for thermoplastic resins* [21].

resistance at 80°C is still quite good, reinforcing the previous conclusion that the phenoxy resins do provide good creep resistance.

Above the T_g, the phenoxy polymers are weak, elastomeric systems. As the temperature is further increased, they will ultimately liquefy. However, exposure to temperatures below 200°C causes little degradation. The thermal stability may thus be rated as good. Processing temperatures up to 315°C may be employed, if required, providing exposure time is short, without severe degradation.

The thermal properties of the phenoxy solution coatings when used without crosslinking agents will decline with temperature rather gradually to about 80°C, or somewhat lower with the lower-molecular-weight species. Above this temperature, properties decline rapidly and adhesive strengths may prove inadequate. The crosslinked coatings give some improvement in strength retention with temperature, but the improvement does not appear to be of a significant order.

The elevated-temperature strength retention of the thermoplastic phenoxy matrix, in a laminated construction, is not noticeably inferior to that obtained with a commercial NEMA-grade G-10 thermosetting epoxy, as shown in Fig. 2.9.

TABLE 2.18   Glass Transition Temperatures of Some Hydroxy-Ether Copolymers [9]

Source of R_1°	Source of R_2°	Mole ratio of R_1/R_2 in monomer feed	Copolymer type	T_g1, °C
Bisphenol A.	. . . .	1/0	. . . .	100
Bisphenol A.	Bisphenol V	3/1	Random	105
Bisphenol A.	Bisphenol V	1/1	Random	110
Bisphenol A.	Bisphenol V	1/3	Random	130
	Bisphenol V	0/1	. . . .	140
Bisphenol ACP.	Bisphenol V	1/1	Random	130
Bisphenol ACP.	. . . .	1/0	. . . .	115
Bisphenol L.	Bisphenol A	1/1	Random	140
Bisphenol L.	. . . .	1/0	. . . .	175
Dichlorobisphenol A.	Bisphenol A	1/1	Random	90
Dichlorobisphenol A.	Bisphenol A	1/1	Alternating	90
Dichlorobisphenol A.	. . . .	1/0	. . . .	85
Bisphenol A.	Tetrachlorobisphenol A	1/1	Alternating	100
	Tetrachlorobisphenol A	0/1	. . . .	115
Bisphenol A.	Hydroquinone	1/1	Alternating	95
	Hydroquinone	0/1	. . . .	60
Bisphenol F.	Tetrachlorobisphenol A	1/1	Alternating	80
Bisphenol F.	. . . .	1/0	. . . .	80
Tetrabromobisphenol A.	Bisphenol A	1/1	Alternating	117

° See Tables 2.1 or 2.3.   For structures of the phenols see Table 2.2.

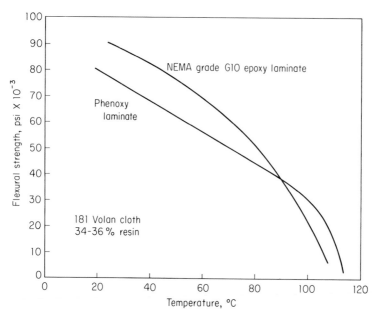

FIG 2.9 *Properties vs. temperature for phenoxy and epoxy laminates* [13].

PHYSICAL-CHEMICAL PROPERTIES

Considerable work has been accomplished in determining the effect of structural variables in the phenoxy resin backbone on the moisture-vapor and oxygen-vapor permeability of films. Data are given in Tables 2.21, 2.22, 2.24, and 2.25. A commercial phenoxy is compared with various other

Bottle and eyecup blow-molded for phenoxy resin. (Union Carbide Corp.)

TABLE 2.19 Influence of Connecting Group in Bisphenol on the Glass I
Transition Temperature of Polyhydroxy-Ethers [8]

$$\left[O - \bigotimes - X - \bigotimes - O - CH_2 - \underset{\underset{OH}{|}}{CH} - CH_2 \right]_n$$

Polymer no.	X	T_g1, °C
1	$-\underset{\underset{CH_3}{|}}{\overset{\overset{CH_3}{|}}{C}} - CH_2 - \underset{\overset{CH_3}{|}}{CH} -$	75
2	$-CH_2-$	80
3	$-\underset{\underset{CH_3 \ \ CH_3}{\diagdown \diagup}}{\overset{\overset{CH}{|}}{CH}}-$	95
4	$-\underset{\underset{CH_3}{|}}{\overset{\overset{CH_3}{|}}{C}}-$	100
5	$-\overset{\overset{CH_3}{|}}{C}-$ with phenyl	115
6	$-\overset{\overset{CH_3}{|}}{\underset{\underset{CH_3}{|}}{C}}$ — ring(S) — CH_3	135
7	ring(S), CH_2-CH_3	140
8	$-\overset{\overset{O}{||}}{\underset{\underset{O}{||}}{S}}-$	155
9	ring(S), CH_3 top and $\underset{\underset{H_3C \quad CH_3}{\diagdown\diagup}}{CH}$ bottom	175

TABLE 2.20 Influence of the Type of Dihydric Phenol on the Glass I Transition Temperature of Polyhydroxy-Ethers [8]

$$\left[O-E-O-CH_2-\underset{\underset{OH}{|}}{CH}-CH_2 \right]_n$$

Polymer no.	E	$T_g 1$, °C
1		60
2		85
3		100
4		115
5		120

polymeric films in Table 2.26. Extensive data are given in [17] regarding the probable suitability of phenoxy blow-molded bottles for packaging various products. The bottles are suited for packaging many foodstuffs, cosmetics, and household chemicals. Flavor and odor retention are excellent. The resin complies with the limitations of the Food Additive Regulation 121,2579 (October 22, 1963), which permits the use of this polymer in all food-contact uses. Stain resistance is given in Table 2.27.

Phenoxy films will vary in their chemical resistance depending on their specific composition. Typical data for modified and crosslinked films are given in Table 2.28. The unmodified film is compared, in terms of chemical resistance, with other films in Table 2.29.

The effect of various chemical environments on adhesive bond strengths is indicated in Table 2.30.

In view of the limited strength retention with temperature, the use of thermoplastic phenoxy coatings in chemical environments much above normal ambient temperatures would probably not be justified, although with some of the crosslinked systems performance might prove satisfactory. The strength retention for adhesive bonds, after short exposures to steam and boiling water, appears satisfactory, although longer exposure times might create difficulties.

ELECTRICAL PROPERTIES

The electrical properties of phenoxy compounds are in the range expected of crosslinked epoxy resins. They are, therefore, quite good electrical insulators. Typical data for molding compounds are given in Table 2.10; data for films in Table 2.31.

As with other properties, however, it might be expected that the insulating properties would decline rather sharply above temperatures of about 80°C. Crosslinked films, while providing values at room temperature in the same range of the thermoplastic materials, might be expected to provide somewhat better elevated-temperature electricals.

PROCESSING

Molding and Extrusion Compounds

The phenoxy resins suitable for molding and extrusion have molecular weights in the 25,000 to 40,000 range. On storage, they tend to pick up moisture to an extent to interfere with optimum processability. Therefore, they are customarily predried at temperatures of about 75°C for several hours.

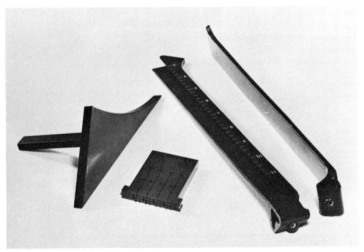

Phenoxy components for computer include two-piece rear paper guide, rectifier case, and disk pack guide processing system. Phenoxy was selected for its high dimensional stability and good electrical properties. (Union Carbide Corp.)

Swimming-pool filter is injection-molded of phenoxy, chosen because its moldability is ideal for the intricate part and because it undergoes no dimensional change when immersed in water. (Union Carbide Corp.)

At the low end of the processing range, the phenoxy resins are highly elastic (Fig. 2.10). On the other hand, above 175 °C, phenoxy resin displays nonelastic behavior (Fig. 2.11). At the higher temperatures the viscosity is quite sharply temperature-dependent (Fig. 2.12). Thus, at the usual molding temperatures from 230 to 275°C, small adjustments in temperature permit regulation of viscosity to meet equipment and application demands. With injection molding equipment, pressures of about 14,000 psi are satisfactory, and the phenoxy can be handled on machinery suited for impact polystyrene at rated capacity. Mold design generally follows thermoplastic practice, but because of low shrinkage, slightly more draft than usual may be required on deep-draw molds.

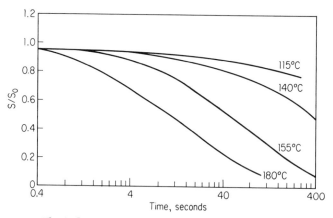

FIG 2.10 *Elastic flow properties of phenoxy resin PRDA*-8060 *at lower processing temperatures* [7]. $S_0 =$ *stress at time zero;* S $=$ *stress at time* t.

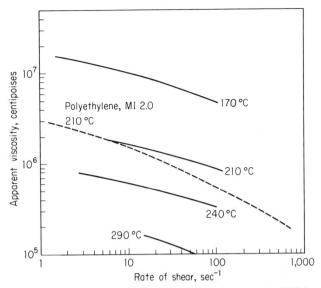

FIG 2.11 *Effect of shear rate on viscosity of phenoxy resin PRDA-8030* [7]. *Phenoxy results obtained with die lengths of* 0.375, 0.500, *and* 1.000 *in. Die orifice* 0.0825 *in.*

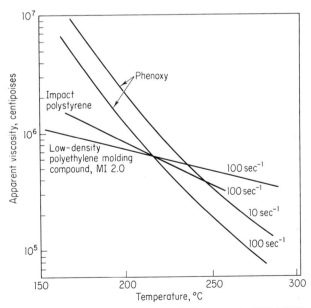

FIG 2.12 *Viscosity vs. temperature of phenoxy resin PRDA-8060 at higher processing temperatures* [7].

For extrusions, the phenoxy is processed at about 230°C using a high-compression-ratio nylon- or polyethylene-type screw. The elasticity at the low end of the processing range facilitates blow-molding operations, insofar as sagging and runaway of the parison are minimized.

POSTMOLDING OPERATIONS

Phenoxy resins may be machined easily, provided temperatures are controlled by use of slow surface speeds and sharp tools. They may be solvent-cemented, using a 25 percent solids solution of the phenoxy in methyl ethyl ketone; or they may be hot-gas-welded in a fashion similar to that used with polyethylene.

Coatings

One of the principal problems encountered with phenoxy coatings is the slow evaporation rate at which solvents are released from the highly polar

TABLE 2.21 Effects of Esterification on Properties of Bisphenol A Polyhydroxy-Ether [10]

R	Esterification %[a]	T_g1, °C	Oxygen permeability, cc-mil/(100 in.²) (24 hr)(atm)	Moisture-vapor transmission, g-mil/(100 in.²) (24 hr)[b]
H	0	100	5	3
Formyl	80	80	10	7
Acetyl	10	90	9	4
	50	80	14	5
	100	60	41	6
Chloroacetyl	10	90	7	7
	50	78	8	
	100	65	8	8
Mercaptoacetyl	25	80	4	7
Propionyl	100	60	47	9
Stearyl	30	60	23	6
	75	25	>100	10
Benzoyl	10	85	8	4
	50	80	18	5
	100	65	30	6
o-Chlorobenzoyl	100	66	9	8
p-Toluenesulfonyl	95	80	16	9
Diphenylphosphinyl	25	80	11	8
Nitryl	25	80	6	9

[a] Determined by either hetero atom analysis or measurement of saponification equivalent.
[b] At 37°C and 90% relative humidity.

TABLE 2.22 Effects of Esterification on Properties of Polyhydroxy-Ethers from Various Diphenols [10]

$$\left[\!\!\begin{array}{c} O-E-O-CH_2-CH-CH_2 \\ | \\ O \\ | \\ R \end{array}\!\!\right]_n$$

Dihydric phenol residue (E)	Ester (R)	T_g1, °C	Oxygen permeability, cc-mil/(100 in.²) (24 hr)(atm)	Moisture-vapor transmission, g-mil/(100 in.²) (24 hr)°
(phenylene)	H	60	0.5	3
	Acetyl	49	3	6
bisphenol A residue	H	100	5	3
	Acetyl	60	23	6
	Benzoyl	65	30	6
tetrachlorobisphenol A residue	H	115	4	3
	Acetyl	100	21	6
bisphenol residue (CH₃, phenyl)	H	115	8	7
	Acetyl	110	25	6
	Benzoyl	126	20	6
thioether bisphenol residue	H	140	15	7
	Acetyl	107	41	9
sulfone bisphenol residue	H	155	2	9
	Acetyl	130	9	

° At 37°C and 90% relative humidity.

vehicle solids. Some improvement may be obtained through the use of solvent blends and appropriate fillers, but the difficulty has not been entirely overcome.

With unpigmented coatings, thicknesses above about ½ mil are customarily force-dried for 30 minutes to an hour to remove solvent. With films where the volume concentration of pigments is relatively high, films as thick as ¾ mil may be satisfactorily air-dried.

Air-dried coating systems are developed from the thermoplastic phenoxy

TABLE 2.23 Bond Strength of Phenoxy PAHJ Bonded Joints (Material: type 2024T3 clad aluminum; glue line 0.001 in.) [5]

Tensile Lap Shear Strength

Test temperature, °C	Shear strength, psi	Minimum requirement, MIL-A-5090D Specification, psi
−55	3,150	2,500
23	3,500	2,500
82	2,800	1,250
105	1,400	

Creep Resistance of Phenoxy-bonded Joints

Dead load	Test temperature, °C	Creep, inches	Maximum allowable by Specification MIL-A-5090D, in.
1,600 psi for 8 days	23	<0.00005	0.015
800 psi for 8 days	82	<0.00005	0.015

TABLE 2.24 Permeability Properties of Some Hydroxy-Ether Copolymers [9]

Source of R_1°	Source of R_2°	Mole ratio of R_1/R_2	Copolymer type	Oxygen permeability, cc-mil/ (100 in.²) (24 hr) (atm)	Moisture-vapor transmission, g-mil/ (100 in.²) (24 hr)†
Bisphenol A	. . . .	. . . .	. . . .	5	3
Bisphenol A	Bisphenol V	3/1	Random	6	4
Bisphenol A	Bisphenol V	1/1	Random	8	4
Bisphenol A	Bisphenol V	1/3	Random	12	5
	Bisphenol V	. . . .	. . . .	15	7
Bisphenol ACP	Bisphenol V	1/1	Random	8	5
Bisphenol ACP	. . . .	. . . .	. . . .	8	7
Dichlorobisphenol A	. . . .	. . . .	. . . .	3	3
Dichlorobisphenol A	Bisphenol A	1/1	Random	6	7
Dichlorobisphenol A	Bisphenol A	1/1	Alternating	4	
Tetrachlorobisphenol A	. . . .	. . . .	. . . .	4	3
Tetrachlorobisphenol A	Bisphenol A	1/1	Alternating	8	6
Hydroquinone	. . . .	. . . .	. . . .	0.5	3
Hydroquinone	Tetrachlorobisphenol A	1/1	Alternating	5	6
Bisphenol F	Tetrachlorobisphenol A	1/1	Alternating	4	4
Tetrabromobisphenol A	Bisphenol A	1/1	Alternating	7	4

° See Table 2.1 or 2.3. For structures of the phenols see Table 2.2.
† At 37°C and 90% relative humidity.

TABLE 2.25 Influence of the Type of Dihydric Phenol on Barrier Properties of Polyhydroxy-Ethers [8]

$$\left[\!\!-\text{O}-\text{E}-\text{O}-\text{CH}_2-\underset{\overset{|}{\text{OH}}}{\text{CH}}-\text{CH}_2-\!\!\right]_n$$

Polymer no.	E	Oxygen permeability, cc-mil/(100 in.²)(24 hr)(atm)	Moisture-vapor transmission, g-mil/(100 in.²)(24 hr)°
1		0.5	3
2		2	9
3		3	3
4		4	
5		4	3
6		5	3
7		8	7
8		8	7

° At 37°C and 90% relative humidity.

TABLE 2.25 (*continued*) Influence of the Type of Dihydric Phenol on Barrier Properties of Polyhydroxy-Ethers [8]

Polymer no.	E	Oxygen permeability, cc-mil/(100 in.^{2}) (24 hr)(atm)	Moisture-vapor transmission, g-mil/(100 in.^{2}) (24 hr)°
9		15	7
10		75	15

or from the phenoxy crosslinked with polyurethanes. In the latter case, two-component packaging is required, with the ingredients mixed just before use. With the phenoxy system crosslinked with urea-, phenol-, or melamine-formaldehyde resins, one-can systems may be developed which provide good shelf stability but require oven cures at 160 to 190°C. Solvent-free phenoxy coatings may be obtained by the fluidized-bed process, which consists of dipping a heated part into a bed of air-agitated powder [14].

TABLE 2.26 Comparison of the Barrier Properties of Some Polymeric Films [8]

Polymer no.	Gas permeability, cc-mil/(100 in.^{2}) (24 hr)(atm)		Moisture-vapor transmission, g-mil/(100 in.^{2}) (24 hr)°
	Oxygen	Carbon dioxide	
1 Vinylidene chloride–vinyl chloride copolymer	<1	2	0.25
2 Polyethylene terephthalate	5	6	2
3 Bisphenol A polyhydroxy-ether	5	8	3
4 Polyvinyl chloride	15	55	2.5
5 Polyethylene (high density)	107	450	0.6
6 Polypropylene	200	750	0.6
7 Bisphenol A polycarbonate	200	1,000	10
8 Polyethylene (low density)	439	1,900	1
9 Polystyrene	530	2,300	6

° At 37°C and 90% relative humidity.

Adhesives

As with high-strength thermosetting adhesives, phenoxy adhesives require careful attention to surface preparation if the inherently high adhesive strengths are to be realized in practice. Surface preparation generally consists of solvent-degreasing followed by light sanding. For maximum bond strengths, metals may be treated with a variety of special chemical preparations, such as the chromate etch frequently used with aluminum surfaces.

The phenoxy resins, when carried in a solvent, do not provide outstanding adhesive properties between two solid surfaces. Difficulty of adequate wetting is compounded by the problem of solvent removal.

Hot-melt adhesive systems are not entirely satisfactory, because it is not practical to maintain the phenoxy resin in the molten state for sufficient time to permit thorough melting prior to thermal degradation. This situation can probably be corrected through the use of suitable plasticizers, but present information is inadequate to permit recommendations.

The preferred physical form of the phenoxy adhesive is as a film. The film is interposed between the adherend faying surfaces, and pressure and temperature are applied for a period of time sufficient to ensure thorough wetting. It is probable that this time-temperature-pressure relationship is critical to optimum bond performance, since wettability is a function of all three parameters in combination. Satisfactory wetting is obtained for

TABLE 2.27 Stain Resistance (0.40-in. bars, immersed 24 hours at 25°C) [21]

Environment	Staining	Remarks
Gasoline	No	
Water	No	
95% ethyl alcohol	Yes	Polished surface
50% ethyl alcohol	Yes°	Polished surface
Ivory soap	No	
Oakite (trisodium phosphite)	Yes	Etched surface
Olive oil	No	
Lemon juice	No	
Mustard	No	
Wax crayon	No	
Shoe polish	No	
Tea	No	
Vinegar	No	
Bluing	No	
Washable ink	No	
Lysol (phenol solution)	Yes	Etched surface
Mercurochrome	No	
Catsup	No	
Chocolate syrup	No	

° Failed to stain in 4 hours.

TABLE 2.28 Corrosion Resistance of Unmodified and Crosslinked
Phenoxy Resin PKHH Coatings [12]

Reagent	Unmodified	TDI° 100/30† (100% stoi-chiometric)	TDI 100/15† (50% stoi-chiometric)	Mondur S‡ 100/59† (50% stoi-chiometric)	Cymel 245-8§ 10/10†	Cymel 245-8 80/20†
Acetic acid, 5%.......	L	S				
Acetic acid, 50%......	L	L				
Carbon tetrachloride..	U	L				
Citric acid, 5%	S	S				
Citric acid, 50%......	S	S				
Ethylene dichloride...	U	U				
Gasoline............	S	S	S	S	S	S
Hydrochloride acid, 5%	S	S				
Methyl ethyl ketone...	U	S	S	L	L	S
Mineral oil..........	S	S				
Mineral spirits........	S	S				
Motor oil............	S	S	S	S	S	S
Nitric acid, 5%.......	S	S¶				
Nitric acid, 50%......	U	U				
Sodium chloride, 3%..	S	L	L	L	S	S
Sodium hydroxide, 5%.	S	S	S	S	S	S
Sodium hydroxide, 20%	S	S	S	S	S	S
Sulfuric acid, 5%.....	S	S				
Sulfuric acid, 50%....	S	S				
Toluene.............	U	S	S	S	S	S
Water, fresh.........	S	S	S	S	S	S

° TDI = toluene diisocyanate.
† Weight ratios based on resin solids.
‡ Mondur S = blocked polyisocyanate sold by Mobay Chemical Co.
§ Cymel 245-8 = a melamine-formaldehyde resin sold by American Cyanamid Co.
¶ Film darkened after 5 days.
NOTE: Thin coatings (0.5 to 1.0 mil) on cold-rolled steel Q panels.
Key: S Satisfactory. No attack after 2 weeks immersion.
    L Limited recommendation. Test before using.
    U Unsatisfactory.

most metals using temperatures of 315 to 345°C for a few seconds or 260°C for a few minutes. Thirty minutes or more may be required if temperatures are restricted to 190°C. Pressure must be sufficient only to maintain contact between faying surfaces and adhesive, since volatiles are not produced for the resin. The usual pressure is 200 psi, but lower pressures may also be satisfactory.

With the phenoxy resins, glue-line thickness has not been found to be critical, comparable results being obtained over the range from ½ to 5 mils on nonporous surfaces. On porous surfaces, such as wood, thicker films are required to accommodate the bleed-off into the adherend. The principal advantage normally obtained through the use of thinner films is faster processing times.

TABLE 2.29 Comparative Performance of Phenoxy Eponol 55 vs. Other
Lacquer-type Resins and Converted Epon Resin Systems [3]

Test conditions	Lacquer resins (all systems force-dried)				Converted Epon resin systems			
	Eponol 55 resin	Vinyl resin	Acrylic resin	Nylon resin	Epon 1001 amine-cured at 23°C	Epon 1007 phenolic-cured at 205°C	Epon ester melamine-cured at 205°C	Epon 1007 urea-cured at 190°C
Chemical resistance:								
20% NaOH								
11 days at 93°C.......	8	6	1	1	8	9	1	5
30% H_2SO_4								
14 days at 23°C.......	10	10	7	1	10	10	8	3
10% HCl								
14 days at 23°C.......	9	9	6	1	8	5	5	2
Distilled H_2O								
20 days at 23°C.......	10	7	5	1	8	10	10	10
11 days at 93°C.......	6	7	1	1	4	10	8	4
Environmental resistance:								
Humidity after 1,000 hours 37°C and 100% relative humidity............	8	7½	8¼	1				
Humidity after 2,500 hours 37°C and 100% relative humidity............	8	7	6	1				
Heat resistance.........	7	1	9	5	7	6	4	3

NOTE: Ratings used: 10 = unaffected.
0 = complete failure.

TABLE 2.30 Environmental Effects on Phenoxy PAHJ Bonded Joints
(Material: type 2024T3 clad aluminum; glue-line thickness 0.001 in.) [5]

Environment	Exposure time	Exposure temperature, °C	Tensile lap shear strength, psi
Air....................	30 days	23	3,000–3,500
Tap water..............	30 days	23	2,600
Salt spray..............	30 days	23	2,500
Autoclave..............	20 minutes	120	2,300
Boiling water...........	2 hours	100	2,300
Acetone................	2 hours	23	2,700
Aircraft hydraulic oils (phosphate ester type)...	7 days	23	1,500
Jet fuel (JP-4)...........	7 days	23	950

TABLE 2.31 Electrical Properties of Phenoxy Resin Eponol 55

Sample	Dielectric constant	Dissipation factor	Power factor	Volume resistivity, ohm-cm
A....................	3.17	0.0014	0.0014	2.6×10^{16}
B....................	3.48	0.0013	0.0013	2.8×10^{16}
C....................	2.59	0.0052	0.0052	2.8×10^{16}

Composites

Phenoxy composites are prepared from dry preimpregnated cloth or from roving. The impregnation may be conducted from a hot melt by an extrusion process, or preferably from solution, with the solvents being flashed off by heat.

Because of the difficulties of solvent removal from thicker sections, and because hot-melt application requires too prolonged an exposure to too high a temperature, wet-winding operations do not appear practical.

Prepreg materials may be stored indefinitely before final processing. Laminates are prepared simply by the application of heat and pressure, while filament windings are prepared by raising the temperature above 200°C just before the roving contacts the mandrel. As quickly as the structure cools, full strength is developed [13].

APPLICATIONS

The largest application for phenoxy resins is as vehicle solids for coatings formulations. In common with epoxy resins, exterior durability and color retention is less satisfactory than with good exterior-grade films. This, together with the difficulty of solvent removal in thicker films, militates

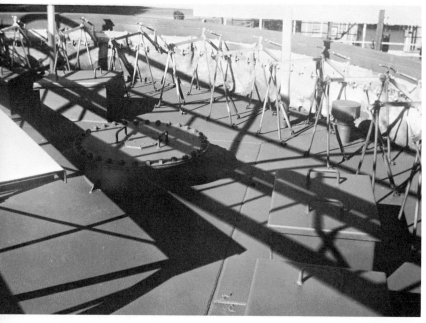

Floating roof of fuel storage tank coated with phenoxy red lead/red iron oxide primer against corrosion. (Shell Chemical Co.)

against their use in topcoat applications. They are exceptionally well suited for primer applications, where their high adhesive strengths, drying speed, and overall compatibility with various topcoats, make them quite attractive.

The phenoxy resins are presently used as primers in automotive applications, where they are applied to the bare metal; they are then coated with a special epoxy ester which is compatible with the acrylic topcoat. In the marine industry, the phenoxy is used in connection with all the commercial topcoats: epoxy ester, alkyd, chlorinated rubber, and two-can epoxies. As heavy-duty maintenance primers, the phenoxy is usually applied in two coats, the second coat some 2 hours after the first. Six hours later, the topcoat may be applied.

The phenoxy resins are excellent vehicle solids for zinc-rich metal primers. They provide the above advantages together with the additional advantage of high polarity in solution which assists in maintaining the sacrificial metal in suspension.

The potential for phenoxy molding compounds is restricted to service conditions below 80°C or so. They provide good impact resistance coupled with excellent dimensional stability within their temperature range. Special grades are also flame-resistant. The phenoxy resins are tough, lightweight, clear, and easily printed, and offer good barrier properties; this combination makes them of interest for blown bottles in the packaging field [22, 23].

Phenoxy film adhesives offer easy processability coupled with high bond strength throughout their temperature range. They appear to offer advantages in certain sandwich constructions and as production adhesives for wooden surfaces.

REFERENCES

1952

1. Carpenter et al., Production of Thermoplastic Resins and the Production from Such Resins of Threads, Fibres, Filaments, and the Like, U.S. 2,602,075.

1961

2. Nikles, Epoxide Resin Compositions, U.S. 3,006,892.
3. Shell Chemical Co., Eponol Resin, SC 61-160.

1962

4. Union Carbide Plastics Co., Some Chemical Modifications of Bakelite Phenoxy, Bulletin 10181.

1963

5. Bugel et al., Phenoxy Resin: a New Thermoplastic Adhesive, ASTM Symposium, Atlantic City, N.J., June 27.
6. Shell Chemical Co., Development of a Fuel and Microbe Resistant Finish, Union Laboratories, Report PT-WD-67.
7. Norwalk et al., How to Process the New Phenoxies, *Plastics Technol.*, February, pp. 34–39.
8. Reinking et al., Polyhydroxyethers, I: Effect of Structure on Properties of High Molecular Weight Polymers from Dihydric Phenols and Epichlorohydrin, *J. Appl. Polymer Sci.* 7:2135–2144.
9. Reinking et al., Polyhydroxyethers, II: Effect of Structure on Properties of High Molecular Weight Copolymers from Dihydric Phenol Mixtures and Epichlorohydrin, *J. Appl. Polymer Sci.* 7:2145–2152.
10. Reinking et al., Polyhydroxyethers, III: Ester Derivatives, *J. Appl. Polymer Sci.* 7:2153–2160.

1964

11. Shell Chemical Co., Plastics and Resins Division, Bulletin R&D R-5.
12. Union Carbide Plastics Co., Bakelite Phenoxy Resins PKHH and PAHJ for Solution Coatings and Adhesives, Bulletin J-2421-B.
13. F. L. Williamson, Application of Phenoxy Thermoplastic Resins to Commercial Filament Winding, 19th Annual Meeting of RIP Division of SPI, Chicago.

1965

14. R. E. Bayes and J. P. Manasia, Base Coated with a Linear Thermoplastic Polyether, U.S. 3,177,090.
15. Ciba Products Co., Technical Bulletin Araldite 488E32, 488 N-40, no. 3101611.5.
16. Dow Chemical Co., Product Technical Data Sheet D.E.R. 686 MK40 and 684 MK40.
17. Elder, Phenoxy Blow Molded Bottles, *SPE J.*, May, pp. 480–485.
18. Jones-Dabney Technical Data, Epi-Rez 2287.
19. Linear Polyether Resins and Processes for Their Production (to Shell Internationale Research), Brit. 980,509.
20. Miles and Spell, Applications of Thin-layer and Gel Permeation Chromatography to the Characterization of Epoxy Resins, 20th Annual Meeting of RIP Division of SPI.
21. Union Carbide Plastics, Bakelite High Impact Phenoxy PRDA 8100 for Molding and Extrusion, Product Data, J-2565A.

1966

22. H. Lee, New Linear Polymers, SPI Conference, Coronado, Calif., April.

1967

23. H. Henriques, What Is the Future of Clear Plastic Bottles?, SPI Conference, Coronado, Calif., April.

3

Poly(phenylene) Oxides

Lower-molecular-weight polyphenylene oxides have been known for half a century prior to the introduction of polyxylenol by General Electric in 1964. Commercialization was made possible by the development of an oxidative coupling method of synthesis by which 2,6-substituted phenols can be polymerized to higher molecular weights in virtually quantitive yields.

These new materials possess exceptionally good elevated-temperature properties (with DTs about 190° C). The unstabilized materials are subject to crosslinking and embrittlement when aged in the presence of oxygen about 120° C, but this problem may be minimized by the development of suitable stabilizers.

Processed on conventional molding and extrusion equipment capable of operating at 290° C and above, the new polymers offer potential challenge to chemically resistant fluorinated molecules and to thermoset plastics in the lower temperature range.

*I*nitial work on unsubstituted poly(phenylene oxides) was begun about 1915 by W. H. Hunter and coworkers [1, 2]. The polymers, obtained by heating metal-halogen phenoxides, although produced in fairly low molecular weights and relatively poor yields, were the subject of continuing interest, with synthesis techniques being refined through the years. In 1957, A. S. Hay of General Electric Company produced poly(2,6-disubstituted phenylene oxides) by an oxidative coupling method in high yields and high molecular weights. Subsequently, in 1961, C. C. Price and co-workers produced similar compounds by reacting 2,6-disubstituted *p*-halophenols through the action of potassium ferricyanide. A variety of related polyphenylene oxides are described in Thermal Degradation of Polymers, Society of Chemical Industries SCI Monograph 13 (1961). A review of the history is given by Faurote and Segal [6], and Price [20]. Resins produced by the oxidative coupling method were introduced commercially as thermoplastic molding compounds in 1964.

SYNTHESIS

The oxidative synthesis is the preferred method for the production of polyphenylene oxides. The method, inherently, is suited as well to the production of other polymers [i.e., poly(aromatic acetylenes)] and is of broader potential significance to the plastic technology than here indicated.

Oxidative Synthesis

The oxidative synthesis of poly(2,6-disubstituted phenylene oxide) may be written in simplified form as [9]:

| 2,6-Xylenol | Oxygen | Poly(2,6-xylenol) | Water |

The reaction is catalyzed by a cuprous salt and a tertiary amine.

The ortho and para positions of phenols are quite reactive under these conditions, but the meta positions are inert. Under the conditions of oxidative synthesis any halogen but fluorine on the ortho or para positions will react to give coupling. Thus, when hydrogen, bromine, or iodine is

63

TABLE 3.1 Oxidation of 2,6-Disubstituted Phenols Yielding Polymers [7]

R_1	R_2	Solvent[a]	Yield, %[b]	Molecular weight[c]	Viscosity,[d] dl/g	Formula	C, % Calculated	Found	H, % Calculated	Found
Methyl.....	Methyl	A	85	31,000	0.72	C_8H_8O	80.0	80.1	6.7	6.8
Methyl.....	Ethyl	B	82	25,400	0.40	$C_9H_{10}O$	80.6	80.8	7.5	8.0
Methyl.....	Isopropyl	A	62	15,350	0.24	$C_{10}H_{12}O$	81.0	81.4	8.2	8.3
Ethyl......	Ethyl	B	81	32,000	0.53	$C_{10}H_{12}O$	81.0	80.7	8.2	8.2
Methyl.....	Chloro[e]	A	83	71,000	0.47	C_7H_5ClO	59.8	61.9	3.6	3.9
Methyl.....	Bromo[f]	A	18	....	0.03	C_7H_5BrO	45.5	58.0	2.7	2.5
Methyl.....	Methoxy	A	60	13,100	0.27	$C_8H_8O_2$	70.6	69.5	5.9	6.0
Methyl.....	Phenyl	A	60	....	....	$C_{13}H_{10}O$	84.8	82.6	6.6	5.1
Phenyl.....	Phenyl	B	46	....	0.05	$C_{18}H_{12}O$	88.5	88.4	5.0	5.2

[a] Solvents: A = pyridine; B = 22% pyridine + 78% nitrobenzene.
[b] Reprecipitated polymer.
[c] Osmotic molecular weight in $CHCl_3$ at 25°C.
[d] In $CHCl_3$ at 25°C.
[e] Analysis: Cl, calculated 25.2%, found 21.7%.
[f] Analysis: Br, calculated 45.4%, found 26.0%.

Atom model of polyphenylene oxide from m-*dimethylbenzene and oxygen.* (The Epoxylite Corporation)

present at more than one of the three positions, a crosslinked polymer will result. Crosslinking can be prevented by hydrocarbon substituents on two of the three positions. For highest-molecular-weight polymers, the reactive site should be in the para position, although low- and intermediate-molecular-weight species may be developed from phenols with active ortho positions. Preferably, 2,6-xylenol is employed, as shown in the preceding equation.

The blocking substituents in the 2,6-positions should not be too bulky, lest the reaction produce diphenoquinones rather than the polyether.

o-Substituted diphenoquinone

Generally, aliphatic substituents with methylene bridges will not hinder polymer formation, while methylidyne bridges substituents will generally produce both polymers. The limiting case appears to be the isopropyl group. 2-Methyl-6-isopropyl phenol is oxidized to both the diphenoquinone and the polyphenylene ether, with the latter predominating; 2-6-diisopropyl phenol gives a reaction product containing a predominance of diphenoquinones. Aryl, alkoxy, and aryloxy groups, if present in both the 2,6-positions, will provide only diphenoquinones. Table 3.1 presents data on the effect of substituents on molecular weight.

Further, the blocking substituents in the 2,6-positions should not contain groups that will react independently under the conditions of synthesis or react with the catalyst.

The exact limits of substituents has, perhaps, not been entirely established. Hay reported that the reaction of 2-methyl-6-allylphenol and 2,6-allyl-phenol by oxidative coupling will produce only low-molecular-weight oils [7]; whereas Faurote reported having applied the direct oxidative coupling technique to produce high-molecular-weight species from the former by this technique [6].

Within the above limitations, a variety of 2,6-disubstituted phenylene oxides may be synthesized by oxidative coupling.

With regard to the catalyst, any cuprous salt that can exist in the cupric state and form a complex with the tertiary amine that is soluble in the reaction medium is satisfactory. Cuprous chloride, bromide, or azide are preferred for producing highest-molecular-weight products [8]. Suitable tertiary amines are aliphatic amines having at least two straight hydro-carbon chains, N-alkylcyclic amines, and aromatic heterocyclic amines. With N-aryl amines, the basicity is reduced to the point where complexing is difficult and oxidative stability is reduced under the conditions of synthesis. The preferred amine is pyridine.

A study of the reaction mechanisms indicates that the first step of the reaction which leads to the high polymer is the oxidation of the phenyl by Cu(II), followed by carbon-oxygen coupling of two phenoxy radicals:

(I)

$2 \, (I) \longrightarrow$

Superficially, the polymerization process, in the physical aspects, resembles the condensation reaction more than the free-radical reaction [5]. Char-acteristically, a small molecule is split out of the reaction to produce coupling, and the reaction appears to proceed in a stepwise fashion, to build a slow-growing polymer in a statistical manner that reaches higher and higher molecular weights until near the end of the reaction, the average molecular weight shows a rapid increase. Characteristically, the free-radical reaction produces high-molecular-weight species in blend with the monomer at a very rapid rate. However, the analogy with the conden-sation reaction is not entirely exact. The actual route by which the polymer chain grows appears to involve a disproportionation mechanism which pro-duces the monomer and higher polymers from any of the polymeric phenols (dimer, trimer, tetramer, etc.). Toward the end of the reaction, when the concentration of monomer is very small but the molecular weight still quite low, two chains then produce a larger chain and another monomeric unit, by way of a quinol ether equilibration,

and the process is repeated [13].   The disproportionation has been shown to occur when the dimer is exposed to the catalyst in an oxygen-free system and equilibrium constants for redistribution of the dimer have been calculated [17].   The equilibration of the oligomer with other phenols has been reported [19].

The best method for regulating polymeric chain growth is through variations in the reaction conditions, and in particular, the amount of oxygen consumed before neutralization of the catalyst with hydrochloric acid or the like.

The reaction proceeds quite rapidly and exothermically, usually being completed in the presence of excess oxygen in 15 to 20 minutes.   A solvent such as nitrobenzene may be employed where the materials are not soluble in the reactants.   The catalyst complex may or may not be oxidized in advance.

Typical Preparation

A typical synthesis, from the literature, is as follows:

Oxygen was passed for 10 minutes into a reaction mixture containing 5 grams of 2,6-dimethylphenol, 1 gram of Cu_2Cl_2, and 100 ml of pyridine.   During the course of the reaction the temperature rose to a maximum of 70°C.   No water was removed during the course of the reaction.   The product was precipitated by pouring the reaction mixture into about 500 ml of dilute hydrochloric acid and was separated by filtration.

The product, poly(2,6-dimethyl-1,4-phenylene) ether ... was produced in substantially quantitative yields.

This product had a molecular weight of light scattering in the range of 300,000 to 700,000 and did not melt at 300°C. The powder produced on precipitation could be molded, calendered, or extruded under pressure of 2,000 psi into a unitary piece at 240°C. Tough films were made from 10 percent solutions of the polymer in each of the following solvents, (1) benzene, (2) toluene, (3) xylene, (4) tetrahydrofuran, (5) pyridine, by spreading the solutions on a glass surface and removing the film after the solvent had evaporated. These films were oriented by stretching and cold drawing. Fibers were prepared by extruding a saturated xylene solution of the polymer into air. These fibers could also be oriented by stretching and cold drawing [8].

Synthesis by p-Bromophenol Route

As indicated previously, the 2,6-substituted poly(phenylene oxide) may be prepared from the substituted p-halophenol, with bromine being the preferred halogen. The reaction may be written, in simplified form, as follows:

$$(n + 1)KOH + nBr-\overset{CH_3}{\underset{CH_3}{\bigcirc}}-OH \xrightarrow{K_3Fe(CN)_6}$$

Potassium hydroxide   2,6-Methyl-4-bromophenol

$$Br-\overset{CH_3}{\underset{CH_3}{\bigcirc}}\left[O-\overset{CH_3}{\underset{CH_3}{\bigcirc}}\right]_n O-\overset{CH_3}{\underset{CH_3}{\bigcirc}}-OH$$

Polymer

$$+ (n + 1)KBr + (n + 1)H_2O$$

The exact mechanism has not been fully elucidated. It is probable that polymerization is initiated by the phenoxy radical, produced by oxidation of the phenoxide ion by potassium ferricyanide [4]. It is possible that the chain termination occurs as a result of free-radical coupling which could be presented, in simplified form, as

$$R-\overset{CH_3}{\underset{CH_3}{\bigcirc}}-O^\bullet + R-\overset{CH_3}{\underset{CH_3}{\bigcirc}}-O^\bullet \longrightarrow R-\overset{CH_3}{\underset{CH_3}{\bigcirc}}-O-\cdots$$

Free radical   Free radical   Hemiquinoil

This mechanism is in accordance with the finding that polymers prepared under nitrogen contain only one phenol group per 10 polymer molecules; it does not account, however, for the observation that only one bromine per molecule is detected [3, 6].

Molecular weight of the polymer may be varied by the reaction conditions. The reaction is usually run at room temperature with the caustic supplied in a benzene and water mixture. Methanol in place of benzene will produce higher polymers, as will increasing catalyst concentration and lower reaction temperatures. Increased yields are obtained by running the reaction in nitrogen, insofar as oxygen retards the potassium ferricyanide-initiated polymerization [4]. The nature of the substituents will also influence molecular weight, and catalysts other than ferricyanide may be preferred with specific substituents. For example, lead oxide appears to be very efficient in the case of diallyl or dipropyl substituents.

The p-bromophenol intermediate, then, may be used when synthesizing some of the more highly substituted poly(phenylene oxides). Typical compounds are indicated in Table 3.2.

Polyxylenols produced by oxidative coupling and through the p-bromophenol intermediate have been investigated with X rays to determine diffraction patterns. It has been established that they show regions of well-ordered crystallinity, with the polymer from the 4-bromophenol intermediate being somewhat more crystalline than the polymer from xylenol [3]. The substituted p-bromophenol may also be employed in the direct oxidative coupling route, but the bromine ion deactivates the catalyst, necessitating that the catalyst be present in equimolar proportions.

TABLE 3.2 Polymerization of 2,6-Disubstituted 4-Bromophenols in Air with Potassium Ferricyanide as Initiator [4]

4-Bromophenol	[Phenol]/[Catalyst]	Time of shaking, days	Conversion, %	Intrinsic viscosity
2,6-Diallyl-	1/0.005	11	1.6	
	1/0.015	9	16.2	0.087
	1/0.038	7	35.3	0.120
	1/0.071	2	35.5	0.129
	1/0.097	2	36.7	0.189
	1/0.142	4	31.0	0.106
2,6-Dipropyl-	1/0.037	4	5.0	0.094
2-Propyl-6-phenyl	1/0.1	8	10.0	0.058
	1/0.2	8	11.8	0.062
	1/0.3	8	26.7	0.076
2-Propyl-6-methyl	1/0.1	7	34.9	0.168
	1/0.2	7	44.4	0.113
	1/0.3	7	48.3	0.074

MODIFICATION AND FORMULATION

As is evident from the previous discussion, copolymers are possible through the use of variously ortho-substituted phenols. Additionally, differing molecular-weight ranges of both the homo- and copolymer may be synthesized, depending upon application requirements.

Modifications to polyxylenol have included oxidation to the carboxy derivative, side-chain bromination, attachment of quaternary amine side chains, and attachment of tetra-alkylsilane side chains. The result of these modifications has been to reduce temperature resistance [3].

Thermosetting polyphenylene oxides have been produced by the use of copolymers derived from 2,6-dimethyl-4-bromophenol with 2-methyl-6-allyl-4-bromophenol and homopolymers of the latter [10]. These may be crosslinked with heat or may be partially epoxidized with less than equivalent amounts of peracetic acid. The resultant epoxy groups may be reacted with conventional epoxy resin curing agents to shorten the cure times [13]. These crosslinked systems have been suggested as improved high-temperature adhesives and offer somewhat better properties than those obtained with polyxylenol, but they suffer from oxidative instability at temperatures at 260°C and above [3].

Although the polyxylenols are soluble in aromatic hydrocarbons and chlorinated solvents, there are presently no data available on their usefulness in coating formulations. Solution systems have been used for adhesives.

PHYSICAL PROPERTIES

The commercial molding material offered by General Electric Company is a polyxylenol with a molecular weight from 25,000 to 30,000.

The physical properties of the commercially available polyxylenol are indicated in Table 3.3.

Adhesive properties have been investigated on a preliminary basis [2]. On aluminum coupons, tested in tensile shear, polyxylenol, cured 2 minutes at 290°C under 200 psi pressure, provided strengths of 3,440 psi. Longer cure cycles appear to result in excessive oxidation, with consequent reduction in bond strengths. With stainless steel, bond strengths are as indicated in Table 3.4. Better values at 260°C with the allyl-substituted polymers may be attributed to crosslinking during the cure cycle. It is likely that room-temperature strengths of polyxylenol might be improved through proper formulation, perhaps involving use of plasticizers to obtain equivalent wetting at lower bonding temperatures.

Particularly notable, in terms of physical properties, is the low thermal expansion rate of the polyxylenol. This results in excellent serviceability to cryogenic temperatures.

TABLE 3.3 Properties of Grade C-1001 Poly(2,6-dimethylphenylene Oxide) [9]

Property	Average value	Test (ASTM unless otherwise noted)
Color	Light beige, opaque	
Specific gravity	1.06	D 792
Impact strength, notched Izod, ⅛-in. bar, ft-lb/in. of notch	1.5–1.9	D 256
Tensile impact strength, L-type samples, ft-lb/in.^{2}	350–450	D 1822
Tensile strength, psi:		D 638
At 23°C:		
Yield	10,000–11,000	
Fail	9,000–10,000	
At 125°C:		
Yield	5,500–6,500	
Fail	4,500–5,500	
Tensile modulus, psi × 10^{-5}		
At 23°C	3.6–3.8	D 638
At 125°C	3.3–3.4	
Elongation at 23°C, %:		
Yield	6–7	D 638
Fail	50–80	
Creep, 300 hours at 3,000 psi at 23°C, %	0.75	D 674
Water absorption in 7 days, %	0.10	D 570
Flexural strength at 23°C, psi	14,000–15,000	D 790
Flexural modulus at 23°C, psi	3.5–3.8 × 10^5	D 790
Fatigue limit, psi	1,200–2,000	Wohler
Rockwell hardness, R scale	118–120	D 785
Coefficient of friction, rotated against self	0.18–0.23	Bell Labs.
Abrasion loss, Taber abraser, CS-17 wheel, grams	0.017	D 1044
Deflection temperature at 264 psi, °C	190–193	D 648
Coefficient of linear expansion, in./(in.)(°F)	2.7–3.1 × 10^{-5}	D 696
Mold shrinkage, in./in.	0.007	D 955
Flammability	Self-extinguishing	D 635

Retention of accurate dimensional tolerances at elevated temperatures is the prime requirement for range clock timer cams molded from polyphenylene oxide. (General Electric Co.)

TABLE 3.4   Lap Shear Tensile Strength of Poly(2,6-Disubstituted 1,4-Phenylene Oxides) on Stainless Steel [10]

				Tensile Strength, psi‡				
					at 23°C	at 260°C			at 315°C
		Cure						
Description°	Bond†	°C	Minutes		0.5 hour	4 hour	17 hour	0.5 hour
PX	P	288	3	1,240	81			
PX	F	288	3	1,530	49			
PX	....	288	3	3,150	129			
Copolymer 50	....	260	5	1,270	703	545	317	577
	P	204	5	2,540			515	
Copolymer 50	....	260	5	2,135	655			
Copolymer 50	F	198	30	138			938	
Copolymer 70	F	260	30	223			1,132	
PMAP	....	182	30	1,930	245	965	750	
PMAP	F	190	30	2,567	153		500	

° PX = Polyxylenol; poly(2,6-dimethylphenylene oxide).   Copolymer 50 from 50 mole % 2-methyl-6-allyl-4-bromophenol.   Copolymer 70 from 70 mole % 2-methyl-6-allyl-4-bromophenol. PMAP = homopolymer of 2-methyl-6-allyl-4-bromophenol.

† P = applied as powder.   F = applied as film from chloroform solution in PX, from acetone "dough" film in the other polymers.

‡ Average of 2 to 6 tests.

THERMAL PROPERTIES

As indicated in Table 3.3, the polyxylenol molding compounds provide deflection temperature (DTs) of about 190°C.   The glass transition T_g is about 15 to 20°C higher, depending on the method of measurement.

Unstabilized polyxylenol is suitable to service in the 110 to 120°C range for continuous exposure in normal atmospheres.   Above this temperature, progressive surface oxidation will lead to a slowly crosslinking structure, with the attendant loss of elongation.   In an inert atmosphere, the polyxylenols are serviceable to their DTs.   Weight loss by thermogravimetric analysis indicates stability to about the DT, with the polymer losing weight rapidly above that temperature as indicated in Fig. 3.1.

When thermal gravimetric analysis (TGA) is employed to analyze poly-(2,6-dimethyl) and (2-methyl-6-isopropyl-1,4-phenylene) ether, the latter displays improved stability in air (Fig. 3.2).   More marked differences have been observed when the polymers were heated in oxygen at 250°C.   At the end of 90 minutes, the dimethyl material was badly charred and had lost 46 percent of initial weight, whereas the isopropyl material, although darkened, had lost only 1.8 percent of its weight [14].   At 200°C, the former gave a sharply exothermic reaction, by DTA; the latter, a less pronounced one (Fig. 3.3).   On the basis of these data, together with

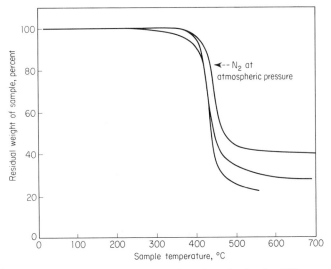

FIG 3.1 *Thermogravimetric analysis of two lots of polyxylenol* [3].

infrared and mass spectrograph data, the oxidative degradation mechanisms proposed in Figs. 3.4 and 3.5 were advanced. The significant difference in performance of the isopropyl polymer indicates that it may be of potential use in higher-temperature applications where crosslinking can be tolerated. Photooxidation proceeds by the same general mechanism as thermal oxidation, but it has been shown to occur initially at a somewhat faster rate [18].

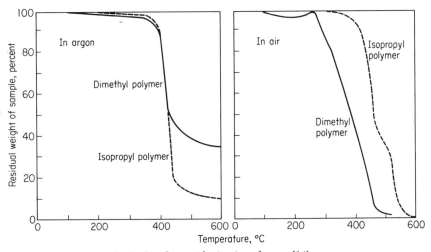

FIG 3.2 *Thermograms of polyphenylene oxides in air and argon* [14].

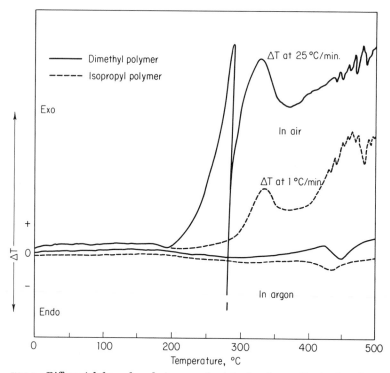

FIG 3.3 *Differential thermal analysis curves for polyphenylene oxides in air and argon* [14].

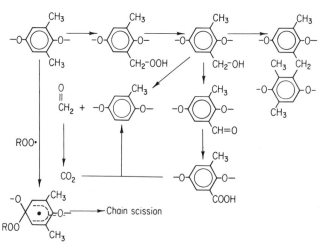

FIG 3.4 *Proposed initial oxidative degradation steps for poly (2,6-dimethyl-1,4-phenylene) oxide* [14].

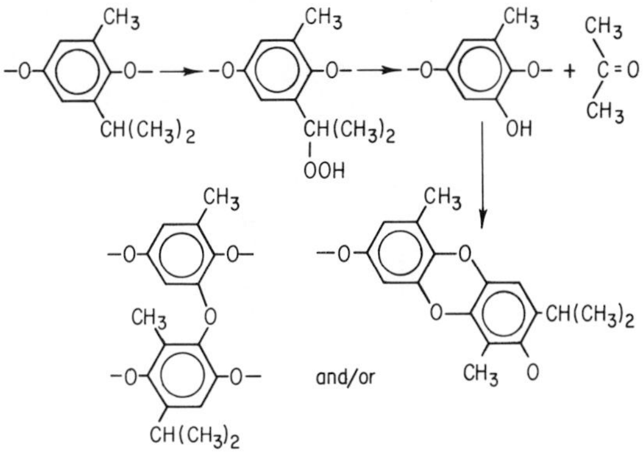

FIG 3.5   *Proposed initial oxidative degradation steps for poly(2-methyl,6-isopropyl-1,4-phenylene) oxide* [14].

PHYSICAL-CHEMICAL PROPERTIES

The polyxylenols provide extremely good resistance to aqueous bases, and acids.   Typical 7-day exposure data are given in Table 3.5.

This good room-temperature chemical resistance is carried over to elevated temperatures.   For example, good resistance to steam autoclaving has been demonstrated.

TABLE 3.5   Chemical Resistance of Grade C-1001 Poly(2,6-dimethylphenylene Oxide) (Immersed 7 days at 23°C) [11]

Reagent	Weight gain, %
Water	0.10
Sulfuric acid, 3%	0.10
Sulfuric acid, 30%	0.08
Nitric acid	0.11
Hydrochloric acid, 10%	0.10
Hydrochloric acid, 38%	0.93
Acetic acid	0.13
Oleic acid	0.08
Sodium hydroxide, 1%	0.11
Sodium hydroxide, 10%	0.09
Ammonium hydroxide, 10%	0.15
Sodium chloride, 10%	0.09
Ethanol, 100%	0.45
Ethanol, 50%	0.34
Sodium carbonate, 2%	0.11
Hydrogen peroxide, 3%	0.12
Dichloroethylene	Dissolved
Toluene	Dissolved
Heptane	0.39
Commercial detergents, 1%	Negligible
Hydrofluoric acid, 48%	2.08

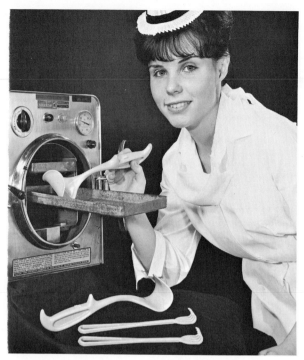

Surgical instruments made of polyphenylene oxide can be sterilized repeatedly in an operating-room autoclave. (General Electric Co.)

Resistance to aliphatic hydrocarbon solvents is somewhat poorer than to acids and bases, with the polymer exhibiting crazing on immersion.

ELECTRICAL PROPERTIES

The dielectric constants of the commercial polyxylenol molding compound are somewhat lower than normally expected of thermoplastics (Table 3.6). The dissipation factor is flatter with temperature and frequency than with similar thermoplastics (Figs. 3.6 and 3.7). Dielectric strength vs. thickness is shown in Fig. 3.8.

PROCESSING CONDITIONS

Because of the high T_g of the polyxylenols, they can be molded only at relatively high temperatures. At these temperatures, the polyxylenols are less sensitive to shear rates than polystyrene, but are somewhat more sensitive than polycarbonates. Typical viscosity data at 338°C are shown in Fig. 3.9.

TABLE 3.6 Dielectric Constant of PPO (C-1001) at a Series of Temperatures and Frequencies [16]

Frequency, cps	Dielectric constant
60	2.56
10^3	2.55
10^4	2.55
10^6	2.55
10^9	2.59

Temperature, °C	Dielectric constant at 60 cps
180	2.52
88	2.54
23	2.56
7	2.55
−196	2.57

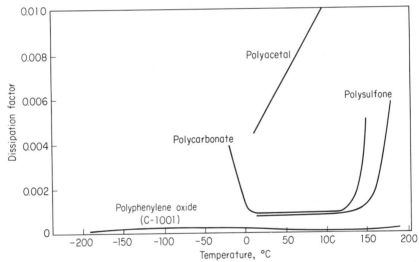

FIG 3.6 *Dissipation factor at 60 cps vs. temperature for high-performance thermoplastics* [16].

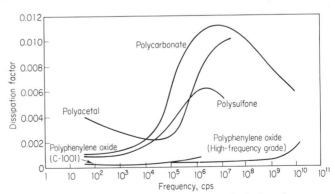

FIG 3.7 *Dissipation factor at 23° C vs. frequency for high-performance thermoplastics* [16].

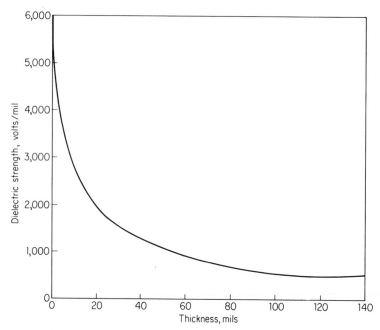

FIG 3.8 *Short-time dielectric strength vs. thickness for PPO* (**C**-1001) [16].

The polyxylenols may be molded in equipment capable of operating above 290°C and with pressures from 8,000 to 20,000 psi. Typical operating data for two different injection presses are given in Table 3.7. The polyxylenols should not be held in the equipment for over 10 minutes at molding temperature.

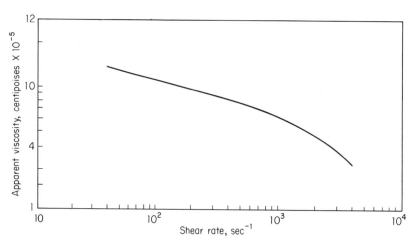

FIG 3.9 *Instron rheometer data for grade* **C**-1001 *poly(2,6-dimethyl*-1,4-*phenylene) oxide at* 338°C [9].

TABLE 3.7 Processing Parameters for Grade C-1001 Poly(2,6-methylphenylene Oxide) [12]

Parameter	Lester ram press		New Britain screw press
Capacity, oz.............	4–6		10
Clamp, tons.............	150		175
Shot size, oz.............	2.5	0.5	5.5
Part description.........	Test bar	Insulator (flat)	Test bar
Part thickness, in........	0.125	0.100 max. 0.019 min.	0.125
Temperatures, °C:			
Hopper	120–135		
Rear	304	304	276
Middle	315	315	315
Front	326	326	321
Nozzle	326	326	326
Mold	135	120	130
Cushion, in.............	⅛–¼	⅛–¼	⅛–¼
Ram speed, in./min			
Screw speed.............	36	60	60
Rpm	....	40	40
Cycle time, seconds:			
Inject	25	7	5
Boost	20	2	2
Hold	20	4	5
Open and close.......	5	5	20
Total	70	16	30

Plastic drinking cups made of polyphenylene oxide remain extremely strong and "squeezable" not only when filled with boiling water (100°C), as shown in the cup on the left, but also when filled with liquid nitrogen (−195°C), at right. (General Electric Co.)

TABLE 3.8 Property-Application Relationship [16]

Property	Connectors	Microwave insulation°	Printed circuits†	Cable wrap‡	Battery cases	Capacitors	Coil forms	Switches	Housings—electrical equipment
Electrical									
High dielectric strength	x	...	...	x	x	x	x	x	x
Low dielectric constant	...	x	x	x	...	x			
Low dissipation factor	x	x	x	x					
Low water absorption	x	...	...	x					
Mechanical and thermal; environmental resistance									
Mechanical properties	x	x	x	...	x	...	x	x	x
High-heat deflection temperature	x	x	x	x	x	x	x	x	x
Dimensional stability:									
Low creep	x	x	x	...	...	...	x	...	x
Low expansion coefficient	x	x	x	...	...	...	x	...	x
Chemical resistance	...	x	x	x	x				
Adhesion to copper	...	x	x	x					
Self-extinguishing, Class 1	x	x	x	x	x	x	x	x	x

° Strip line, radomes, lens, etc.
† Miniaturization, etc.
‡ Flexible, high voltage, etc.

Polyxylenols may be extruded on conventional equipment, operating at 290°C or higher.

APPLICATIONS

Polyxylenol may be supplied as sheets, wire coatings, molded parts, and extrusions.

The combination of high chemical resistance coupled with excellent thermal resistance indicates a market as a replacement for fluorocarbons. The electrical properties make the material suitable for a variety of applications in the electrical-electronics industry as indicated in Table 3.8. A particularly promising potential is in hot-water and steam-pipe applications.

With the elevated temperature resistance, it is possible that the polyxylenol plastics will challenge thermosetting compounds in molding applications.

REFERENCES

1916

1. W. H. Hunter, A. O. Olson, and E. A. Daniels, A Catalytic Decomposition of Certain Phenol Silver Salts, *J. Am. Chem. Soc.* **38**:1761–1771.
2. G. H. Woolett, The Silver Salt of Triiodophenol and Its Catalytic Decompositions, *J. Am. Chem. Soc.* **38**:2474–2478.

1961

3. J. Dickstein and B. D. Halpern, High Temperature Resistant Adhesives, AD 266 452.
4. C. J. Kurian and C. C. Price, Polyethers, XII: Poly(2,6-disubstituted-1,4-phenylene Oxides), *J. Polymer Sci.* **49**:267–275.
5. G. F. Endres and J. Kuriatek, Polymerization by Oxidative Coupling, III: Mechanistic Type in the Copper-Amine Catalyzed Polymerization of 2,6-Dimethylphenol, *J. Polymer Sci.* **58**:593–609.
6. P. D. Faurote and C. L. Segal, Poly(phenylene Oxides): a Brief Review and Some Experimental Results, ACS Pacific Southwest Meeting, December.
7. A. S. Hay, Polymerization by Oxidative Coupling, II: Oxidation of 2,6-Disubstituted Phenols, *J. Polymer Sci.* **58**:581–591.

1963

8. Improvements Relating to the Oxidation of Phenols (to General Electric Co.), Brit. 930,993.

1964

9. R. P. Anderson and A. C. Gowan, PPO Polyphenylene Oxide, a New High Performance Polymer, General Electric Co., Pittsfield, Mass., Chemical Development Operation.
10. H. E. Hoyt et al., Evaluation of Poly(2,6-dimethyl)-1,4-phenylene Oxides and Related Copolymers for High Temperature Adhesive Applications, *J. Appl. Polymer Sci.* **8**:1633–1641.

11. PPO Property and Application Data, Grade C-1001, General Electric Co., Polymer Products Section.
12. PPO Technical Report, Processing, General Electric Co., Polymer Products Section.
13. K. C. Tsou, H. E. Hoyt, and B. D. Halpern, Epoxidation of Poly-2-methyl-6-allyl-1,4-phenylene Oxide and Copolymer of 2-Methyl-6-allyl-4-bromophenol and 2,6-Dimethyl-4-bromophenol, *J. Polymer Sci.*, part A, vol. 2, pp. 4425–4431.

1965

14. R. T. Conley and W. M. Alvino, The Thermo-oxidative Degradation of Poly(phenylene) Ether, ACS Symposium, Atlantic City, N.J., September.
15. G. D. Cooper, H. S. Blanchard, G. E. Endres, and H. Finkbeiner, Studies on the Mechanism of Oxidative Polymerization of 2,6-Xylenol, Preprints of Contributed Papers on Polymer Chemistry, ACS Western Regional Meeting, Los Angeles, November.
16. A. Gowan and P. Shenian, Properties and Electrical/Electronic Applications for Polyphenylene Oxide Plastics, *Insulation*, September, pp. 129–132.

1966

17. G. D. Cooper, A. R. Gilbert, and H. Finkbeiner, The Redistribution of Hydroxyarylene Ethers, ACS Symposium, Phoenix, Ariz., January.
18. P. G. Kelleher, L. B. Jassie, and B. D. Gesner, Thermal and Photo-oxidation of Poly(2,6-dimethyl-1,4-phenylene) Oxide, ACS Meeting, New York, September.
19. D. M. White, Synthesis of Hydroxyarylene Ethers by Equilibration of Poly(2,6-xylylene Oxide) with Phenols, ACS Symposium, Phoenix, Ariz., January.
20. C. C. Price, Polyxylenol, *J. Paint Technol.* 38:705–709.

Poly(p-Xylylenes)

Poly(p-xylylenes) are prepared by the pyrolytic decomposition of di-p-xylylene and the subsequent polymerization of the active intermediate, p-xylylene, on a cooled surface. The materials are commercially available in chlorinated and nonchlorinated grades; they are also supplied in film form and are suitable for thin-film decomposition by, essentially, vacuum-deposition techniques. As of 1966, pilot-plant capacity was limited to the processing of only several thousand pounds of material per year.

4

Poly(p-xylylene) was first obtained by conversion of p-xylene to the reactive intermediate, p-xylylene, by vacuum pyrolysis at from 900 to 950°C. The intermediate, on condensation, spontaneously polymerizes. Other methods have been employed, involving the reactive intermediate from p-xylyltrimethylammonium hydroxide or organometallic intermediates [1]. In 1961, a series of patents to Union Carbide Corporation disclosed a new synthetic route for the production of the polymer. This work, involving the intermediate di-p-xylylene, was more fully described by W. F. Gorham in 1965 [6]. The new synthesis route resulted in the commercial introduction of poly(p-xylylene) films under the generic name, parylene. Subsequently, Union Carbide reported additional work on the synthesis of substituted poly(p-xylylenes) by alternate routes.

Errede and coworkers have produced poly(p-xylylene) at low temperatures in toluene [2] and investigated its moldability and thermal stability [3] in addition to synthesizing phosphorus-containing poly(p-xylylenes) of improved processability [4].

SYNTHESIS

Vacuum Pyrolysis

The commercial synthesis of poly(p-xylylene) is accomplished by vacuum, vapor-phase pyrolysis of di-p-xylylene to the reactive intermediate, p-xylylene, which then spontaneously polymerizes, on cooling, to the polymer. The reaction is as follows:

Di-p-Xylylene p-Xylylene

Poly(p-xylylene)

The reaction continues through the free-radical mechanism to produce the polymer. The yield is quantitative, and, provided temperatures are not too high, the polymer is linear with a molecular weight of about 500,000 [5].

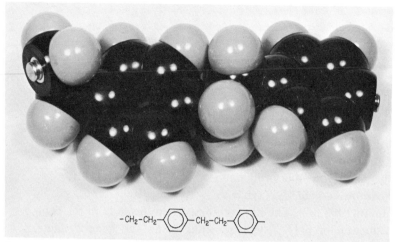

*Atom model of poly-*p-*xylylene.* (The Epoxylite Corporation.)

The di-*p*-xylylene is produced by pyrolyzing *p*-xylene in steam at 950°C and is collected in a 15 percent yield with a 60 percent efficiency [5].

Tests conducted with unsymmetrically substituted di-*p*-xylylenes indicate that both methylene bridges are cleaved either simultaneously or sequentially during pyrolysis, and that the reactive intermediate is, in fact, the *p*-xylylene. Two molecules of *p*-xylylene react as indicated in the previous formula to produce the dinuclear species; growth then continues by the addition of new *p*-xylylene molecules. The polymer grows to the point where it interacts with an adjacent polymeric unit or until the reactive sites become buried in the polymer network. Produced from di-*p*-xylylene, poly(*p*-xylylene) will contain a radical concentration of 5–10×10^{-4} mole of free electrons per mole of xylylene [8].

A description from the literature indicates the synthesis:

The pyrolysis reactions were carried out in a 24-in. section of 1-in. I.D. Vycor tubing. The first 6 in. of the tube served as a distillation zone and the following 18-in. section as the pyrolysis zone. The pyrolysis tube was connected by appropriate glass connections to a glass deposition chamber. A measured quantity of di-*p*-xylylene or ring-substituted derivative was placed in a porcelain boat and the boat placed in the distillation zone. The system was then closed and evacuated to 1 to 100 microns, depending on the derivative in question. The di-*p*-xylylene was distilled at the rate of 1 gram every 3 or 4 minutes through the pyrolysis zone. To achieve this rate, the distillation zone was maintained at temperatures ranging from 140 to 220°C, depending on the derivative. The pyrolysis zone was heated to 600°C.... The pyrolysis gases were then led into a deposition chamber. The glass joints leading from the pyrolysis zone to the deposition chamber were maintained at about 200°C to prevent premature polymerization.   The deposition chamber was usually held at room temperature, although with some derivatives it was heated as high as 160°C to permit deposition of polymer over a fairly broad area [8].

p-Xylylenes produced from di-p-xylylene by the vacuum pyrolysis technique may contain substituents.   A number of these have been investigated, among them chlorinated and brominated versions, and compounds with alkyl, cyano, acetyl, and carbomethoxy groups.   Experimental data on

Semi-works-scale parylene production unit at Union Carbide's Plastics Division facility in Bound Brook, N.J.   The polymerization chamber at far left is a 10-pass foil-coating unit which produces insulated foil used in the construction of capacitors.   Parylene N dimer is charged into the sublimator (horizontal tube at far right).   The vapor passes through a throttle which controls the rate of admission to the furnace (large horizontal section).   Pyrolysis takes place in the furnace, and the resulting p-xylylene is introduced into the polymerization chamber where it condenses and polymerizes on the foil.   Dozens of sensing elements provide accurate readout of temperature, pressure, vapor concentration, and other factors in all sections of the reactor and polymerization chamber, and make possible precise control of the process.   (Union Carbide Corp.)

the preparation of several of these species are given in Table 4.1. With the unsymmetrically substituted di-p-xylylenes, two homogeneous polymers can be obtained as a result of pyrolysis: one substituted, the other unsubstituted, the two condensing with spontaneous polymerization at different temperatures.

Synthesis from Para-substituted Styrenes

By the selection of suitable substituents, styrenes have been equilibrated to p-xylylenes, these spontaneously polymerizing to the linear polymers.

A suitable substitution is the p-cyanophenyl methyl group. A styrene containing this substituent will, in the presence of a base catalyst sufficiently strong to allow substantially complete ionization of the acetonitrile proton, rearrange to the p-xylylene. The reaction in simplified form is as follows:

α-Cyano-α-phenyl-α′-methyl-p-xylylene

The p-xylylene intermediate then polymerizes by a free-radical mechanism to give the polymer

I

A suitable catalyst for the reaction is potassium *tert*-butoxide in *tert*-butyl alcohol. The solvent provides a high concentration of labile protons together with low reactivity toward the nitrile group.

The actual reaction, however, is somewhat more complicated than indi-

TABLE 4.1 Experimental Data on Preparation of Several Poly-p-xylylenes [8]

Di-p-xylylene (DPX) derivative	Polymer produced	Weight of dimer, grams	Distillation temperature, °C	Pyrolysis temperature, °C	Length of run, minutes	Weight of product, grams°	Weight of extracted polymer, grams†	Conversion, %
Di-p-xylylene	Poly-p-xylylene	1.50	175	600	20	.....	1.50	100
Di-p-xylylene	Poly-p-xylylene	1.00	175	550	20	.....	1.00	100
Di-p-xylylene	Poly-p-xylylene	1.00	175	500	20	.....	0.50	50
Di-p-xylylene	Poly-p-xylylene	1.00	175	400	20	.....	0.06	6
Dichloro-DPX	Poly(chloro-p-xylylene)‡	3.00	150–160	600	30	3.00	3.00	100
		2.00	150–160	500	20	1.96	0.29	16
Dibromo-DPX	Poly(bromo-p-xylylene)§	3.00	165–175	660	18	2.86	2.86	
Dicyano-DPX	Poly(cyano-p-xylylene)	4.00	170–180	660	15	3.52	3.52	
Tetrachloro-DPX	Poly(dichloro-p-xylylene)	2.00	165–175	660	20	.....	1.82	
Dimethyl-DPX	Poly(methyl-p-xylylene)	2.00	150	660	12	1.5		
Diethyl-DPX	Poly(ethyl-p-xylylene)	2.00	160	660	12	1.8		

° Stripped from walls of deposition chamber. Remainder of polymer deposited in tubing and traps.
† Product extracted with refluxing toluene or carbon tetrachloride for 1 hour and then dried to constant weight.
‡ An elemental analysis was obtained on the polymer. Calculated for C_8H_7Cl: C, 69.35; H, 5.05; Cl, 25, 60. Found: C, 69.3; H, 5.1; Cl, 25.6.
§ A bromine analysis was obtained on the polymer. Calculated for C_8H_7Br: Br, 43.7. Found Br, 43.7.

cated in the above equation, and competing reactions occur.   One that appears of practical consequence is the following, in simplified form:

$$\underset{C_6H_5}{\overset{C{\equiv}N}{\ominus C}}{-}\langle C_6H_4\rangle{-}CH{=}CH_2 + \underset{C_6H_5}{\overset{C{\equiv}N}{HC}}{-}\langle C_6H_4\rangle{-}CH{=}CH_2 \xrightarrow{+H}$$

$$\underset{C_6H_5}{\overset{C{\equiv}N}{HC}}{-}\langle C_6H_4\rangle{-}CH_2{-}CH_2{-}\underset{C_6H_5}{\overset{C{\equiv}N}{C}}{-}\langle C_6H_4\rangle{-}CH{=}CH_2$$

II

The resultant structure is incapable of further polymerization by the first route.

Analysis of the reaction product of the polymerization of the substituted styrenes through the p-xylylene intermediate indicates that in a typical run, the resultant polymer contained approximately 25 percent of the reaction product expected of reaction II and 75 percent of that expected of reaction I.

A typical description of the synthesis is as follows:

> (p-Vinylphenyl)phenylacetonitrile, 2.0 grams (0.0096 mole), was refluxed over-night under argon in 10 ml of anhydrous tert-butyl alcohol containing 0.0044 mole of potassium tert-butoxide. The polymeric product, 1.5 grams, was recovered by pouring the red reaction mixture into water and washing the resultant precipitate with water and methanol. The crude product was purified by reprecipitation from acetone into cyclohexane and from methylene chloride into petroleum ether (b.p. 40 to 60°C) to yield 0.8 gram of polymer softening at about 190°C [10].

During the course of the same research [10], the structure of the substituted poly(p-xylylene) was confirmed by the independent synthesis of the material from the 1,6-elimination of hydrogen chloride from α-cyano-α-phenyl-α′-methyl-α′-chloroxylene.   In this reaction, the expected 1,2-elimination did not occur, and this fact, together with the speed of the reaction, led to the conclusion that the reaction proceeded through a xylylene intermediate.

MODIFICATION AND FORMULATION

The modifications which may theoretically be introduced in the poly-(p-xylylenes) may be affected through the selection of suitable substituted precursors. The effect of selected substituents on mechanical properties is given in Table 4.2. The unsubstituted species are poorly soluble, except in strong solvents and at elevated temperatures. The alkyl-substituted products may be dissolved in chlorinated solvents at room temperature, but their properties as coatings have not been reported in the literature.

PHYSICAL PROPERTIES

The commercially available poly(*p*-xylylenes) are of two types: parylene N [poly(*p*-xylylene)] and parylene C [poly(monochloro-*p*-xylylene)]. Comparison of the commercial materials with other linear polymers is shown in Table 4.3. Comparative light-transmission data are given in Fig. 4.1; comparative stress-strain data in Fig. 4.2.

The commercially available materials are supplied as the dimer or as vacuum-deposited films in a custom coating service.

Replication of submicroscopic detail is shown by this parylene C replica of a screw dislocation in a crystal of polyethylene. Magnification 36,300×. *The heights of the dislocation lines average* 100 Å *or about* 1/2500 mil. (Union Carbide Corp.)

TABLE 4.2 Mechanical and Thermal Properties of Several Poly-*p*-xylylenes [8]

Property	Poly-*p*-xylylene	Poly(chloro-*p*-xylylene)	Poly(bromo-*p*-xylylene)	Poly(dichloro-*p*-xylylene)	Poly(cyano-*p*-xylylene)	Poly(methyl-*p*-xylylene)	Poly(ethyl-*p*-xylylene)
Room-temperature Tensile Properties°							
Tensile strength, psi	9,000	13,000	8,000	6,000	8,700	9,500	11,000
Secant modulus, psi	350,000	400,000	400,000	400,000	435,000	400,000	175,000
Elongation at break, %	10–200	200	30	5–10	7–12	230	275
Thermal Properties†							
Crystalline melting point, °C	<400	280–300	270	>300	270	200–210	160–170
Glass transition temperature, °C	60–70	80–100	80	110	90	50–60	25
Tensile modulus at 200°C, psi	25,000	25,000	20,000	25,000	20,000	<1,000	<100

° Measured on 1- to 2-mil films in Instron tensile tester at 10% strain/min.
† From secant modulus-temperature curve. Melting points also obtained from x-ray data and from melting behavior in sealed melting-point tubes.

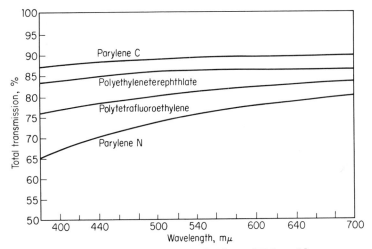

FIG 4.1 *Comparison of light transmission of Mylar and Teflon with parylenes* [6].

THERMAL PROPERTIES

As indicated in Table 4.2, the melting points of the poly(*p*-xylylenes) range from 290 to about 400°C. The T_g is from 60 to 100°C. The secant modulus of typical compounds is indicated in Fig. 4.3. Even at cryogenic temperatures excellent flexibility is maintained. For example, a 2-mil film will withstand six 180° bends before failure at −200°C. Physical properties are unaffected by thermal cycles from 2°K to room temperature.

The thermal stability of the poly(*p*-xylylenes) in air is not exceptional.

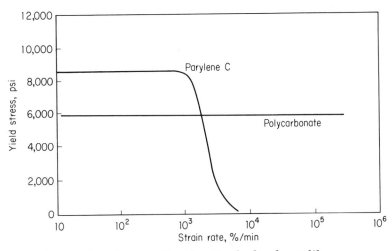

FIG 4.2 *Stress-strain performance of parylene C and polycarbonate* [6].

TABLE 4.3   Physical Properties of Parylene and Other Polymers [6]

Property	Parylene N	Parylene C	PE terephthalate	TFE resin
Secant modulus, 1% strain, psi.......	350,000	400,000	650,000	85,000
Tensile strength, psi°..............	9,000	13,000	26,000	3,400
Elongation to break, %°...........	200	200	170	300
Density, g/cc...................	1.103–1.120	1.289	1.397	2.16
Index of refraction................	1.669	1.629	1.50–1.57	
T (melting), °C†..................	>400	280–300	260	330
T (glass) transition, °C†.............	60–70	80–100	95–105	−100
T_5 (where modulus is 100,000), °C†...	165	125	130	10
T_4 (where modulus is 10,000) °C†....	....	250	245	200

° Measured at 10% strain/min.
† Taken from secant-modulus-temperature curve (Fig. 4.3).

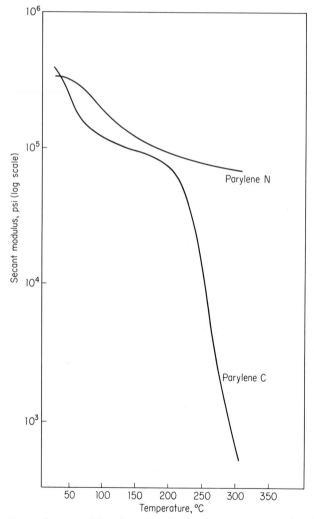

FIG 4.3   *Secant modulus of parylene N & C vs. temperature* [6].

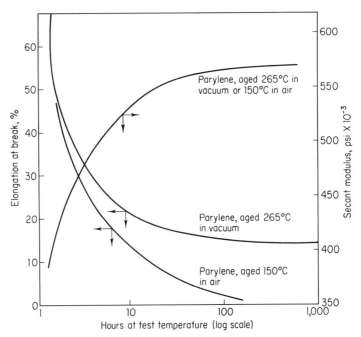

FIG 4.4 *Percent elongation and secant modulus of parylene N vs. aging time* [6].

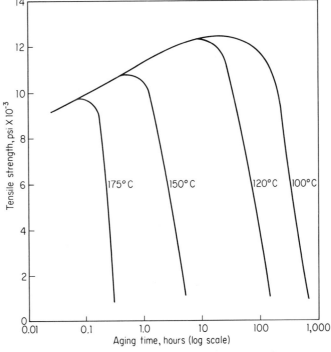

FIG 4.5 *Tensile strength of parylene N vs. aging time at various temperatures* [6].

Short-time service is limited to about 100°C or slightly higher for the chlorinated species. The effect of aging on elongation and modulus is shown in Fig. 4.4, and on tensile strength in Fig. 4.5. In inert atmospheres, the chlorinated material is not serviceable to as high temperatures as the unsubstituted material (i.e., 265 vs. 350°C), in accordance with its lower melting point.

A study of the oxidative degradation process indicates that the following is the most probable route:

The activation energy for the oxidative degradation was determined to be 16.8 kcal [7].

PHYSICAL-CHEMICAL PROPERTIES

The poly(p-xylylenes) show good dimensional stability in the range of 35 to 95 percent relative humidity, as indicated in Table 4.4. Gas permeability is shown in Table 4.5 and compared with other linear polymers in Table 4.6. The polymers are generally insoluble up to about 150°C. At 270°C they are soluble in chlorinated biphenyls, but upon cooling to 160°C they crystallize as a gel.

Weathering of the polymers, from accelerated testing, indicates unsatisfactory performance on exposures for extended periods to sunlight and standard atmospheres, embrittlement being the main problem encountered.

TABLE 4.4 Comparison of Dimensional Stability of Films over Range 35 to 95% Relative Humidity at 40°C [6]

Film	*Change* $\times 10^{-5}$ *in./(in.)* (*% relative humidity*)
Parylene C..........................	0.25
Polycarbonate	0.70
Phenoxy	2.9
Cellulose triacetate..................	3.2
Polyethylene terephthalate.............	3.0

TABLE 4.5 Permeability Characteristics of Several Poly-p-xylylenes [8]

Polymer	Test gas				
	Moisture vapor†	Hydrogen°	Carbon dioxide°	Oxygen°	Nitrogen°
Poly-p-xylylene	14	250	225	30	9
Poly(chloro-p-xylylene)	1.0	200	12	5	0.7
Poly(bromo-p-xylylene)	0.6	75	6	4	0.1
Poly(dichloro-p-xylylene)	5.0		130	30	4.5
Poly(cyano-p-xylylene)	30	295	50	15	
Poly(methyl-p-xylylene)	1.1	166	44	9.5	2.6
Poly(ethyl-p-xylylene)	4.1	716	314	83	15

° Permeability to test gases at 23°C, in $(cc)(STP)(mils)/(100\ in.^2)(24\ hr)$.
† Permeability to moisture vapor at 23°C, in $g\text{-}mils/(24\ hr)(atm)(100\ in.^2)$.

TABLE 4.6 Barrier Properties of Parylene and Polymer Films [6]

Polymer 2-mil films	Gas permeability, $cc\text{-}mil/(100\ in.^2)(24\ hr)(atm)$			Moisture-vapor transmission, $g\text{-}mil/(100\ in.^2)$ (24 hr)
	N_2	O_2	CO_2	
Parylene N	9	30	225	14
Parylene C	0.7	5	12	1
Polyvinylidene chloride	0.2	1.0	3.8	1
Polyethylene terephthalate	1.0	1.8	25	3
Polyethylene	135	350	1,400	21
Polytetrafluoroethylene	290	770	1,833	3
Polystyrene	40	200	900	120

TABLE 4.7 Electrical Properties of Several Poly-p-xylylenes [8]

Electrical properties	Poly-p-xylylene	Poly(methyl-p-xylylene)	Poly(chloro-p-xylylene)	Poly(dichloro-p-xylylene)
Dielectric constant at 1,000 cps	2.65	2.48	3.1	2.82
Dissipation factor at 1,000 cps	0.0002	0.0025	0.02	0.003
Dielectric strength, volts/mil (1–3-mil films)	6,000	6,000	3,700	5,000

ELECTRICAL PROPERTIES

The electrical properties of various poly(p-xylylenes) are given in Table 4.7 and compared with other plastics in Table 4.8.

PROCESSING CONDITIONS

Vacuum-deposited films of poly(p-xylylene) may be applied to small objects in thicknesses from 0.002 (500 Å) to about 5 mils, provided the objects to be coated are stable to vacuum. The films are in the main deposited at or near room temperature.

If polymerization is conducted in an aqueous solution, the material may be obtained in the particulate form. The powders have no present commercial use.

Free films may be obtained by deposition onto a cold condenser, then stripping off. Free-film membranes up to 3 in. in diameter and as thin as 500 Å have been produced.

APPLICATIONS

Because they are in the early experimental stages, the poly(p-xylylenes) are quite expensive, prices for thin films being about $1,000 per lb.

The presence of the almost invisible film of parylene N aluminum foil used in capacitors is readily demonstrated by exposing it to a chemical that will react with aluminum. Sodium hydroxide solution dropped on the coated film at left shows no reaction; uncoated foil at right is rapidly attacked. (Union Carbide Corp.)

TABLE 4.8 Typical Electrical Properties of Parylene and Other Polymers
(Tests conducted on 3-mil films) [6]

Property	Parylene N	Parylene C	Polyethylene terephthalate	TFE resin
Dielectric strength at standard temperature,				
volts/mil	6,500	3,700		
Corrected to ⅛ in.	700	520	780	480
Dielectric strength, step by step, volts/mil	6,000	1,200		
Corrected to ⅛ in.	550	410	510	430
Volume resistivity at 23°C, ohms	1.4×10^{17}	8.8×10^{16}	1.6×10^{16}	2.8×10^{16}
Surface resistivity at 23°C, ohms:				
At 50% relative humidity	10^{13}	10^{14}		
At 90% relative humidity	9×10^{11}	7×10^{11}	10^{12}	3×10^{12}
Dielectric constant:				
At 60 cps	2.65	3.1	3.27	2.08
At 1 kc/sec	2.65	3.1	3.27	2.08
At 100 kc/sec	2.65	3.0	3.19	2.08
At 1,000 kc/sec	2.65	2.9	....	2.08
Dissipation factor:				
At 60 cps	0.0002	0.02	0.00145	0.00012
At 1 kc/sec	0.0002	0.0195	0.00424	0.00013
At 100 kc/sec	0.0004	0.0156	0.0163	0.00004
At 1,000 kc/sec	0.0006	0.0128	....	0.00005

Encapsulation of reactive chemicals in thin parylene C coatings provides protection. Parylene-coated lithium metal granules at left exhibit no reaction with water on which they float. Unprotected granules at right react instantly and violently with water. (Union Carbide Corp.)

The material is used as the primary dielectric in special capacitors (Kemet Brand ML-1), which can be used at 170°C (vs. 123°C for comparable capacitors), which have better frequency response and lower dissipation factor, and yet are only one-fifth the size of a polystyrene capacitor of equivalent rating [9].

The polymer can be deposited on heat-sensitive surfaces, provided only that the surface is stable to vacuum. Solid chemicals may be encapsulated in it.

In addition to its use in electrical applications, it has potential for thin-film use in holding reactive chemicals, for specialized packaging, and as thin-film windows in optical instruments. The polymer has also been used experimentally as a coating for heat-transfer condensers, where it provides an economic advantage over noble metals [11]. In this application, the coating promotes drop condensation, thus eliminating films of the condensate and increasing heat-transfer efficiencies up to 38 percent over uncoated metal.

REFERENCES

1958

1. L. A. Errede and M. Szwarc, Chemistry of p-Xylylene and Analogs and Polymers, *Quart. Rev.* (London) **12**:301.

1962

2. L. A. Errede and R. S. Gregorian, Xylylenes, XIII: Crystallinity and Cross Linking in Poly(p-xylylene), *J. Polymer Sci.* **60**:21–32.
3. L. A. Errede and N. Knoll, Xylylenes, XIV: Moldability and Thermal Stability of Poly-(p-xylylene) and Related Polymers, *J. Polymer Sci.* **60**:33–42.

1963

4. L. A. Errede, Phosphorus Containing Poly-p-xylylenes and Related Polymers, Brit. 920,515.

1965

5. Aromatic Polymers Move into Specialties, *C&E News*, March 1.
6. Bakelite Parylene, Union Carbide Plastics Product Data Sheet, J-2660,026-5.
7. R. T. Conley, Stability of Condensation Polymers in Oxygen Containing Atmospheres, Proceedings of the Symposium on High Temperature Polymers: Synthesis and Degradation, ACS Western Regional Meeting, Los Angeles, November.
8. W. F. Gorham, A New, General Method for The Preparation of Linear Poly(p-xylylenes), ACS Symposium, Detroit, April.
9. The Invisible Polymer, *Bakelite Rev.*, July, pp. 7–8.
10. Kluiber, Equilibrium of *para*-Substituted Styrenes to Produce p-Xylylenes, *J. Org. Chem.* **6**:2037–2041.
11. Parylene Coating Promotes Dropwise Condensation Tubes, *C&E News*, October 18.

5

Aromatic Polysulfones

Although the aliphatic polysulfones have been known since the beginning of the twentieth century, the aromatic materials were not synthesized until the late 1950s and were not offered commercially until 1965. The materials are produced through the reaction of p,p'-dichlorodiphenyl sulfone and the disodium salt of bisphenol A to give linear polymers having molecular weights ranging from 30,000 to 60,000.

The aromatic polysulfones were introduced as molding powders, where they provide exceptionally good physical and electrical properties to temperatures of about 150°C. The oxidative stability at these temperatures is exceptionally good, although resistance to weathering and ultraviolet is less satisfactory. Adhesive systems have also been developed.

The molding materials generally can be processed on conventional molding equipment, although processing temperatures higher than normal are required. The adhesive materials are applied by hot-melt or solution techniques.

The aliphatic polysulfones were originally synthesized in 1898 by Russian workers and subsequently investigated by German, Dutch, and English researchers. They were originally prepared through the reaction of sulfur dioxides with olefins; and subsequently, by the oxidation of polymeric sulfides as well as by condensation of bifunctional reactants of which at least one contained a sulfone group. Lack of thermal stability of the aliphatic polysulfones has been one of the chief difficulties in commercial utilization of these resins. Many are thermodynamically unstable at temperatures below their softening point. A comprehensive review of the aliphatic polysulfones, together with 214 references, is given by Gaylord [2].

In 1958 production of aromatic polysulfones was claimed [1]. The materials were produced from the reaction of p,p'-dihalodiphenyl sulfone with the disodium salt of an aromatic dithiol. Subsequently, in 1964, aromatic polysulfones containing ether links were introduced commercially by Union Carbide Plastics Company. In 1965, they came on stream with a plant having a capacity of 10 million lb per year.

SYNTHESIS

The commercial aromatic polysulfones are produced by reacting the disodium salt of bisphenol A with p,p'-dichlorodiphenyl sulfone in dimethyl sulfoxide and chlorobenzene [4].

The reaction can be written:

Disodium salt of bisphenol A p,p'-Dichlorodiphenyl sulfone

Polysulfone   Salt

The commercial materials have n numbers from 60 to 120 with corresponding molecular weights from 30,000 to 60,000.

MODIFICATION AND FORMULATION

Aromatic polysulfones may be developed from any of the wide variety of diphenols available to the technology, and results might be expected to follow, broadly, those obtained when other phenols are substituted for bisphenol A in the phenoxy technology. However, data are not available on the effect of these modifications.

The selection of bisphenol A introduces the isopropylidine link in the linear polymers. This, without sacrifice to hydrolytic stability, improves processability by lowering the melting point of the polymer. The aromatic ether links provide rotation points and contribute toughness to the final structure. The combination of properties, coupled with the low cost of the bisphenol A, may well approach optimum for molding-grade aromatic polysulfones. Higher heat-resistance polymers, however, remain a possibility by the use of phenols other than bisphenol A.

The aromatic polysulfones may be dissolved in a number of more active solvents. Typical of the solvents, and the resultant viscosities, are those shown in Table 5.1. The effects of solvent blends on viscosities are shown in Table 5.2.

The commercially available aromatic polysulfone moldings compounds are suited to dry coloring with certain dyes, but dry coloring with pigments is not recommended (see Table 5.3). A variety of colors, both opaque and transparent, can be supplied by the manufacturer.

Other modifications, such as the use of plasticizers and ultraviolet stabilizers, have not been suggested in the literature. Stabilizers for the polysulfones have been suggested [3].

Atom model of aromatic polysulfone from bischlorophenyl sulfone and bisphenol A. (The Epoxylite Corporation.)

PHYSICAL PROPERTIES

Aromatic polysulfones are presently available in two injection molding grades, P-1700 (light amber) and P-1710 (opaque ivory) from Union Carbide Plastics Company. Corresponding extrusion grades, those having higher molecular weights, are P-3500 and P-3510. Various colors are supplied on special order. An adhesive grade is available under the designation Sulfone Resin 47. An infrared spectrum of a film of polysulfone is shown in Fig. 5.1.

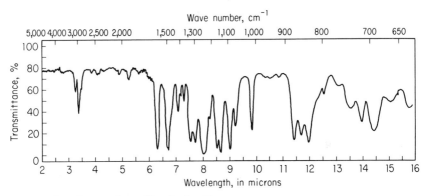

FIG 5.1   *Infrared curve of cast film of polysulfone.*

Physical properties of typical aromatic polysulfones are shown in Table 5.4. Properties are compared with those of other thermoplastics in Table 5.5. A comparison of creep properties is given in Fig. 5.2. Tensile fatigue resistances for several polymers are compared in Fig. 5.3.

When used as adhesives, applied in the 100 percent solids form by heating to the liquid stage, followed by cooling, the aromatic polysulfones provide

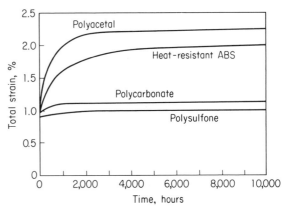

FIG 5.2   *Creep resistance of thermoplastic polymers* (3,000 psi *stress at* 23°C) [9].

*Flexural creep tests of polysulfone and other plastics at 150°C and 1,500 psi
tensile stress after 100 hours. Transparent and opaque specimens of polysulfone at left have undergone a barely visible deformation. Polycarbonate
at right front has deformed to the limit allowed by the holder, and polyacetal
at right rear has failed by fracture.* (Union Carbide Corp.)

lap shear strengths relatively independent of molecular weights, as shown
in Table 5.6. Bond strengths, too, are relatively independent of glue-line
thickness, as indicated in Fig. 5.4 for lap shear aluminum joints and in
Table 5.7 for peel strengths on aluminum joints. Bond strengths to steel
joints are indicated in Table 5.8. Creep, at room temperature, under
a dead load of 1,600 psi for 8 days is <0.00005 in., compared to the allowable limit of 0.015 in. in MIL-A-5090D.

THERMAL PROPERTIES

The aromatic polysulfones are relatively resistant to oxidation because
the sulfur atom is in its highest oxidation state and because the sulfone

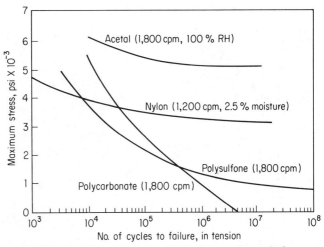

FIG 5.3 *Tensile fatigue strength of thermoplastic polymers* [11].

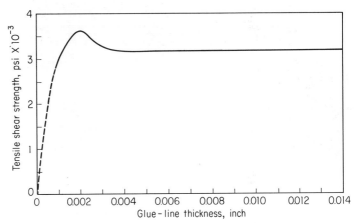

FIG 5.4 *Effect of glue-line thickness on aromatic polysulfone bonded joints* [16].

TABLE 5.1 Viscosities of Aromatic Polysulfone Solutions [16]

Solvent	Solids, %	Gardner-Holdt viscosity	Brookfield viscosity, centipoises
Acetophenone	20	Z	2,250
Chloroform	20	X	1,300
Cyclohexanone	20	Z1	2,700
Chlorobenzene	20	K	275
Chlorobenzene	30	Z4–Z5	8,000
Dimethylformamide	20	Z	2,250
Dioxane	20	X–Y	1,500
Methylene chloride..............	20	W	1,070
Tetrahydrofuran	20	L	300

Polysulfone, exposed to the flame of an acetylene torch, burns but is self-extinguishing as soon as the flame is removed. Formation of a crust of porous carbon insulates the interior of the bar and greatly slows combustion. (Union Carbide Corp.)

TABLE 5.2   Viscosities of Solvent Blends [16]

Solvent blend	Weight ratio of solvents	Solids, %	Gardner-Holdt viscosity	Brookfield viscosity, centipoises
Toluene/cyclohexanone	50/50	20	U	627
Toluene/cyclohexanone	75/25	20	U	627
Toluene/acetone°	70/30	30	Z–ZI	2,500
Toluene/acetone/cyclohexanone	65/25/10	20	P	400
		25	X–Y	1,500
		30	Z–ZI	2,500
	35/15/50	20	T	550
Xylene/cyclohexanone	50/50	20	M	325

° Cannot be diluted below 30% solids.

TABLE 5.3   Colorants to Use with Polysulfone [6]

Color	Manufacturer	Trade name
Blue	American Aniline	Oil Blue
Blue-green	American Cyanamid	Cyan Blue Toner
Green	American Cyanamid	GT Solvent Green 3
	Hilton Davis	1915
		Synthaline Green
Orange	American Aniline	Amaplast Red GG
Purple	American Aniline	Amaplast Violet PT
Violet	American Cyanamid	Oil Violet IRS
Red	American Aniline	Amaplast Rubinol
Yellow	American Aniline	Quinoline Yellow

groups tend to draw electrons from the adjacent benzene rings to stabilize them against oxidation.

The deflection temperature of the commercial polymers is about 175°C under 264 psi fiber stress. Above this temperature, deflection is relatively rapid. At 180°C, 10-mil deflection will occur under 66 psi fiber stress. The glass transition temperature lies in this region, depending on the

TABLE 5.4   Typical Properties of Aromatic Polysulfone [10]

Property	Value
Specific gravity	1.24
Tensile strength at yield, psi	10,200
Tensile modulus, psi	360,000
Tensile elongation, %:	
To yield	5–6
To break	50–100
Tensile creep after 2 years at 3,000 psi, %	1.05
Flexural strength at yield, psi	15,400
Flexural modulus, psi	390,000
Compressive strength at yield, psi	13,900
Compressive modulus, psi	370,000
Shear strength, psi:	
At yield	6,000
Ultimate	9,000
Notched Izod impact strength, ft-lb/in.:	
¼ in.	1.3
⅛ in.	1.3
⅛ in. at −40°C	1.2
Rockwell hardness	M69(R120)
Coefficient of thermal expansion, in./(in.)(°F)	3.1×10^{-5}
Mold shrinkage, in./in.	0.0076
Taber abrasion resistance, CS-17 wheel, 1,000-g load, 1,000 cycles, mg weight loss	20
Coefficient of friction (static):	
Against polysulfone	0.67
Against steel	0.40

TABLE 5.5 Properties at Room Temperature of Aromatic Polysulfone vs. Other Polymers [14]

Property	ASTM method	Poly-sulfone	PPO	PVDC
Specific gravity	D 792	1.24	1.06	1.54
Water absorption in 24 hr, %	D 570	0.22	0.06	0.11
Tensile yield strength, 10^{-3} psi	D 638	10.2	10–11	7.3
Tensile modulus, psi $\times 10^{-5}$	D 638	3.6	3.6–3.8	3.7
Elongation at failure, %	D 638	50–100	50–80	65
Flexural strength, 10^{-3} psi	D 790	15.4	14–15	14.5
Flexural modulus, psi $\times 10^{-5}$	D 790	3.9	3.5–3.8	3.8
Izod impact strength, ft-lb/in.:				
Notched	D 256	1.3	1.5–1.9	6.3
Unnotched		>60	....	....
Hardness, Rockwell	D 785	R–120	R118–120	R118
Deflection temperature, °C at 264 psi	D 648	174	190–193	101
Maximum recommended continuous-use temperature, °C		150	107–120	93–101
Flammability, in./min	D 635	Self-extinguishing	Self-extinguishing	Self-extinguishing
Mold shrinkage, in./in.		0.007	0.007	0.007

NOTE: Values shown should not be considered precise figures, but average values taken from various sources.

TABLE 5.6 Effect of Molecular Weight of Aromatic Polysulfone on Strength of Bonded Joints [16]

Molecular weight	Reduced viscosity (0.2 g in 100 cc $CHCl_3$)	Melt flow, g/10 min at 350°C and 44 psi	Tensile lap shear strength, psi
20,000	0.40	24.0	3,200
30,000	0.51	9.3	3,330
55,000	0.73	1.0	3,260

TABLE 5.7 Peel Strength of Aromatic-polysulfone-bonded Laminates [16]

Glue-line thickness, in.	Peel strength at 180°, lbs. per inch width
0.002	28–30
0.003	40–41
0.005	37–40
0.006	47–50
0.010	40–44

TABLE 5.5 (*continued*)

Poly-carbonate	Acetal	30% glass–nylon 66	Wood flour phenolic	Mineral (HF) phenolic	Asbestos DAP	Putty alkyd
1.2	1.42	1.37	1.32–1.55	1.72–1.92	1.65–1.70	2.05–2.15
0.15	0.25	0.07	0.3–0.8	0.01–0.07	0.4–0.5	0.05–0.08
8.5	10	20	5–8.5	5–7	4–5.5	3–4
3.0	4	. . . .	8–12	. . . .	. . . .	15
80	15	1.5	0.4–0.8	0.1–0.5		
13.5	. . . .	. . . .	10			
3.4	4.1	9.85	8.5–12	30–40	12	22–27
15	1.4–2.3	2.5	0.24–0.5	0.3–0.38	0.3–0.45	0.3–0.35
>60	21					
R118	R120	. . . .	R120	M100	. . . .	Barcol 65
132	124	260	126–170	110–163	150–176	176–204
120–132	85	. . . .	150	71	. . . .	163
Self-extinguishing	1.1 (drips)	Self-extinguishing drips	Self-extinguishing	Self-extinguishing	Not ASTM°	Self-extinguishing
0.006	0.025	. . . .	0.007	. . . .	. . . .	0.007

° 70 seconds ignition time.

TABLE 5.8 Bond Strength of Aromatic-polysulfone-bonded Steel Joints [16]

Type of steel	Surface preparation	Tensile lap shear strength, psi
18–8 stainless.	Acid-dichromate	4,280
18–8 stainless.	Solvent wipe	3,070
Carbon	Solvent wipe	3,100

TABLE 5.9 Strength of Aromatic-polysulfone-bonded Joints vs. Temperature [16]

Test temperature, °C	Tensile lap shear strength, psi	Minimum requirements, MIL-A-5090D, type II, psi
−55	3,300	2,250
23	3,500	2,250
82	2,700	
150	2,200	2,000
175	1,950	
205	520	

method of measurement.   A reported value for glass transition is 190°C. The brittle point is − 100°C.

The aromatic polysulfones appear suitable for service, in air, at temperatures from 140 to 170°C.   No changes in the infrared spectrum were observed on heating a sample of polysulfone at 125°C in air for 3,000 hours; also 7,000 hours heating gave less than 0.25 percent weight loss; 9,000 hours at 140°C in oxygen gave 3 percent weight loss [18].

Thermal stability studies in vacuum indicate that sulfur dioxide is the first measurable decomposition product at 400°C; other products obtained at temperatures below 500°C include methane, phenol, bisphenol A, and p-isopropenylphenol [17].

The aromatic polysulfones provide quiet flat creep properties with temperature, as indicated in Figs. 5.5 and 5.6.   Flexural modulus vs. temperature is shown in Fig. 5.7 as compared with other thermoplastics. Creep at 150°C in comparison with polycarbonate is shown in Fig. 5.8. Figure 5.9 shows tensile strength at yield vs. temperature for the aromatic polysulfone and polyphenylene oxide.   Specific heat is 0.24 at 23°C and 0.37 at 160°C.   Thermal conductivity is 1.8 Btu/(hr)(ft²)(°F)(in.).

In sections thicker than 70 mils, the material is classified as self-extinguishing.   This is a characteristic of the polymer, not the result of an additive. It has been hypothesized that the aromatic polysulfones have a quenching effect on the flame due to the formation of a carbonaceous layer that acts as an intumescent coating rather than through the liberation of an inert gas.

The good creep strength at higher temperatures, observed with the molding compounds, is equally in evidence with adhesive formulations.

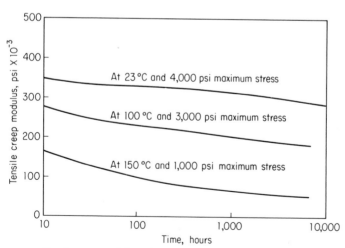

FIG 5.5   *Tensile creep modulus of aromatic polysulfone at varying stress levels and temperatures vs. time* [5].

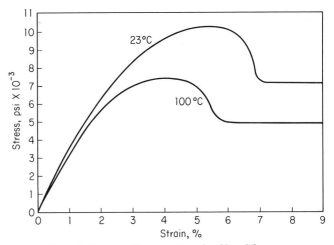

FIG 5.6 *Stress-strain curves for aromatic polysulfone* [5].

Creep, under 800 psi dead load for 8 days, at 150°C, is less than 0.00005 in., as compared with the allowable maximum of 0.015 in. specified in MIL-A-5090D. Performance of the joint with temperature is indicated in Table 5.9.

PHYSICAL-CHEMICAL PROPERTIES

The aromatic polysulfones provide dimensional stability as indicated in Table 5.10. Resistance to mineral acids, alkalies, and salt solutions is good, as is resistance to detergents and hydrocarbon oils, even at elevated temperatures under moderate stress levels. The materials are attacked by

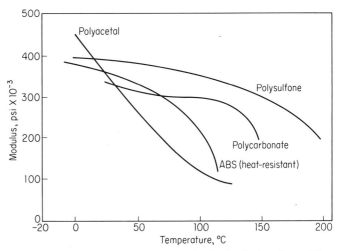

FIG 5.7 *Flexural modulus vs. temperature for thermoplastic polymers* [5].

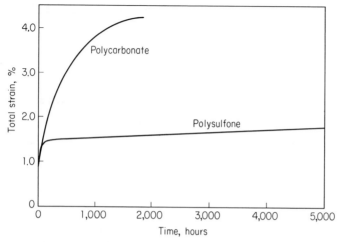

FIG 5.8   *Comparison of creep behavior of aromatic polysulfone and poly-carbonate at* 100°C *and* 3,000 *psi tension* [5].

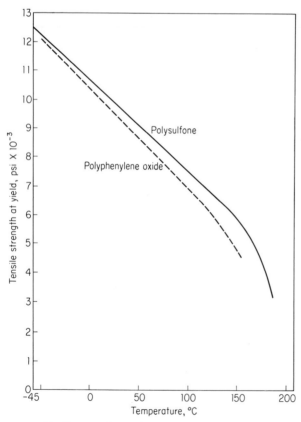

FIG 5.9   *Tensile strength at yield vs. temperature for aromatic polysulfone and polyphenylene oxide* [11].

114

TABLE 5.10 Dimensional Stability of Aromatic Polysulfone (Effect of moisture and thermal cycling after dehydration for 16 hours at 130°C under vacuum) [10]

Time and environment	Weight change, %	Linear change, in./in.
28 days at 23°C, 50% relative humidity	+0.23	<0.001
28 days in water at 23°C	+0.62	<0.001
7 days in water at 100°C	+0.85	+0.0011
10 cycles between 150°C air and 60°C water (4 hours each condition):		
24 hours at 150°C at end	−0.03	<0.001
28 days at 150°C	−0.10	−0.001

polar organic solvents and are partially soluble in aromatic hydrocarbons and soluble in chlorinated hydrocarbons. Typical chemical resistance data are shown in Table 5.11. Resistance of lap shear joints to various fluids is indicated in Table 5.12. Permeability data are given in Table 5.13.

The aromatic polysulfones offer resistance to weathering exposure and to ultraviolet similar to phenoxy and other aromatic ring polymers.

ELECTRICAL PROPERTIES

Electrical properties for aromatic polysulfones are given in Table 5.14 and Fig. 5.10. These properties are compared with other thermoplastics in Table 5.15 and Figs. 5.11 and 5.12.

TABLE 5.11 Chemical Resistance of Aromatic Polysulfone [11]

Medium	Weight change after 7 days' immersion at 23°C, %	Time to failure at 23°C and 1,000 psi, hours
Water	0.58	>500
Sulfuric acid, 40%	0.36	
Hydrochloric acid, 20%	0.42	>500
Sodium hypochlorite, 5.25% . . .	. . . .	>500
Acetic acid, 20%	−0.52	>500
Oleic acid, 100%	0.066	>500
Ethanol, 100%	0.08	>500
Glycerin, 100%	−0.15	>500
Turpentine, 100%	. . . .	14.8
Jet fuel, JP4	0.05	>500
Auto gasoline	0.05	>500
Lemon oil, 100%	. . . .	22.8
Motor oil no. 10	0.009	>500
Brake fluid	−0.04	1.2

TABLE 5.12 Effect of Fluids on Bond Strengths of Aromatic Polysulfones [16]

Environment	Exposure time, days	Exposure temperature, °C	Tensile lap shear strength at 23°C, psi
Air	60	23	3,370
Air	8	150	2,200
Isopropanol	7	23	3,400
Hydraulic oil (phosphate ester type)	7	23	3,100
Jet fuel (JP-4)	7	23	3,010
Distilled water	7	23	2,300

TABLE 5.13 Permeability Data for Aromatic Polysulfone [11]

Property	ASTM method	Value
Water absorption in 24 hours, %	D 570	0.22
Permeability:		
Moisture vapor, g/(mil)(100 in.²)(24 hr)	....	18
Oxygen, cc/(mil)(100 in.²)(24 hr)	....	230
Carbon dioxide, cc/(mil)(100 in.²)(24 hr)	....	950

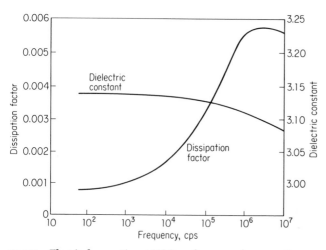

FIG 5.10 *Electrical properties at 23°C vs. frequency for aromatic polysulfone* [14].

TABLE 5.14 Electrical Properties of Aromatic Polysulfones

Property	Value

Dielectric constant:
  At 60 cps:
    Condition A 3.14
    Condition B 3.31
    150°C 2.8
    176°C 2.8
  At 10^3 cps:
    Condition A 3.13
    Condition B 3.29
    176°C 2.8
  At 10^6 cps:
    Condition A 3.10
    Condition B 3.23
    150°C 2.8
    176°C 2.7
    At 50×16^6 cps, condition A. 2.06
Dissipation factor:
  At 60 cps:
    Condition A 0.008
    Condition B 0.006
    150°C 0.0015
    176°C 0.008
  At 10^3 cps:
    Condition A 0.0011
    Condition B 0.0010
    176°C 0.003
  At 10^6 cps:
    Condition A 0.0056
    Condition B 0.0073
    150°C 0.0025
    176°C 0.003

Surface resistivity, ohms. . . . . 3 × 10^{16}
Volume resistivity at 50% relative humidity, ohm-cm. . . . . 5 × 10^{16}
Arc resistance, seconds. 122

Dielectric Strength, volts/mil

Mils	At 23°C	At 100°C	At 160°C
130	425	530	
10	2,200	2,250	1,600
1	7,500	8,600	6,200

Condition A = 23°C and 50% relative humidity.   Condition B = after 48 hours immersion in water at 50°C.

TABLE 5.15 Comparison of Electrical Properties of Aromatic Polysulfones with Other Plastics [14]

Property	ASTM method	Poly-sulfone	PPO	PVDC	Poly-carbonate	Acetal	30% glass–nylon 66	Wood flour phenolic	Mineral (HF) phenolic	Asbestos DAP	Putty alkyd
Dielectric strength, short-time, volts/mil . . .	D 149	425	400–500	1250	400	500	500	200–425	300–375	450	300–400
Volume resistivity, ohm-cm at 50% relative humidity.	D 257	5×10^{16}	10^{17}	8×10^{15}	2.1×10^{16}	6×10^{14}	5×10^{15}	10^{9}–10^{13}	10^{13}	10^{14}	10^{14}
Dielectric constant at 60 cps and 50% relative humidity.	D 150	3.14	2.58	3.08	3.17	3.7	4.0	5–9	4.7–5.5	6.4	6–6.5
Dissipation factor at 60 cps.	D 150	0.0008	0.00035	0.019	0.0009	0.003	0.018	0.05–0.03	0.01–0.07	0.09	0.035–0.04

NOTE: Values should not be considered as precise figures, but as averages taken from various sources.

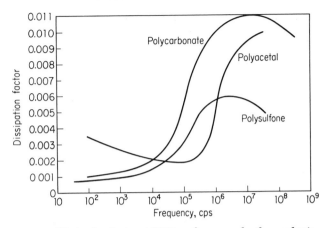

FIG 5.11 *Dissipation factor at* $23°C$ *vs. frequency for thermoplastic polymers* [5].

PROCESSING

Molding Compounds

It is recommended that, before processing, aromatic polysulfone stock be dried for at least 5 hours at $120°C$ to reduce moisture content below 0.05 percent. Higher moisture contents, while not adversely affecting the polymer, will result in imperfections in the resultant part.

Aromatic polysulfones are processed on standard thermoplastic processing equipment. In general, stock temperatures are higher than for most other thermoplastics, ranging from 340 to $370°C$ for injection equipment.

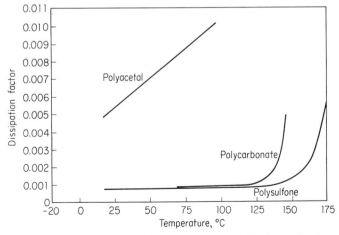

FIG 5.12 *Dissipation factor at* 60 cps *vs. temperature for thermoplastic polymers* [5].

TABLE 5.16   Spiral Flow Molding of Aromatic Polysulfone (Mold channel 0.625 in. wide, 3-oz. Lester ram machine) [5]

Material	Stock temperature, °C	Pressure, psi	Mold temperature, °C	Depth of channel, mils	Flow, inches
Polysulfone	350	23,400	93	80	7.5
P-1700	388	23,400	93	80	10.5
	412	23,400	93	80	13.25
	412	23,400	162	80	14.0
	412	46,800	93	80	17.5
	412	23,400	93	80	3.0
Polycarbonate	304	23,400	93	80	7.5
Styrene-acrylonitrile copolymer, RMD-4511	260	23,400	70	80	19.5
Polystyrene, SMF-3600............	232	23,400	65	80	21.0
Polyethylene (0.96 d, 3.5 MI)........	232	23,400	43	80	20.0

Typical flow-index data for a ram injection machine are given in Table 5.16. Screw machines are preferred, with maximum pressure being used and cylinder temperatures maintained at 25 to 50°C below the stock temperature. With the screw machines, the heat history is reduced, cycles are faster, and more complex and longer flow pieces can be producd [12].

Because of the relatively high melt index of the aromatic polysulfones, (Figs. 5.13 and 5.14) long flow or thin parts may cause difficulty. Flow characteristics of polysulfone compared with other thermoplastics are given in Fig. 5.15. In general, mold temperatures of about 100°C are adequate for simple parts thicker than about 100 mils. Other parts may require mold temperatures as high as 150 to 160°C. Increasing stock temperature,

Subminiature printed-circuit card-edge connector at left, and rack-and-panel cable connector at right are precision-molded from polysulfone. (Union Carbide Corp.)

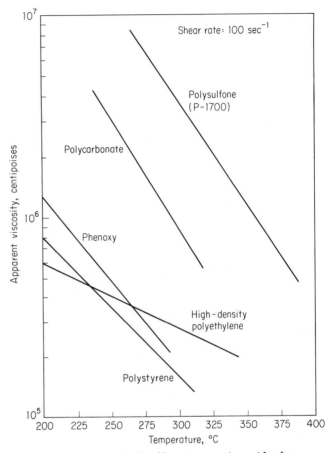

FIG 5.13 *Melt viscosity of polysulfone in comparison with other thermoplastics* [6].

however, is more effective than increasing mold temperature, in terms of flow. Wall thickness and temperature also sharply influence flow (Fig. 5.16).

In the design of injection molds for polysulfones, the molds should be capable of withstanding the high pressures normally used. Sprues and runners should be heavier and shorter than in a mold for free-flowing thermoplastics. Large gates, and flow from thick to thin sections, are required. Experiments have shown that only a few inches of flow can be expected in thin sections. In a 30-mil cavity, for example, flow will be only a few inches, even with relatively high stock temperature and pressure. Since the polysulfone does not flash easily into thin cavities, vents may be 3 to 4 mils deep. The ejection system should be suitable for rigid parts, and a shrinkage factor of 7 mils per in. should be used in designing the mold [8].

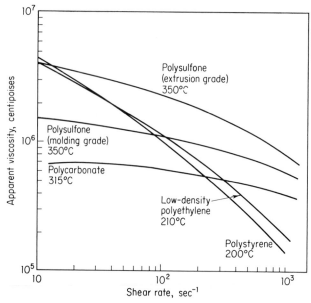

FIG 5.14 *Melt viscosity vs. shear rate for thermoplastics at optimum processing temperatures* [5].

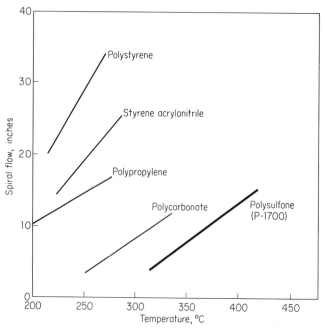

FIG 5.15 *Spiral flow vs. temperature for polysulfone in comparison with other thermoplastics* [6]. *Mold temperature,* 93° C; *injection pressure,* 23,400 *psi; channel,* 0.0800 × 0.625 *in.*

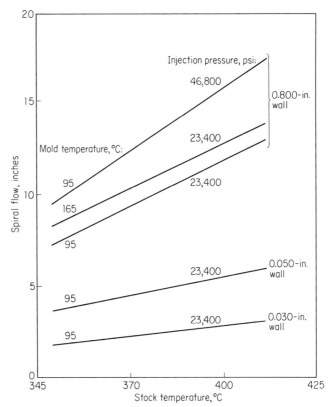

FIG 5.16   *Spiral flow vs. stock temperature for polysulfones as a function of wall thickness and injection pressure* [6].

Molding and forming conditions can produce slight changes in creep behavior due to strain and orientation effects.   Annealing at the anticipated use temperature or in glycerol at 165°C can minimize such changes [7].

For extrusions, temperatures from 315 to 370°C are used, although wire coating and thin films may require temperatures to 410°C.   Best results are obtained with metering-type screws (with 0.120 to 0.150 in. depth for 2.5-in. screws) and a compression ratio of 2 to 3/1.   *L/D* ratios of 20/1 or higher are considered most effective.   Screw speeds up to 60 rpm have been used.   Since sheet will require take-off temperatures of at least 175°C, this may necessitate conversion of equipment from water to steam or hot oil.

Blow molds from parisons formed by both ram- and screw-type extruders at temperatures of 275 to 300°C have produced bottles with good wall-thickness uniformity on standard equipment.   With maximum injection rates and minimum feed, 4-oz bottles with wall thicknesses of 35 to 40 mils

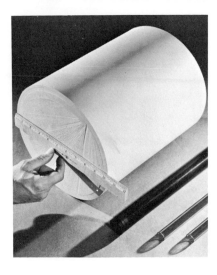

Small rod and tubing to massive 10-in.-diameter solid rod extruded from polysulfone plastic. (Union Carbide Corp.)

have been obtained from a 0.500-in. die and a 0.400-in. pin. Typical blow-molding conditions are shown in Table 5.17.

Because of exceptional melt stability, aromatic polysulfones can be recycled many times without decomposition and loss of properties or yield of finished parts. Higher temperatures, however, for prolonged periods, may cause discoloration of the stock.

The finished parts may be easily machined on standard equipment.

The aromatic polysulfones may be solvent bonded or heat sealed. In the heat-seal method, the surfaces to be joined are pressed against a Teflon-coated heated platen (at 370°C) for 10 seconds and then immediately

TABLE 5.17 Typical Extrusion Blow-molding Conditions
(Type of part: quart bottle) [6]

Screw	
Diameter, in.	2½
L/D ratio	20/1
Compression ratio	3.3/1
Stock temperature, °C	310
Cylinder temperature, °C:	
Feed zone	315
Transition zone	345
Metering zone	345
Extruder head temperature, °C	300
Die bushing temperature, °C	300
Extrusion pressure, psi	2,000
Blow air pressure, psi	80
Mold temperature, °C	55
Mold shrinkage, in./in.	0.008–0.010
Overall cycle, seconds	50

joined. However, since the aromatic polysulfones normally contain a small amount of moisture, the heat sealing is best effected by drying the part for 3 to 6 hours at 120°C in advance of the sealing operation. Solvent bonding is accomplished by use of a 5 percent solution of the aromatic polysulfone in methylene chloride. The joints are cold-pressed for 5 minutes at 500 psi. In solvent bonding films to metals, a 3- to 5-mil film of aromatic polysulfone should first be applied to the metal and dried, the solvent seal subsequently being made against this film. In general, the strength of the solvent-bonded joints will improve with aging as the residual solvent evaporates. Ultrasonic bonding may also be used when short processing cycles are required.

The aromatic polysulfones may be painted and baked after treatment with a primer and may be electroplated with about the same efficiency as ABS plastics. A commercial process for plating the material has been developed by Union Carbide, the process being exclusively leased to Enthone, Inc., of West Haven, Connecticut. By it, a peel strength of the metal-to-plastic bond of 16 to 22 lb is obtained.

Adhesives

The aromatic polysulfones may be melted on the surface, or more conveniently, films of the aromatic polysulfone may be used. At 370°C and 80 psi pressure, joints having optimum strengths may be developed on a 5-minute press cycle. When lower-temperature bonding is required, the faying surfaces should be spray-coated or flow-coated with a thin film of resin, which is then baked for 10 minutes at 260°C. The primed metal may then be bonded with a film adhesive by pressing for 1 minute at 260°C. When using the hot-melt technique, the aromatic polysulfone adhesive should be predried to remove residual moisture before making the bond.

When the solvent technique is used to make the bond, room-temperature processing can be employed if the faying surfaces have been clad in advance with films of the aromatic polysulfone. Cladding can be accomplished by priming the surface with a dilute solution of the polymer, flashing off the solvents, and then ironing on the adhesive film at from 260 to 315°C. A dilute solution of the aromatic polysulfone in methylene chloride is then used as the adhesive by the technique previously described.

APPLICATIONS

Because of long-term, high-temperature resistance to 150°C and their balance of strength and toughness, the aromatic polysulfones have poten-

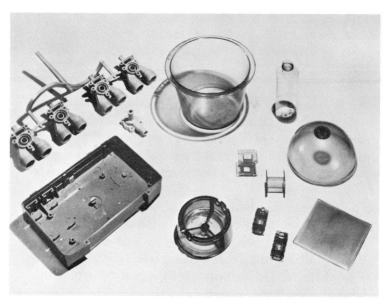

A variety of products molded from polysulfone indicates the versatility of this new plastic. Complete fill-out of thin sections and long flows are accomplished with standard equipment. (Union Carbide Corp.)

tial markets as under-the-hood automotive parts, housings for power tools, computer parts, appliance housings and dishwashing machine tubes, electric switches and circuit breakers, and extruded pipe and sheet.

The aromatic polysulfone adhesives offer strong, ductile joints with good creep and temperature resistance. Such joints can be produced rapidly, since to obtain good bonding it is necessary only to heat the parts for a sufficient time for the resin to wet both surfaces. Interest has developed in the use of polysulfones for wire and cable insulation.

REFERENCES

1958

1. A. Kreuchunas, Polysulfone Condensation Polymers and the Preparation of Same, U.S. 2,822,351.

1962

2. Gaylord, "Polyethers," part III, Interscience, pp. 225–270.

1964

3. E. H. Hill and J. R. Caldwell, Polysulfones of Norbornene and Derivatives, *J. Polymer Sci.,* part A, vol. 2, p. 1251.

1965

4. Aromatic Polymers: the List Lengthens, *C&E News*, Apr. 26, p. 48.
5. Bakelite Polysulfone P-1700 and P-1710 for Injection Molding, Union Carbide Plastics Co., Product Data, Bulletin J-2700, 036-6.
6. H. D. Bassett, A. M. Fazzari, and R. B. Staub, How to Process Polysulfones, I: Injection and Blow Molding, *Plastics Technol.*, September, pp. 50–53.
7. H. D. Bassett, A. M. Fazzari, and R. B. Staub, How to Process Polysulfones, II: Extrusion and Thermoforming, *Plastics Technol.*, October, pp. 49–51.
8. H. D. Bassett, A. M. Fazzari, and R. B. Staub, Tips on Tooling for Polysulfone Resins, *Mod. Plastics*, October, pp. 117–119, 184.
9. New Engineering Thermoplastic: Polysulfone, *Mod. Plastics*, May, pp. 87–89, 196.
10. New High-temperature Thermoplastic: Polysulfone, *Plastics Design Process.*, May, pp. 16–19.
11. New Polysulfone Thermoplastic Stands Up to 300+ F, *Mater. Design Eng.*, May, pp. 89–91, 196.
12. Now, Polysulfone, *Plastics World*, May, pp. 22–23.
13. Polysulfone, a New High Temperature Thermoplastic, *Insulation*, July, pp. 22–24.
14. Polysulfones: Tough, Heat Resistant Thermoplastics, *Plastics Technol.*, May, pp. 15–17, 59.
15. Thermoplastic Polysulfones: Strength at High Temperature, *Chem. Eng.*, May 10, pp. 108–110.
16. Union Carbide Plastics Co. Bulletin, Polysulfones: a Unique Structure Adhesive Resin, no. 5-1416, July.

1966

17. W. F. Hale et al., Thermal Stability of Polyarylethers Prepared by Aromatic Nucleophilic Substitution, ACS Meeting, New York, September.

1967

18. P. G. Kelleher and B. D. Gesner, Thermal and Photo-oxidation of Polysulfone, ACS Spring Meeting, Miami Beach, Fla., April.

6

New Linear Polyamides

The linear, thermoplastic polyamides, generically, have been known since the late 1920s, when they were first synthesized by W. H. Carothers. The aliphatic-based species have been commercially available since 1939.

In the late 1950s, there was increased interest in high-temperature polymers, and the aromatic polyamides were a promising candidate. The aromatic nylons may be produced by either solution or the interfacial polycondensation techniques from aromatic amines and aromatic acid chlorides. The best of the materials require specialized solvents for fiber formation and are produced in fibrid form by interfacial polycondensation techniques. The fibers are used in yarns and cloth. They are chopped and combined with the fibrids to produce papers. The materials have extremely high heat resistance and outstanding Class 180 electrical properties, and are useful as electrical insulation and in applications where heat- and chemical-resistant cloths are needed.

Polycyclamides, produced by conventional nylon tehniques, are available in molding grades, introduced in 1965. These contain alicyclic ring structures and offer improved moisture resistance over the all-aliphatic-based nylons.

The first linear polyamides were synthesized in the late 1920s by W. H. Carothers of E. I. du Pont de Nemours & Company. They were prepared from the homopolymerization of amino acids or caprolactams, or by the condensation of diamines and dibasic acids. The work led, some 10 years later, in 1939, to the commercial introduction of the so-called "nylons," which is the generic term preferred for the linear thermoplastic polyamides having molecular weights ranging from 15,000 to about 30,000. Although other nylons were investigated experimentally over the next 20 years, the commercial materials continued to be aliphatic-based. Among the more prominent materials introduced during that period were nylon 6 (self-condensation of ε-caprolactam), nylon 66 (condensation of hexamethylene-diamine and adipic acid), nylon 610 (condensation of hexamethylenediamine and sebacic acid), and nylon 11 (self-condensation of 11-aminoundecanoic acid).

From the late 1940s, there has been increasing interest in the so-called "superpolyamides." These are partially or wholly aromatic structures. Early work employed alicyclic diamines reacted with a diphenyl ester of phthalic acid [1, 2], and research has continued on these species [17]. Fully aromatic species, except for methylene bridges, were produced from *m*-xylylenediamine and isophthalic acid in the early 1950s [3]. Subsequently, polyamides were made from aromatic acid chlorides and piperazine and methyl-substituted piperazine [14].

This activity culminated in 1961 with the experimental introduction of fibers and papers manufactured from aromatic-based nylons by E. I. du Pont de Nemours & Company; production reached full commercial scale in 1966. In 1965, Monsanto Company was granted patent coverage on a series of aromatic polyamides derived from *m*-aminobenzoyl chloride hydro-chloride and similar materials and the monomers in mixture with aromatic acid chlorides and amines [20]. Concurrently, work proceeded on species of nylon based on alicyclic precursors, specifically aimed at producing systems possessing improved hydrolytic stability over the aliphatic-based polymers, but with similar handling properties. In 1965, alicyclic species were introduced as molding compounds by Tennessee Eastman, who sug-gested the generic name *polycyclamides* for these compounds. More recently, high-molecular-weight polyamides have been produced by the reaction of enamines (derived from cyclic ketones and isocyanates) with diisocyanates. Typically, the reaction of *N*-morpholino-1-cyclopentene with phenylmethane diisocyanate produces a polymer with aromatic and alicyclic rings joined by amide and methylene links [26].

SYNTHESIS

Chemistry

The synthesis of various types of nylons is well known in the technology and has been fully explored in the literature. Essentially, the new linear materials, which are the subject of this chapter, are produced by similar techniques. The basic reaction of interest is as follows:

$$(n + 1)\text{HOC}-\text{R}-\text{COH} + (n + 1)\text{H}_2\text{N}-\text{R}'-\text{NH}_2 \longrightarrow$$

$$\text{HOC}-\text{R}-\text{C}\left[\text{N}-\text{R}'-\text{NHC}-\text{R}-\text{C}\right]_n\text{N}-\text{R}'-\text{NH}_2$$

The ingredients are generally blended at an equal molar ratio to provide highest molecular weights. Lower-molecular-weight species are obtained through the use of excess of one reactant, or by the use of a monofunctional chain-stopping element such as monobasic acid. An acid catalyst may be used to accelerate the reaction.

Under the conditions of synthesis, the secondary amide nitrogen is not normally reactive, the primary amine condensing preferentially, thereby preventing undesirable side-chain formation and polymerization.

In actual practice, the synthesis of the conventional nylons is conducted in two steps. In the first step the amine-acid salt is formed and recrystallized or otherwise purified to ensure equal molar proportions of ingredients and reproducible molecular weights. The salt may then be reacted in solution in a heated vessel at 250 to 300°C with venting to allow escape of water from the solution. Alternatively, the salts may be directly fused

Atom model of alicyclic polyamide from adipic acid and cyclohexanebis(methylamine). (The Epoxylite Corporation.)

without solvents by heating them to above their melting points in an inert atmosphere under conditions that permit water removal.

There are obviously many changes that may be effected in the basic procedure to improve yields, facilitate synthesis, and control the molecular weight of the resultant nylons. Short-chain alkyl or phenyl esters may be used in place of the acids, the phenyl esters liberating phenol which is soluble in the reactants and which can subsequently be removed by washing rather than distillation. Reaction conditions can be varied and catalysts can be selected to provide the desired properties.

The poly(cyclamides) are synthesized by these general procedures. The present commercial material is produced from 1,4-bis(aminomethyl)cyclohexane and aliphatic diacids, for example, the following:

Poly-1,4-cyclohexylenedimethylene suberamide
(Tennessee Eastman's Q2)

Production of the fully aromatic nylons, however, poses more of a problem. Aromatic amines are generally not sufficiently reactive to achieve high-molecular-weight products by conventional techniques. Therefore, an early method for producing aliphatic nylon is employed: use of the more reactive acid chloride. The acid chloride and the amine may be reacted in a common solvent; or, alternatively, the reaction may be conducted by the interfacial polycondensation process.

Interfacial polycondensation involves dissolving the amine in water and dissolving the acid chloride in an immiscible solvent, such as benzene or preferably cyclohexanone [9]. The two solutions are then mixed with high-speed agitation to create the largest possible interface for reaction. Assuming the proper choice of solvents and concentration of reactants, even higher molecular weights may be obtained by this process than by the fusion process.

The overall reaction proceeds, in simplified form, as follows:

Isophthaloyl chloride   *m*-Phenylenediamine   Salt and water

Poly(*m*-phenyleneisophthalamide)

Atom model of aromatic nylon (Nomex) from m-*phenylenediamine and isophthaloyl chloride.* (The Epoxylite Corporation.)

In the interfacial polycondensation reaction, the reaction occurs at the interface or just inside the solvent boundary, with the polymer growing on the solvent side. The low solubility of the acid chlorides in water protects them from hydrolysis, and the reaction proceeds with extreme speed until the physically available reactants are exhausted. Caustic is used to neutralize the hydrogen chloride to prevent formation of insoluble and nonreactive amine salts. The extent to which the reaction progresses is a function of reaction conditions, purity of ingredients, type of solvents, concentration of ingredients, and proportion of ingredients. It has been shown, for example (Fig. 6.1), that the best molar ratio of diamine to acid chloride for *m*-phenylenediamine and isophthaloyl chloride is in the range of 0.90 to 0.93.

The higher-melting-point polymers indicated in Table 6.1 are only difficultly soluble. Poly(*m*-phenyleneisophthalamide) is dissolved slowly in concentrated sulfuric acid at room temperature, in boiling phosphoric acid, and in boiling dimethylacetamide upon the addition of 3 percent calcium chloride [13]. This latter solvent system, or similar ones as described in [8], are employed in the production of continuous fibers from the polymer obtained by solution polymerization.

Studies using aromatic amines with *n*-alkyl substituents resulted in products of improved solubility which permitted a determination of molecular weight by light-scattering techniques. The molecular weights of the aromatic materials produced by interfacial polycondensation were found to range from 50,000 to 60,000 [12]. It is probable that the materials obtained by solution polymerization give somewhat lower values.

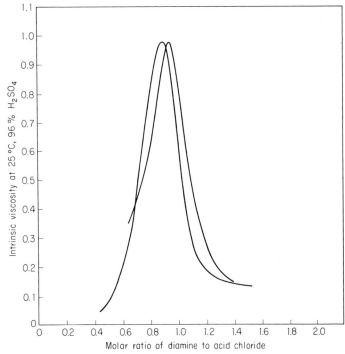

FIG 6.1 *Relationship between intrinsic viscosity and molar ratio of diamine/acid chloride: poly-m-phenyleneisophthalamide* [9].

TABLE 6.1 Aromatic Polyamides Prepared by Interfacial
Polycondensation [11]

Acid chloride	Diamine	Polymer yield, %	Softening point, °C
Phthaloyl chloride.......	o-Phenylenediamine	27	~185
	m-Phenylenediamine	40	~200
	p-Phenylenediamine	74	185–190
Isophthaloyl chloride	o-Phenylenediamine	87	~240
	m-Phenylenediamine	86	>360
	p-Phenylenediamine	86	>360
Terephthaloyl chloride...	o-Phenylenediamine	89	~295
	m-Phenylenediamine	97	>360
	p-Phenylenediamine	77	>360
Terephthaloyl chloride ...	Benzidine	90	>360
	Dianisidine	50	Decomposition ~200
	4,4'-Diaminodiphenylmethane	85	>360
	4,4'-Diaminostilbene	60	>360
	4,4'-Diaminostilbene-2,2-disulfonic acid	80	>360
	4,4'-Diaminodiphenyl sulfoxide	92	~260
	4,4'-Diaminodiphenyl sulfone	65	~275
	2,4'-Diaminoazobenzene	70	Decomposition ~320
	1,5-Diaminonaphthalene	75	Decomposition ~320
	3,6-Diaminoacridine	55	

Preparative Procedure

The synthesis by solution polymerization of a typical aromatic nylon has been described as follows:

m-Phenylenediamine dihydrochloride in the amount of 5.4 parts is placed in a reaction vessel fitted with a high-speed stirrer, and a solution of 12.1 parts of triethylamine in 200 parts methylene chloride is added rapidly. Triethylamine hydrochloride is formed in situ. The mixture is stirred for 1 minute to dissolve the diamine salt. 6.1 parts of isophthaloyl chloride in 200 parts of methylene chloride is then added. Polymerization is completed, and poly(m-phenylene-isophthalamide) is precipitated by addition of a volume of hexane equal to the volume of the reaction mass. The product is water-white and has an inherent viscosity of 1.71 and a polymer melt temperature of 375°C. It is obtained in 91 percent yield [8].

Typical of the reaction conditions and products for the interfacial polycondensation technique are the data given in Table 6.2. The general procedure is to dissolve the amine in water in the presence of 2 moles of sodium hydroxide per 1 mole of diamine. The aromatic acid chloride, in solvent, is added with vigorous stirring. The temperatures are kept in the range of 5 to 10°C during the reaction [21].

An infrared spectrum of the commercial aromatic polyamide fiber is shown in Fig. 6.2.

A typical preparative procedure for the production of aromatic polyamides from m-aminobenzoyl chloride hydrochloride is as follows:

To a 500-ml container, 75 ml water, 4.24 grams sodium carbonate, 0.2 gram sodium lauryl sulfate, and 25 ml acetone were added. To this rapidly stirred emulsion was added 7.86 grams of m-aminobenzoyl chloride hydrochloride suspended in a mixture of 18 ml benzene and 9 ml acetone. Stirring was continued

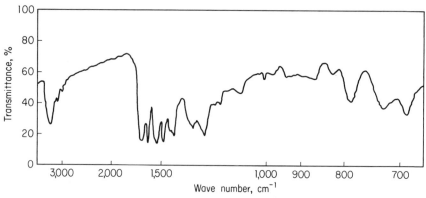

FIG 6.2   *Infrared spectrum of the commercial aromatic polyamide fiber* [13].

TABLE 6.2 Interfacial Polycondensation of *p*- or *m*-Phenylenediamine and Tere- or Isophthaloyl Chloride with Cyclohexanone Solvent for Acid Chlorides [9]

Dibasic acid	Acid chloride concentration, mole/liter	Diamine	Diamine concentration, mole/liter	Polymer yield, %	Polymer viscosity in 96% H_2SO_4, poise
Isophthalic acid...	0.05	*m*-Phenylenediamine	0.02	51	0.41
			0.04	19	0.34
			0.05	37	0.28
			0.06	38	0.11
			0.08	19	0.08
			0.10	8	0.09
	0.10	*m*-Phenylenediamine	0.05	39	0.08
			0.07	36	0.50
			0.09	39	0.99
			0.10	67	0.59
			0.11	30	0.26
			0.13	37	0.14
			0.15	11	0.15
	0.15	*m*-Phenylenediamine	0.10	28	0.40
			0.12	55	0.62
			0.14	66	0.99
			0.15	77	0.70
			0.16	65	0.70
			0.18	21	0.21
			0.20	23	0.17
	0.50	*m*-Phenylenediamine	0.40	70	0.24
			0.50	75	0.29
			0.60	80	0.25
Isophthalic acid...	0.10	*p*-Phenylenediamine	0.05	83	0.34
			0.08	100	0.40
			0.09	100	0.40
			0.10	100	0.39
			0.13	100	0.16
			0.15	100	0.15
Terephthalic acid..	0.10	*m*-Phenylenediamine	0.05	59	0.16
			0.08	67	0.21
			0.09	76	0.27
			0.10	84	0.30
			0.11	100	0.28
			0.13	100	0.27
			0.15	100	0.30
Terephthalic acid..	0.10	*p*-Phenylenediamine	0.05	0	
			0.08	0	
			0.09	2	
			0.10	2	
			0.11	6	
			0.13	26	0.40
			0.15	69	0.41

for 10 minutes to ensure complete polymerization. The polymer was washed and dried and had an inherent viscosity of 0.456 and a melting point of about 420 to 424°C, with discoloration beginning at about 400°C [20].

MODIFICATION AND FORMULATION

The nylons, generically, are supplied by the basic manufacturers (such as Du Pont and Monsanto) to the user in final form ready for processing.

However, by selection of starting ingredients, the chemical structure of the nylons may be varied to achieve desired physical properties or handling characteristics. With the aromatic species, this may be done by varying the reactants, as shown in Table 6.1. In going, for example, from phthaloyl chloride to iso- or terephthaloyl chloride, the softening point is increased from about 200 to in excess of 360°C. This increase can be attributed to the influence of steric factors. Oxidative stability of these species is shown in Table 6.3. Relative stabilities in vacuum are given in Fig. 6.3. In addition to varying the reactants, copolymers may be developed, as indicated in Table 6.4. Alternating aromatic copolyamides have been produced from amines containing m- or p-aminobenzoyl moieties. Melting points of typical polymers in this class are shown in Table 6.5. Also suitable are preformed aromatic diamines based on naphthalene groups or biphenyl ring structures, and containing carbonamide linkages [19].

The homopolymers (as from ε-caprolactam) are generally more crystalline than the copolymers and are lower-melting and more soluble. When blends of acids or of amines are used, or when the precursors contain aliphatic substituents, the hydrogen bonding ability of the polymer is

TABLE 6.3   Oxidative Stabilities of Aromatic Polyamides Based on Terephthaloyl Chloride [11]

Diamine	Weight loss, %, in air at 300°C after:						
	2 hours	2.5 hours	7 hours	8 hours	40 hours	72 hours	74 hours
m-Phenylenediamine	1.8	....	....	2.4	5.3	6.8	
p-Phenylenediamine	2.7	....	....	3.0	7.4	10.6	
Benzidine	1.2	....	....	1.9	3.2	4.4	
4,4'-Diaminodiphenylmethane	....	+1.4	....	0.9	7.7	14.2	
4,4'-Diaminostilbene	2.2	....	....	8.2	....	21.7	
4,4'-Diaminostilbene-2,2'-Disulfonic acid	....	3.3	....	4.2	4.8	....	5.1
4,4'-Diaminodiphenyl sulfoxide	4.2	....	....	4.5	7.4	8.7	
4,4'-Diaminodiphenyl sulfone	2.8	....	....	2.2	4.3	5.5	
2,4-Diaminoazobenzene	2.3	....	3.0	....	4.7	6.2	
1,5-Diaminonaphthalene	1.0	....	1.9	....	3.3	4.7	
3,6-Diaminoacridine	....	4.2	5.1	....	12.3	....	19.7

decreased, and as a consequence, solubility is improved and heat resistance is lowered.

Thus, nylons may be developed with a range of properties varying from those of nylon 6 up to those of the aromatic nylons.   The basic backbone may contain combinations of alicyclic, aliphatic, and aromatic constituents. By suitable selection of the reactants a wide range of physical properties and handling characteristics may be obtained.

As with the older materials, the new nylons are used as supplied.   The

TABLE 6.4   Copolyamide from *p*- or *m*-Phenylenediamine and Tere- or Isophthaloyl Chloride (Solvent for acid chlorides = cyclohexanone; concentration of monomers = 0.1 mole/liter; molar ratio between acid chloride and diamine = 1) [9]

	Dibasic acid			Copolyamide	
Diamine	Terephthalic acid, mole %	Isophthalic acid, mole %	Yield, %	Viscosity at 25°C, poise	Melting point, °C
m-Phenylenediamine	0	100	67	0.59	380–390
	20	80	67	0.57	340–345
	40	60	55	0.73	310–320
	60	40	46	0.46	450–460
	80	20	35	0.38	480–490
	100	0	84	0.30	490–500
p-Phenylenediamine	0	100	100	0.39	490–500
	20	80	86	0.23	465–470
	40	60	99	0.15	450–455
	60	40	100	0.20	480–485
	80	20	100	0.14	500
	100	0	2	....	500

	Diamine			Copolyamide	
Dibasic acid	*p*-Phenylene-diamine, mole %	*m*-Phenylene-diamine, mole %	Yield, %	Viscosity at 25°C, poise	Melting point, °C
Isophthalic acid.............	0	100	67	0.59	380–390
	20	80	43	0.93	375–380
	40	60	54	1.04	340–345
	60	40	45	1.04	480
	80	20	75	0.86	500
	100	0	100	0.39	490–500
Terephthalic acid	0	100	84	0.30	490–500
	20	80	80	0.38	480–485
	40	60	78	0.38	470–475
	60	40	88	0.40	500
	80	20	90	0.36	500
	100	0	2	....	500

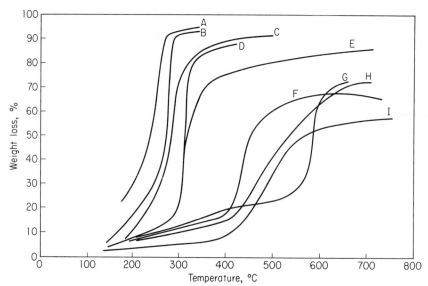

FIG 6.3 *Relative thermal stability of aromatic nylons in vacuum at a constant heating rate of* 3° *per min* [11].

Phenylenediamine	Chloride		
	Phthaloyl	Isophthaloyl	Terephthaloyl
meta	A	F	I
ortho	B	D	E
para	C	H	G

TABLE 6.5 Aromatic-ordered Copolyamides [16]

Diamino derivative	Diacid chloride	Polymer melting temperature, by DTA,° °C
N,N'-m-Phenylenebis(m-aminobenzamide)	IC	430
	TC	430
	NDC	500
	BBC	435
N,N'-m-Phenylenebis(p-aminobenzamide)	IC	475
	TC	490
N,N'-p-Phenylenebis(m-aminobenzamide)	IC	460
	TC	467
N,N'-p-Phenylenebis(p-aminobenzamide)	IC	500
	TC	500
N,N'-Dimethyl-p-phenylene(m-aminobenzamide)	IC	265†
	TC	300†

° Differential thermal analysis.
† Approximate melting points observed by heating the film; not by DTA.
IC = isophthaloyl chloride.
TC = terephthaloyl chloride.
NDC = 2,6-naphthalenedicarbonyl chloride.
BBC = 4,4'-bibenzoyl chloride.

140

TABLE 6.6 Properties of 30% Glass-filled Polycyclamide Q2 [25]

Property	As molded	Annealed
Hardness, Rockwell L.	115	116
Tensile strength, psi.	19,000	20,000
Elongation at break, %.	5	5
Modulus, psi $\times$ 10^{-5}.	8.5	9.0
Notched Izod impact strength, ft-lb/in. notch.	1.0	0.8
Deflection temperature at 264 psi stress, °C.	150	290

exact chemical composition may or may not be revealed, the modifications being considered proprietary and designed for end-use applications.

The aromatic nylons are nonreceptive to dyes, and their properties as supplied (in cloths or yarns) cannot conveniently be modified by the user. The poly(cyclamides), supplied as molding compounds, on the other hand, are capable of limited modification by the user, through addition of plasticizers, dyes, fillers, etc. One method which may be used, and which is also useful with a number of the other new thermoplastic polymers, is through the incorporation of reinforcing fibrous fillers. Typical properties of a reinforced polycyclamide molding compound are shown in Table 6.6.

The preferred reinforcement for the thermoplastic polymers is chopped glass fiber, normally about ¼ in. long. The fibers are used at 20 to 40 percent by weight, with strength properties improving and surface gloss and processing convenience declining with increasing glass content. In addition to providing improved physical properties and increased impact resistance, usually at the expense of reduced elongation, the reinforced systems provide reduced shrinkage by factors as high as 30 percent. The effect of the reinforcement on the processability of the compound is usually not too great. Higher injection pressures and temperatures are normally required than are employed with the unreinforced system, but the temperature increase is usually nominal, on the order of 10 to 25°C. A review of the techniques for using fiber-reinforced molding compounds is given by Murphy [21].

PHYSICAL PROPERTIES

Polycyclamides

The physical properties of the commercially available polycyclamides are shown in Table 6.7.

Aromatic Nylons

Du Pont has compiled a brochure entitled "Suppliers of Laminates and Fabricated Parts of Nomex Paper and Yarn." Laminates composed entirely

TABLE 6.7   Properties of Polycyclamide Q2 and Some Engineering Plastics [25]

Property	Q2	Nylon 66	Acetal	Polycarbonate	ASTM method
Molding temperature, °C.............	325–345	290	205	275–325	
Average mold shrinkage, %............	0.7	1.7	2.5	0.5	
Density, g/ml	1.12	1.14	1.43	1.20	D 1505(5)
Hardness:					
Rockwell L	110	99	104	96	D 785(5)
Rockwell M	84	52	76	54	
Tensile yield strength, psi............	12,000	10,000	10,000	9,000	D 638(5)
Elongation at break, %..............	30	70	50	100	D 638(5)
Flexural modulus, psi × 10^{-5}........	3.7	3.8	3.8	3.6	D 790(5)
Notched Izod impact strength, ft-lb/in. of notch.................	0.7	0.9	1.2	12	D 256(5)
Deflection temperature, °C:					
Under 66 psi stress...............	130	124	160	150	
Under 264 psi stress..............	90	70	90	145	
Abrasion, sandpaper, mg/100 cycles	12	13	28	13	
Coefficient of friction, dynamic, on stainless steel	0.29	0.35	0.21	0.53	
Deformation under load at 50°C, %.....	0.3	2.4	1.0	0.2	D 621(5)

TABLE 6.8   Properties of HT-1 Experimental Yarn (10-in. sample, 60% elongation per minute, at 23°C and 65% relative humidity, except as indicated) [5]

Property	Value
Denier, filament...	2.0
Tenacity, g/denier	5.8
Break elongation, %...	15.2
Initial modulus, g/denier	156
Loop tenacity, g/denier	5.6
Loop elongation, %	13.1
Tenacity at 200°C, g/denier	4.2
Tenacity at 2.5% elongation, g/denier	2.7
Tenacity at 5% elongation, g/denier	3.8
Wet tenacity, g/denier	4.2
Wet elongation, %..	14.0
Shrinkage, %:	
Boil-off	1.6
Dry at 350°C..	7
Extractables, %...	0.9
Ash, %..	0.15
Finish, %..	1.3
Equilibrium moisture at 23°C and 65% relative humidity, %, ca...........	4.9
Density, ca...	1.38

of Nomex paper are offered, as are composites of Nomex and mica; flexible laminates of Nomex and other plastic films; various types of round, square, and rectangular tubing; bobbins and coil forms; bushings, wedges; slot insulation; and die-cut and formed parts of all types. Tapes, braids, cords, and sewing threads are available, these finished to specifications. In addition to the fibers, Du Pont supplies paper in thicknesses of 2, 3, 5, 7, 10, 15, 20, and 30 mils.

Aromatic nylon continuous yarns are made in 200- and 100-denier counts. Fabrics containing 30 denier have been produced. Stress-strain properties of the fiber are given in Fig. 6.4. Calculated crystallinity of the fiber, from moisture-regain data, is about 47 percent [13]. Properties of a typical yarn are given in Table 6.8. Stress-strain properties of the yarn, in comparison with those of an aliphatic nylon, are given in Fig. 6.5. Creep and recovery

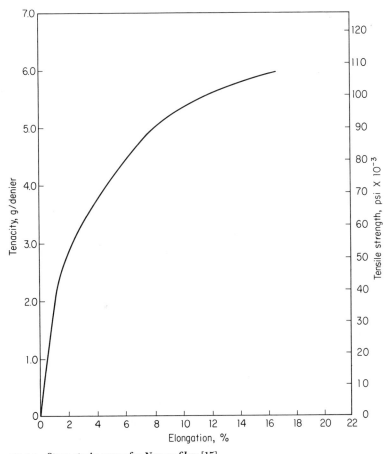

FIG 6.4 *Stress-strain curve for Nomex fiber* [15].

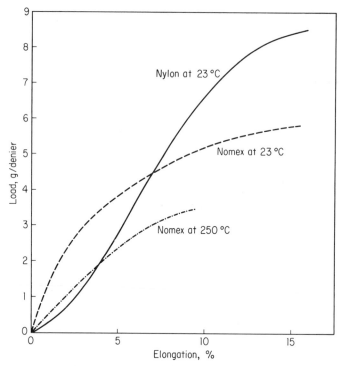

FIG 6.5 *Typical stress-strain curves for Nomex yarn and Du Pont 700 nylon* [5]. *10-in. sample, 60% elongation per minute; samples tested at 65% relative humidity.*

data are shown in Fig. 6.6.   Fabric properties are given in comparison with those of Dacron in Table 6.9; stress-strain properties of a typical fabric, in Fig. 6.7.   The aromatic nylon yarns are gray to silvery white in color with a high luster.   The yarns have low flammability, leaving a frangible char with flame-out times of about 5 seconds.   Tinting of the fibers should be avoided when practical, but if required, the procedures are given in [28].   The same reference provides processing information, as does [27].

Satisfactory adhesion to rubber goods (with proper stock) and to synthetic elastomers has been obtained when the yarns are used as high-temperature reinforcing fibers.

The aromatic polyamide paper is rated as nonporous with densities ranging from 0.7 to 1.0 depending on the thickness.   Properties of typical papers are given in Table 6.10.   Papers coated with a polyimide varnish (Chap. 8) to provide heat-sealing characteristics give properties as indicated in Table 6.11.   Typical properties of 100 percent solid laminates are given in Table 6.12.

TABLE 6.9 Fabric Physical Property Information [15]

Physical properties	Dacron Fabric			Nomex Fabric		
	Lightweight	Medium weight	Heavy weight	Lightweight	Medium weight	Heavy weight
Yarns:						
Warp	220/50/5,100/3S	1,100/250/5,200/3Z	3-ply/1,100/250/5,200/3Z/3S	200/100/3Z	2/5-ply/200/0/3Z/3S	3/5-ply/200/100/0/3Z/3S
Fill	220/50/5,100/3S	1,100/250/5,200/3Z	3-ply/1,100/250/5,200/3Z/3S	200/100/3Z	2/5-ply/200/100/0/3Z/3S	3/5-ply/200/100/0/3Z/3S
Width, inches	23.63	22.75	22.38	23.88	22.50	21.88
Weight, oz/yd	1.69	9.06	18.01	1.66	9.66	15.48
Count:						
Ends/in.	29	31	20	29	17	18
Picks/in.	31	30	19	30	16	17
Thickness, inches	0.0059	0.0174	0.0346	0.0060	0.0210	0.0304
Tensile strength, lb/in.:						
1-in. strip method:						
Warp	107	558	915	70	425	637
Fill	108	560	940	68	405	628
Grab method:						
Warp	124	693	1,018	106	433	920
Fill	121	662	1,100	103	420	870
% elongation at break:						
Warp	11.0	20.0	25.0	23.3	25.0	38.3
Fill	12.7	16.7	16.7	24.3	33.3	35.5

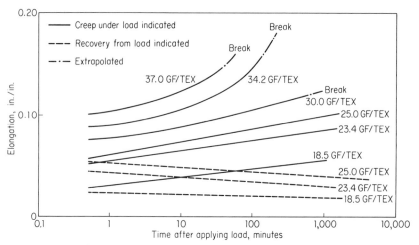

FIG 6.6   *Creep and recovery of Nomex yarn at* 20°C *and* 65% *relative humidity* [13].

THERMAL PROPERTIES

Polycyclamides

By differential thermal analysis commercial polycyclamide gives a T_g of 86°C as compared to 45°C for nylon 6 and 66. The melting point is 296°C as against 218 and 257°C [25]. Further comparisons are given in Table 6.7.

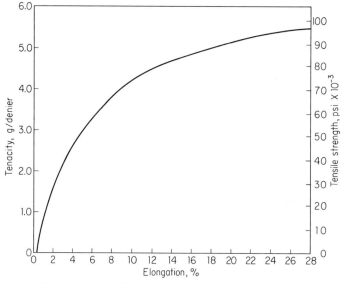

FIG 6.7   *Stress-strain curve for Nomex fabric, yarn* ⅗ *ply,* 200/100/0/3Z/3S [15].

TABLE 6.10 Properties of Typical Nomex Papers [24]

| Property | Direction | Thickness, mils | | | | | | | | ASTM test |
		2	3	5	7	10	15	20	30	
Tensile strength, psi	MD	22	37	59	120	170	300	440	550	D 828-60
	XD	13	23	35	68	100	180	250	380	
Elongation, %..............	MD	7	10	10	15	17	22	19	19	
	XD	6	9	9	12	13	15	15	15	
Elmendorf tear, grams	MD	95	150	290	380	550	850	1100	2000	D 689
	XD	140	250	470	620	900	1400	2100	2700	
Finch edge tear, psi...........	MD	13	23	43	77	100	110	150	190	D 827-47
	XD	6	10	18	22	32	43	54	76	
Shrinkage at 285°C, %........	MD	1.6	1.2	0.9	0.5	0.3	0.3	0.3	0.2	
	XD	1.9	1.6	1.3	1.0	0.4	0.4	0.4	0.4	
Thermal conductivity, (Btu)(in.)/(hr)(ft²)(°F)		....	....	....	....	0.76	....	....	....	C 177-45
Basic weight, oz/yd².........		1.2	1.9	3.2	5.1	7.3	11	15	23	

MD = machine direction. XD = cross direction.

Aromatic Nylons

The aromatic nylon yarns provide elevated-temperature properties in comparison with other plastics, as shown in Figs. 6.8 to 6.11. Initial load-carrying capacity is not quite so good as with nylon fibers, but with continued aging the improved thermal stability of the aromatic polymer becomes manifest. Yellowing is evidenced on aging at temperatures of 230°C. Additional elevated-temperature data on the yarns are given in Figs. 6.12 to 6.15.

TABLE 6.11 Mechanical Properties of Pyre ML Polyimide-coated Nomex Nylon Papers at Room Temperature [24]

| Property | 5 and 5.1–5.6 mils | | | 10 and 10.5–11.0 mils | | | Remarks |
	Uncoated	B-staged	Cured	Uncoated	B-staged	Cured	
Tensile strength, psi...........	12,000	12,000	12,000	....	....	....	ASTM D 828
Tensile modulus, psi × 10⁻⁴....	2.8	4.6	3.0	....	....	....	ASTM D 828
Elongation, % (MD)...........	10	9	8	....	....	....	ASTM D 828
Elmendorf tear, g/mil (MD)....	58	53	45	55	27	43	ASTM D 689
Specific gravity	0.87	0.90	0.90	0.96	0.98	0.96	
Cut-through temperature, °C°..	390	390	430				
Moisture absorption, %........	7	6	4	7	7	6	48 hours at 23°C and 95% relative humidity
Basis weight, oz/yd²	3.2	3.7	3.5	7.3	8.1	7.9	
Coating weight, oz/yd²........	....	0.5	0.3	....	0.8	0.6	

° Equipment specified in ASTM D 876-61. A ¹⁄₁₆-in.-diameter steel ball is pressed into sheet material under a 1-kg load. Equipment is located in an oven, and a temperature rise of 0.5° C/min is used. Cut-through temperature is reported as temperature at which a 110-volt circuit is completed between the ball and the steel backing plate.
MD = machine direction.

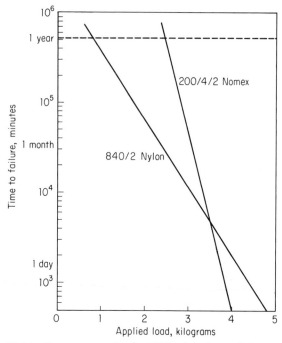

FIG 6.8 *Nomex yarn vs. Du Pont* 700 *nylon, time to failure under dead load at* 175° *C* [5].

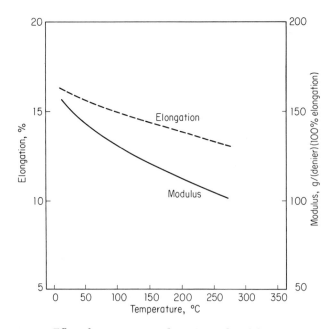

FIG 6.9 *Effect of temperature on elongation and modulus of Nomex yarn* [5]. *10-in. sample, 60% elongation per minute.*

TABLE 6.12   Properties of Laminates of Nomex Nylon Paper [10]

Property	Value	Test (ASTM unless otherwise noted)
Specific gravity	1.3	
Tensile strength, psi	22,000	D 638
Elongation, %	5–13	D 638
Flexural strength, psi	24,600	D 790
Flexural modulus, psi	790,000	D 790
Shear strength, psi	21,300	D 752
Impact strength, ft-lb/in.	3.5	D 256
Bond strength, lb	1,300	D 229
Hardness, Rockwell F	116	D 785
Deflection temperature at 264 psi, °C	280	D 640
Abrasion resistance, mg/kc	46	Taber
Coefficient of friction	0.24	Static
Coefficient of thermal conductivity, Btu/(hr)(ft²)(°F/in.)	0.8–1.0	L 177-45
Coefficient of thermal expansion, in./(in.)(°C):		
Parallel	2.1×10^{-5}	D 696
Perpendicular	8.6×10^{-5}	D 696
Water absorption, % after 24 hours:		
Water absorption, % after twenty-four hours:		
¹⁄₃₂ in.	0.9–3.3	D 570
⅛ in.	0.3–1.1	D 570
½ in.	0.1–0.6	D 570
Compressive creep, %, 35 mil	0.68	D 352

For the aromatic nylon paper, elevated-temperature physical properties are indicated in Figs. 6.16 to 6.18. The polyimide-coated papers provide almost identical properties. Properties of the 100 percent aromatic nylon laminates are given in Figs. 6.19 and 6.20. Oxidative stability at elevated

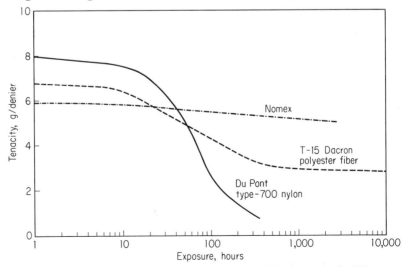

FIG 6.10   *Tenacity of yarns after exposure in air at 175°C [5]. 10-in. sample, 60% elongation per minute, at 23°C, 65% relative humidity.*

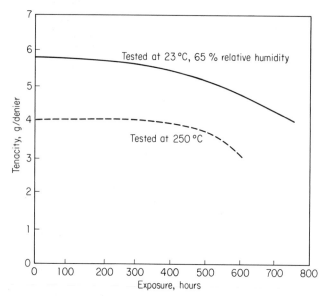

FIG 6.11 *Tenacity of Nomex yarn after exposure in air at 260° C* [5]. *10-in. sample, 60% elongation per minute.*

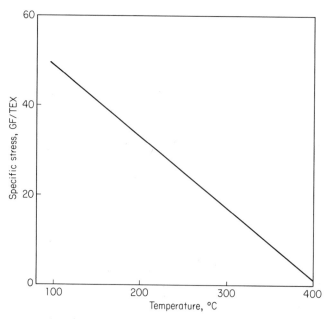

FIG 6.12 *Specific stress vs. temperature for Nomex yarn* [13].

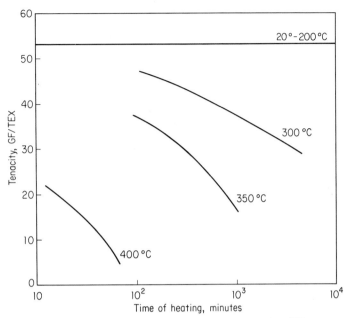

FIG 6.13   *Effect of aging at elevated temperatures on tenacity of Nomex yarn* [13].

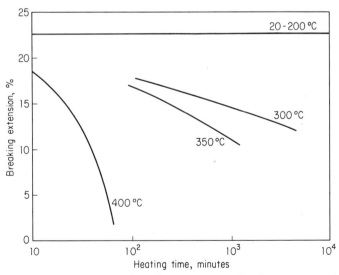

FIG 6.14   *Effect of aging at elevated temperatures on breaking extension of Nomex yarn* [13].

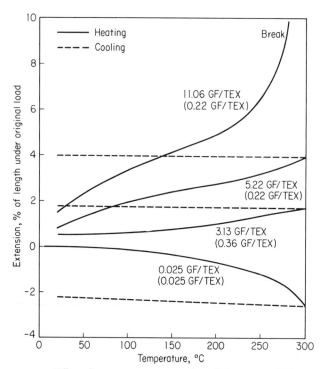

FIG 6.15 *Effect of temperature on extension of Nomex yarn* [13].
Figures in parentheses are original loads; other figures against curves are total acting loads during heating.

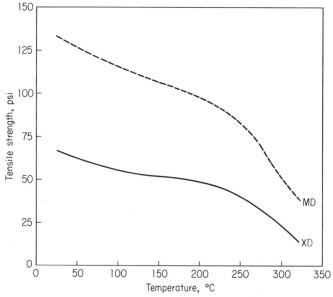

FIG 6.16 *Tensile strength vs. temperature for Nomex paper* [10]. MD = *machine direction.* XD = *cross direction.*

152

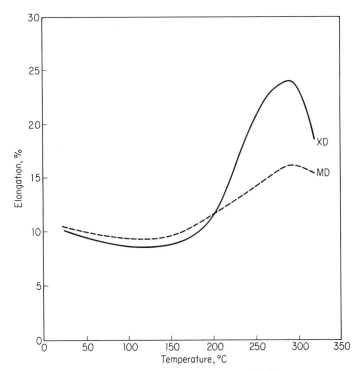

FIG 6.17   *Elongation vs. temperature for Nomex paper* [10].   MD =
machine direction.   XD = *cross direction.*

temperatures appears to be superior to that obtained with most other commercial polymers described in this volume.

PHYSICAL-CHEMICAL PROPERTIES

Polycyclamides

One of the principal weaknesses of conventional nylon 6 and 66 is the
susceptibility of the materials to moisture.   In this respect, the commercial
polycyclamide bears marked superiority, as described in Tables 6.13 and
6.14.

Aromatic Nylons

The aromatic nylons provide extremely good chemical resistance against
both acids and bases.   Stronger acids will reduce strength properties with
prolonged immersion.   Moisture causes loss of strength and elongation, the
loss being partly irreversible [13].   The dimensional stability of the aromatic
nylon paper to changes in relative humidity is given in Table 6.15.

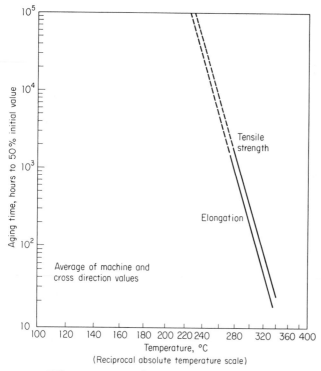

FIG 6.18 *Life vs. temperature for Nomex paper as measured by 50% loss of initial strength and elongation* [10].

The chemical resistance of aromatic nylon yarn is indicated in Table 6.16 and Figs. 6.21 through 6.28. The chemical resistance of the paper, both coated with a polyimide varnish and uncoated, is given in Table 6.17. Radiation resistance is outstanding, as indicated in Table 6.18.

ELECTRICAL PROPERTIES

Polycyclamides

The electrical properties of the commercial polycyclamide are indicated in Fig. 6.29. Properties are superior to nylon 66 at all test temperatures.

Aromatic Nylons

The electrical properties of the aromatic nylon paper are given in Tables 6.19 and 6.20 and in Figs. 6.30 through 6.35. Motorette tests, using aromatic nylon paper, indicate that the governing factor of service life is the lives of the magnet wire insulation and of the varnish, not the life of the paper. Data are indicated in Table 6.21.

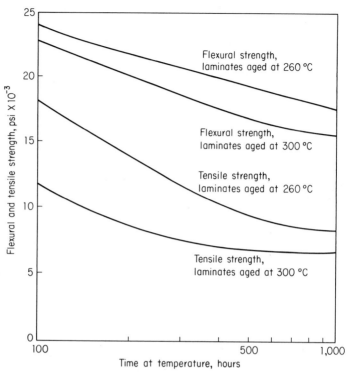

FIG 6.19 *Flexural and tensile strength of laminates of Nomex paper after aging at elevated temperatures* [10].

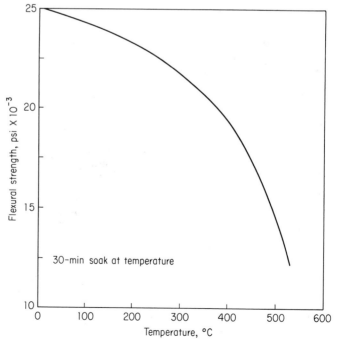

FIG 6.20 *Flexural strength vs. temperature for laminates of Nomex paper* [10].

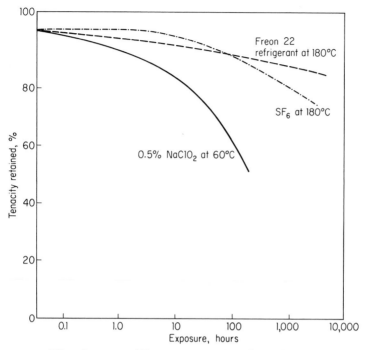

FIG 6.21 *Effect of exposure of Nomex yarn to various chemicals* [5].

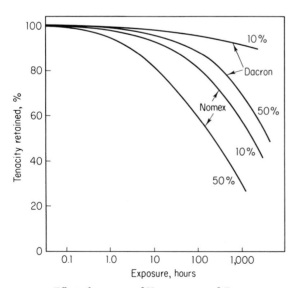

FIG 6.22 *Effect of exposure of Nomex yarn and Dacron (polyester) to dilute and concentrate sulfuric acid at* 60° C [5].

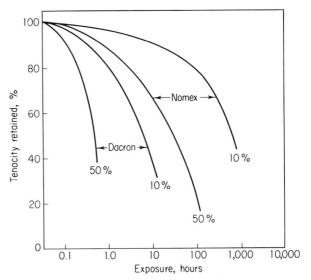

FIG 6.23 *Effect of exposure of Nomex yarn and Dacron (polyester) to dilute and concentrate sodium hydroxide at* 60°C [5].

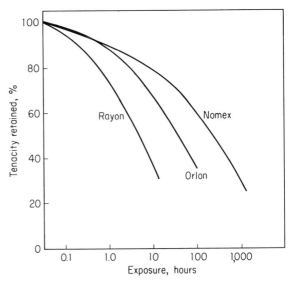

FIG 6.24 *Effect of exposure of Nomex yarn, Orlon (acrylic), and rayon to water vapor at* 155°C [5].

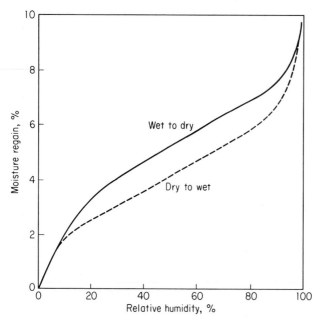

FIG 6.25 *Moisture regain of Nomex yarn* [5].

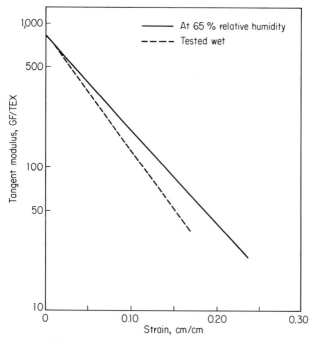

FIG 6.26 *Effect of moisture on tangent modulus vs. strain data of Nomex yarn* [13].

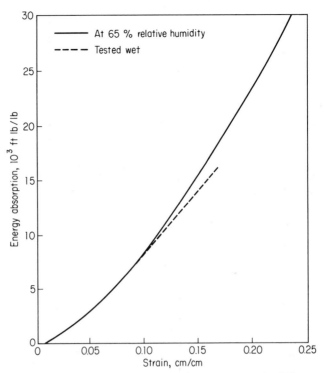

FIG 6.27 *Effect of moisture on energy absorption vs. strain of Nomex yarn* [13].

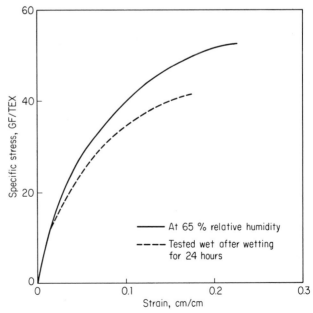

FIG 6.28 *Effect of moisture on stress-strain performance of Nomex yarn* [13].

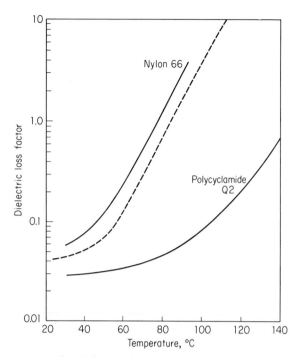

FIG 6.29 *Electrical properties vs. temperature of polycyclamide* Q2 *vs. nylon 66* [24].

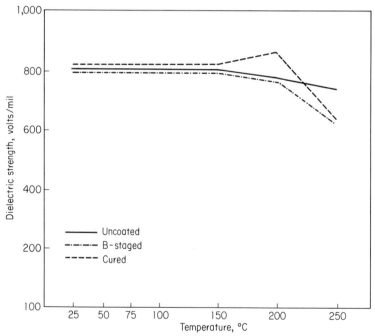

FIG 6.30 *Dielectric strength vs. temperature for* 10-mil *coated and uncoated Nomex paper* [23].

160

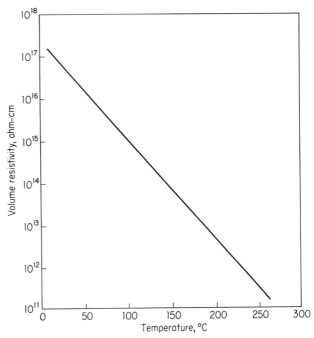

FIG 6.31 *Volume resistivity vs. temperature of* 10-*mil Nomex paper* [22].

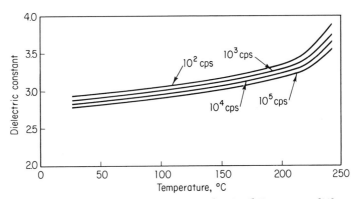

FIG 6.32 *Dielectric constant vs. temperature for* 10-*mil Nomex paper* [22].

TABLE 6.13 Moisture Susceptibility of Plastics [25]

Plastic	Water absorption after 24 hours in boiling water, %	Flexural modulus, psi	
		As molded	After 24 hours boiling
Q2	3.5	370,000	370,000
Nylon 66	8.2	380,000	80,000
Nylon 6	9.0	380,000	70,000
Acetal	2.0	380,000	320,000
Polycarbonate	0.4	360,000	360,000

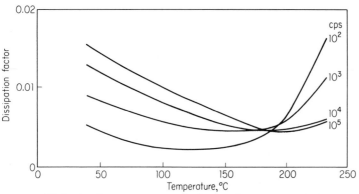

FIG 6.33 *Dissipation factor vs. temperature for 10-mil Nomex paper* [22].

PROCESSING

Polycyclamides

The commercial polycyclamide may be molded on equipment suitable for aliphatic nylons. Apparent melt viscosity vs. shear rate at 320°C is shown in Fig. 6.36. Because of the relatively high melt index, molding temperatures may be somewhat higher than with the more conventional

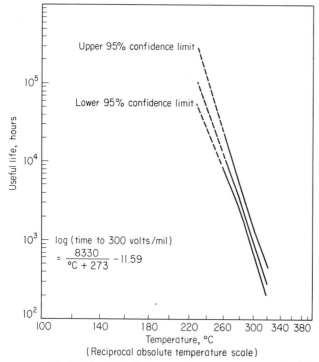

FIG 6.34 *Useful life of* 10-*mil Nomex paper vs. temperature (useful-life end point at dielectric strength less than* 300 *volts per mil)* [10].

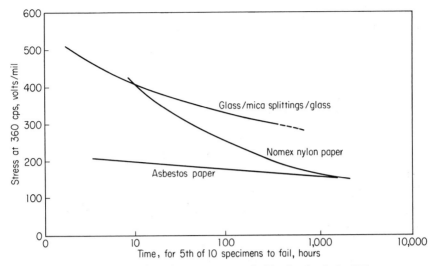

FIG 6.35 *Voltage endurance of Nomex paper compared with other insulation* [22].

materials. Satisfactory parts have been injection-molded, using a screw preplasticizer. Use of the screw permits slightly lower temperatures than does a plunger machine but is not necessary for satisfactory molding. Molding temperatures range from 325 to 345°C. Molds designed for use with both polycarbonates and acetals have proved satisfactory.

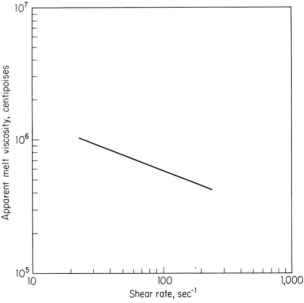

FIG 6.36 *Apparent melt viscosity of polycyclamide* Q2 *at* 320°C *as a function of rate of shear* [24].

TABLE 6.14 Hydrolytic Stability of Plastics [25]

A. At High Temperature and Humidity (110°C, 100% Relative Humidity)

	Properties of specimens after:			
	4 days		14 days	
Plastic	Flexural strength, % retained	Specimen condition	Flexural strength, % retained	Specimen condition
Q2	100	No change	100	No change
Acetal	....	Cheesy; formaldehyde odor	....	Disintegrated
Nylon 66	100	No change	84	Roughened; surface cracked
Polycarbonate	100	Internal cracks	71	Very brittle

B. In Launder-Ometer with Wash Solution (1% Sodium Carbonate, ½% Soap) at 70°C Specimens Tumbled with Steel Balls 4 hours per day)

	Properties of specimens after:			
	4 weeks		8 weeks	
Plastic	Flexural strength, % retained	Specimen condition	Flexural strength, % retained	Specimen condition
Q2	....	No change	100	No change
Acetal	78	Edges cracked	63	Severe crazing
Nylon 66	70	Etched surface	78	Surface crazed; discolored
Polycarbonate	100	One specimen brittle	100	Internal cracks

Aromatic Nylons

MANUFACTURE OF LAMINATES

The aromatic nylon paper may be self-bonded to make thicker laminates. The procedure is to stack the sheets, alternating machine (MD) and cross direction (XD) to equalize properties of the laminate in both directions. The sheets are then heated in a press for 5 minutes at 280°C at contact

TABLE 6.15 Dimensional Stability of Nomex Nylon Paper to Changes in Relative Humidity [23]

	3-mil Nomex paper			10-mil Nomex paper		
Relative humidity, %	Regain, %	Expansion, %		Regain, %	Expansion, %	
		MD	XD		MD	XD
Oven dry	0	0	0	0	0	0
50	2.9	0.4	0.5	3.5	0.4	0.5
65	4.9	0.6	0.5	5.1	0.6	0.9
95	7.7	0.9	1.6	8.4	1.1	1.8

MD = machine direction. XD = cross direction.

TABLE 6.16 Chemical Resistance of Nomex Yarn [5]

No loss after 10 hours at 23°C	No loss after 100 hours at 23°C	50% tenacity retained
10% H_2SO_4	10% H_2SO_4	70% HNO_3, 100 hours at 23°C
70% H_2SO_4	70% H_2SO_4	35% HCl, 100 hours at 23°C
10% HNO_3	10% HNO_3	10% HCl, 8 hours at 95°C
35% HCl	10% NaOH	70% H_2SO_4, 8 hours at 95°C
10% NaOH	28% NH_4OH	10% NaOH, 8 hours at 95°C
40% NaOH		Air + 5% H_2O + 5% SO_2, 100 hours at 175°C
90% HCOOH		
Sodium chlorite		
Sodium hypochlorite		
Peracetic acid		
Stoddard solvent		
Perchloroethylene		
Phenol		
Benzoic acid		

pressure, after which the pressure is increased to about 300 psi and held for 3 minutes. Breathing steps (i.e., pressure release to permit escape of entrapped gases) are conducted on 3-minute cycles until inspection indicates that the gases have all been removed. Pressure is increased to 1,000 psi, and the laminates are again breathed as necessary. Cure time at this pressure is a function of laminate thickness and may range from 40 minutes for a ⅛-in. laminate to 120 minutes for a 1-in. laminate.

TABLE 6.17 Chemical Resistance of 5-mil Pyre ML Polyimide-coated Nomex Paper [24]

Solvent	Dielectric strength, volts/mil			Tensile strength, psi		
	Uncoated	B-staged	Cured	Uncoated	B-staged	Cured
None	675	750	800	8,000	8,000	10,000
Xylene	600	675	700	7,500	7,500	8,000
Hexane	625	700	750	8,500	7,500	9,000
Methyl ethyl ketone	725	700	775	9,000	7,500	8,500
Ethyl acetate	750	750	800	9,000	8,000	8,500
Dimethylformamide	250	275	500	2,500	3,000	5,000
1% NaOH	700	675	750	7,500	7,000	8,500
10% NaOH	600	600	600	6,000	6,000	8,000
1% H_2SO_4	700	550	650	8,000	6,500	8,500
10% H_2SO_4	575	475	650	5,000	4,500	4,000
H_2O	550	600	675	7,000	6,500	8,000
H_2O (boiling)°	675	650	675	7,000	6,500	8,000
H_2O (95% relative humidity)†	600	750	875	7,000	8,500	9,000

Samples soaked 7 days at 25°C and air-dried 16 hours at 25°C, 50% relative humidity before testing, except as noted.

° Sample boiled in water 7 days, air-dried 16 hours and tested.

† Sample held at 23°C and 95% relative humidity; then tested.

TABLE 6.18   Radiation Resistance of Nomex Yarn, Dacron (Polyester), and Nylon 66 [5]

Dosage	Tenacity, % retained		
	Nomex	Dacron	Nylon
β-Van de Graaf			
200 megareps	81	57	29
600 megareps	76	29	0
x-rays 50 kv			
50 hours...................	85	22	
100 hours..................	73	0	
250 hours..................	49	0	
Brookhaven Pile, 50°C			
200 megareps..............	70	45	32
1,000 megareps.............	55	Radioactive	Crumbled
2,000 megareps.............	45	Radioactive	Crumbled

The density of the laminates is about 1.3 as against a theoretical value of 1.38. Films of the aromatic nylon, virtually transparent and approaching the theoretical density, may be prepared by blending the fibers and fibrids in a water slurry to produce a paper which, in appearance, resembles blotter paper. This is then hot-pressed or calendered to soften the fibrids and cause flow to fill the interstices. Such films have been produced experimentally but are not a commercial item.

MANUFACTURE OF FIBERS

Aromatic nylon fibers are produced from solution, a typical procedure from the literature being:

The polymer . . . is dissolved to a concentration of 17 percent in a mixture of 95 parts dimethylformamide and 5 parts lithium chloride. This solution at 128°C is spun through a five-hole spinneret, in which the orifice has a diameter of 0.10 mm, into an air column maintained at 225°C. The resulting fiber is wound up at the rate of 92 yards per minute, and thereafter drawn to approximately 4.75 times its original length and boiled off in water [8].

TABLE 6.19   Moisture Content and Dielectric Strength of 10-mil Nomex Paper as a Function of Relative Humidity [10]

Relative humidity	Dielectric strength, volts/mil	Moisture content, %
Oven dry	892	0
25%	905	3.9
50%	796	4.1
64%	848	6.3
95%	870	10.7

TABLE 6.20 Volume Resistivity of 10-mil Nomex Paper as
a Function of Relative Humidity [10]

Relative humidity	Volume resistivity, ohm-cm.
Oven dry (24 hours at 100°C)	2.0×10^{16}
50%	1.2×10^{16}
95%	1.4×10^{14}

The fibers may be heat-treated to improve physical properties, as
described as follows:

Fibers of poly(m-phenyleneisophthalamide) having a melting point of 427°C and
an intrinsic viscosity of 0.99 are produced . . . to give a yarn of 30 filaments.
The yarn is drawn to 3.5 times its original spun length in steam at atmospheric
pressure to give a highly oriented but amorphous fiber. Following orientation,
the yarn is led over a heating plate which is at 345°C. The plate is 15 in. long,
and the yarn contacts it while under the tension of 45 grams and is wound up at
a speed of 10 yards per minute, giving a contact time of the yarn with the hot
plate of about 2.5 seconds. The yarn is stretched by 50 percent. The yarn so
obtained has a very high degree of crystallinity as shown by x-ray diffraction
pattern analysis [6].

MANUFACTURE OF PAPERS

The aromatic nylon papers are produced from a combination of chopped
fibers (approximately ¼-in. long) and fibrids. The latter are produced
under U.S. patent 2,999,788, which describes a process for removing a film
continuously during interfacial polycondensation and then reducing the
film to fibrid structures with a Waring Blendor [7]. The commercial papers
from this combination are free of binders and ingredients other than the
aromatic nylon.

TABLE 6.21 Projected Lives of Motorette Systems [18]

Set no.	Insulation	Wire	Varnish	Temperature to give life of 20,600 hours, °C
1	Rag paper	Polyvinyl Formal	Phenolic	(105°C control)
2	Polyamide paper	Polyvinyl Formal	Phenolic	105
3	Polyester fiber–film fiber	Epoxy	Epoxy	125
4	Polyamide paper	Epoxy	Epoxy	124
5	Polyester-glass	Crosslinked polyester	Polyester	144
6	Polyamide paper	Crosslinked polyester	Polyester	144
7	Polyimide-glass	Polyimide	Polyimide	226
8	Polyamide paper	Polyimide	Polyimide	216
9	Glass–mica–glass silicone	Polyimide	Silicone	225
10	Polyamide paper	Polyimide	Silicone	228

APPLICATIONS

Polycyclamides

The polycyclamides are expected to prove useful in replacing nylon 6 and 66 in applications where the moisture resistance of the nylons are marginal or unsatisfactory. This improved moisture resistance is obtained without substantial sacrifice of physical properties and with an improvement in electrical insulation resistance.

Aromatic Nylons

The aromatic nylon yarns are suggested for use in protective fabrics exposed to high temperature and for reinforcement of rubber and synthetic elastomers. The aromatic nylon paper has established superiority in electrical insulating applications, where it offers service to Class 180 temperatures and above with outstanding dimensional stability and moisture resistance. Other applications include filter bags for high-temperature gas filtration and laundry pads and covers for home and industrial uses.

REFERENCES

1950

1. D. C. Pease, Synthetic Linear Polyamides Containing Interlinear Cyclic Groups and Process for Obtaining Same, U.S. 2,516,585.

1954

2. D. C. Pease, Transparent Synthetic Linear Polyamide and Process for Producing Same, U.S. 2,696,482.

1956

3. F. G. Lum, E. F. Carlson, and J. C. Butler, Synthetic Plastics from *Meta*-Xylylene Diamine and Isophthalic Acid, U.S. 2,766,222.

1959

4. E. L. Wittbecker and P. W. Morgan, Interfacial Polycondensation, I, *J. Polymer Sci.* **40**:289.

1961

5. W. R. Clay and W. C. Long, Physical and Chemical Properties of HT-1, E. I. du Pont de Nemours & Co., Inc., Textile Fibers Department, May.
6. Improvements Relating to the Treatment of Aromatic Polyamide Structures (to E. I. du Pont de Nemours & Co., Inc.), Brit. 877,885.
7. P. W. Morgan, Synthetic Polymer Fibrid Paper, U.S. 2,999,788.
8. Polyamide Structures and Process for Their Production (to E. I. du Pont de Nemours & Co., Inc.), Brit. 871,581.

1962

9. H. E. Mark et al., Aromatic Polyamide, *J. Polymer Sci.* **61**:S49.

1963

10. Properties and Processing of Nomex, Bulletin NP-31, E. I. du Pont de Nemours & Co., Inc., Textile Fibers Department, September.

1964

11. R. A. Dine-Hart et al., Aromatic Polyamides, *J. Polymer Sci.*, part B, vol. 2, no. 4, pp. 369–373.
12. O. Ya. Fedotova et al., Some Properties of Aromatic and Arylaliphatic Polyamides Prepared by Interfacial Polycondensation, *Vysokomolekul. Soedin.* **6**(3):452–458.
13. E. Mikolajewski and J. E. Swallow, Mechanical and Thermal Properties of an Aromatic Yarn, Royal Aircraft Establishment, Technical Note CPM 57, January.
14. P. W. Morgan and S. L. Kwolek, Low Temperature Solution Polycondensation of Piperazine Polyamides, *J. Polymer Sci.*, part A, vol. 2, pp. 181–201.
15. M. Moss and L. M. Roseland, Expandable Space Structure Material Research, AD 437 107.
16. J. Preston and F. Dobinson, New High Temperature Aromatic Polyamides, *J. Polymer Sci.*, part B, vol. 2, pp. 1171–1174.
17. V. P. Sarzhevskaya et al., Polyamides with Aromatic and Heterocyclic Links in the Chain, V: Polyamides Based on Bis(4-aminocyclohexyl)methane and Some Heterocyclic Dicarboxylic Acids, *Ukr. Khim. Zh.* **30**(1):83.

1965

18. G. H. Bowers, High Temperature Motorette Systems Testing, Proceedings of 6th Electrical Insulation Conference (IEEE and NEMA), September.
19. F. Dobinson and J. Preston, New High Temperature Polymers, II: Ordered Aromatic Copolyamides Containing Fused and Multiple Ring Systems, Proceedings of Symposium on High Temperature Polymers: Synthesis and Degradation, ACS Western Regional Meeting, Los Angeles, November.
20. W. A. H. Huffman, R. W. Smith, and W. T. Dye, Jr., Process for Preparing Polyamides from Aromatic Amino Acids, U.S. 3,203,933.
21. P. W. Morgan, "Condensation Polymers: Interfacial and Solution Methods," Interscience.
22. T. P. Murphy, How to Mold FRTP Resins, *Mod. Plastics,* June.
23. Properties and Performance of Nomex High Temperature Resistant Nylon Paper, Bulletin N-195, E. I. du Pont de Nemours & Co., Inc., Textile Fibers Dept., September.
24. Properties and Processing of Heat-sealable Pyre-ML Polyimide-coated Nomex Nylon Paper, E. I. du Pont de Nemours & Co., Inc., Textile Fibers Department.
25. M. T. Watson and G. M. Armstrong, Q2: a New Polycyclamide Engineering Plastic, *SPE J.*, May, pp. 475–479.

1966

26. W. H. Daly, Novel Polyamide Synthesis via Enamines, ACS Meeting, New York, September.
27. Shipping Information and Processing of Nomex High Temperature Resistant Nylon Filament Yarn, Bulletin NP-32, E. I. du Pont de Nemours & Co., Inc.
28. Yarns and Fabrics of Nomex, High Temperature Resistant Nylon, Bulletin N-199, E. I. du Pont de Nemours & Co., Inc.

7

Aromatic Polyamide-Imides and Polyester-Imides

High-temperature properties intermediate between the aromatic polyamides and the aromatic polyimides may be obtained with the polyamide-imides and polyester-imides. These provide improved elevated-temperature strength over the former and improved processability over the latter. They are presently being marketed as wire coatings and varnishes and provide extremely good thermal stability for operations at temperatures to 220°C.

The polyamide-imides are generally produced from aromatic diamines or dianhydrides containing amide links in the central chain. These are then reacted with a dianhydride to produce a polyamic acid capable of being converted to the polyimide through the action of heat. The polyester-imides are produced from aromatic amines and dianhydrides containing aromatic ester links in the central chain. In their production and processing, both types share many points in common with the aromatic polyimides discussed in the following chapter.

*T*he polyamide-imides and the polyester-imides are a logical bridge between the aromatic polyamides, described in Chap. 6, and the aromatic polyimides, described in Chap. 8.

The polyamide-imides were disclosed in 1942 [2] through the reaction of a diamine with a triacid, the reaction proceeding ideally in two steps:

$$
\underset{\substack{\text{1,2,3-Propanetricarboxylic}\\\text{acid}}}{\text{HOCCH}_2\text{CHCH}_2\text{COH}} + \underset{\text{Diamine}}{\text{H}_2\text{N—R—NH}_2} \longrightarrow
$$

with the triacid bearing two O (double-bonded) groups on the terminal carbons and a C=O / OH branch on the central carbon.

Polyamic acid

Polyamide-imide

The early materials, based on aliphatic species, were not of commercial importance. With the introduction of aromatic dianhydrides, derived from polymethyl benzenes from petroleum sources, the reaction assumed significance. The aromatic polyamide-imides were thus disclosed in the earliest pertinent literature on the aromatic polyamides and aromatic polyimides. As early as 1945, E. I. du Pont de Nemours & Company claimed polyamide-imides and polyimides from the reaction of both aliphatic and aromatic diamines with tri- or tetracarboxylic aromatic and aliphatic acids [1].

To give an example of the interrelationship between the technologies: In 1960, Du Pont disclosed production of aromatic polyamides: from the intermediate *N,N'*-bis(3-aminophenyl)isophthalamide [4]. This amine-terminated diamide could be further reacted with additional isophthaloyl chloride to produce the high-molecular-weight aromatic polyamide, as discussed in Chap. 6. On the other hand, the amine-terminated diamide could be reacted with pyromellitic dianhydride to produce a linear polymer containing both imide and amide linkages.

In 1965, Westinghouse Electric Corporation was granted a composition of matter patent covering polymers from a variety of amide-containing aromatic diamines reacted with dianhydrides such as pyromellitic dianhydride [15].

Much of the early Westinghouse work and additional research by Narmco Division of Whittaker Corporation was under government sponsorship and was aimed at the development of high-molecular-weight heat-resistant polymers for aerospace adhesive and laminating applications in the 300°C range. The general finding was that the aromatic polyamide-imide polymers were less thermally stable than the aromatic polyimides, and research was therefore virtually discontinued by the services in 1965 in favor of molecules potentially more favorable for the ultrahigh-temperature ranges.

In spite of the less than optimum elevated-temperature resistance, interest in the polyamide-imides continued at several companies, applications as electrical insulation being envisioned. In 1964, Amoco Chemicals Corporation introduced a special polyamide-imide polymer from methylene-dianiline and trimellitic anhydride. The Amoco polymer was offered for magnet wire enamels and for electrical-grade varnishes capable of continuous operation at 220°C.

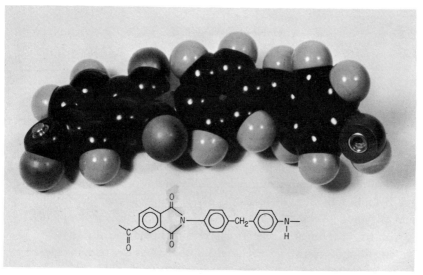

Atom model of polyamide-imide from trimellitic anhydride and methylene dianiline. (The Epoxylite Corporation.)

In 1966, polyester-imides were being developed experimentally by General Electric Company. These materials were derived from a dianhydride which contained aromatic diester groups [17, 18].

Special polyester-imides produced by the reaction of polyhydroxy-terminated polyesters with a diacid diimide from trimellitic anhydride and *m*-phenylene-diamine [8] are available commercially in Europe under the trade name Terebec. These are crosslinked rather than linear polymers. Polyester-imides in some respects similar to these are available as polyimide-modified branched polyesters from Schenectady Chemicals, Inc., in the United States, under the trade name Isomid.

SYNTHESIS

Chemistry

POLYAMIDE-IMIDES

The polyamide-imide polymers are more easily prepared and processed than either the high-molecular-weight aromatic polyamides or polyimides.

Three general methods may be employed in the synthesis: (1) An amine-terminated polymer may be developed from the reaction of a diacid chloride with excess primary diamine, by essentially the interfacial polycondensation technique described in the preceding chapter; this is then reacted in a solution with a dianhydride and the resultant polymer ring-closed by techniques described in the following chapter. (2) The dianhydride may be reacted with excess diamine to obtain a low-molecular-weight polymer which is further reacted with a diacid chloride by the interfacial polycondensation or solution technique. (3) The polymer, containing alternating amide-imide links, may be developed from a diprimary amine and trimellitic anhydride (TMA).

A considerable number of amide-containing diamine intermediates have been synthesized, such as the following:

3,3'-Diaminobenzanilide

Isophthaloyl(4-aminoanilide)

By varying the reaction ratios of the acid chloride and the amine, amide-containing precursors can be developed with virtually any molecular weight, and in this fashion the final ratio of amide to imide linkages in the polymer can be controlled.

The overall reaction, in simplified form, would progress as follows:

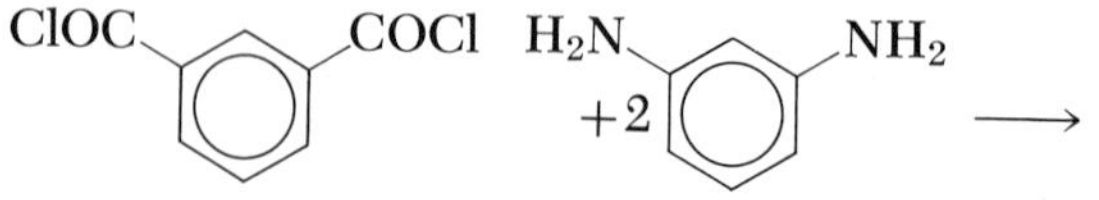

Isophthaloyl chloride

m-Phenylenediamine

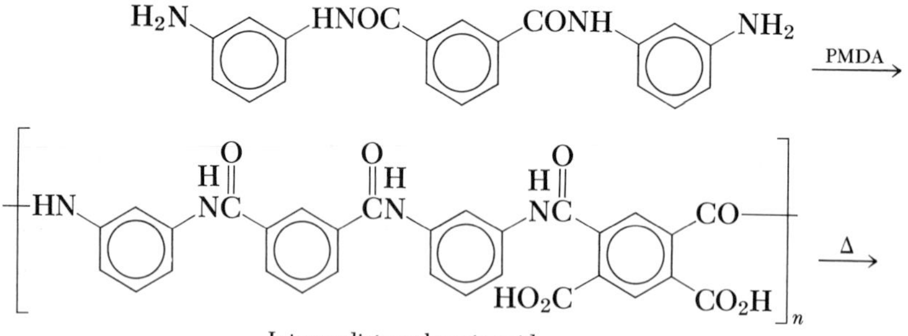

Intermediate polyamic acid

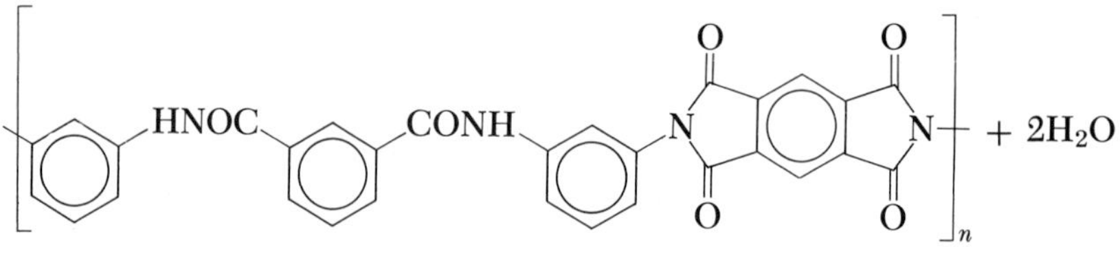

Polyamide-imide

The polyamide-imides from TMA may be produced from the 4-acetyl chloride of TMA and a diamine, with the two components used in almost equimolar amounts. The resulting structure will contain a carboxyl group in either the 1- or the 2-position, and further heating will create the imide group, leading to a polymer of the following general structure [9]:

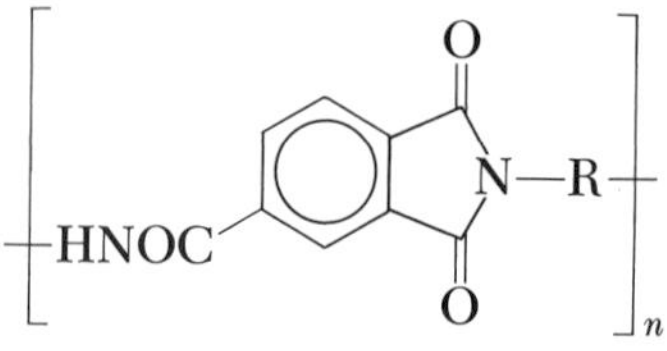

It has been disclosed that polyamide-imides may also be produced from TMA through the reaction of the anhydride with the diacyl derivative of the amine [17], the reaction proceeding:

$$CH_3CONHRHNOCCH_3 + 2 \quad [\text{Trimellitic anhydride}] \longrightarrow$$

Amide   Trimellitic anhydride

$$[\text{Dianhydride}] + 2CH_3CO_2H$$

Dianhydride   Acetic acid

This acidolysis reaction, which takes place at 125 to 325°C, gives the desired product only under very carefully controlled conditions. An unidentified side reaction involving the anhydride ring has been observed. The resulting dianhydride may be further reacted with a diamine to provide a polyamide-imide.

It has been found that as the ratio of amide to imide links in the final polymer is increased, flexibility is improved but, as would be expected, is not preserved to high temperatures, embrittlement being observed at about 300°C or less. The use of high amide-to-imide linkages, however, does improve processability of the polymer, since the amount of water eliminated in the final ring-closing operation is minimized. The water, as indicated in Chap. 8, poses a special volatile-release problem with the 100 percent polyimide polymers.

With aromatic species, best flexibility has been observed with bonds in the meta and para positions on the benzene ring, with highest viscosities being obtained through para positions. The positions, however, appear to have little effect on thermal stability.

It has been observed that the interfacial polycondensation technique is not well suited to the preparation of short-chain amine-terminated polyamides, and hence is more suitable for the preparation of polyamide-imide polymers high in amide linkages [5].

The product of trimellitic anhydride and diamines appears to provide a more convenient method for obtaining higher imide-to-amide ratios and consequently improved thermal stability.

POLYESTER-IMIDES

The polyester-imides are produced by essentially the same technique as the polyamide-imides. The precursor, however, is a dianhydride containing aromatic ester links. These materials are prepared by the reaction of trimellitic anhydride with a diacetoxy derivative of an aromatic diol. Of the aromatic diols investigated, hydroquinone seems to offer best properties. The dianhydride from this diol has the following structure:

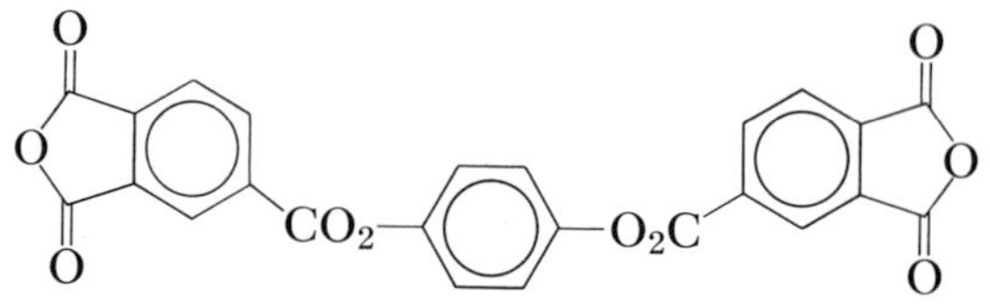

Dianhydride from hydroquinone and
trimellitic anhydride

The actual reaction is believed to involve a four-membered ring transition state as follows [23]:

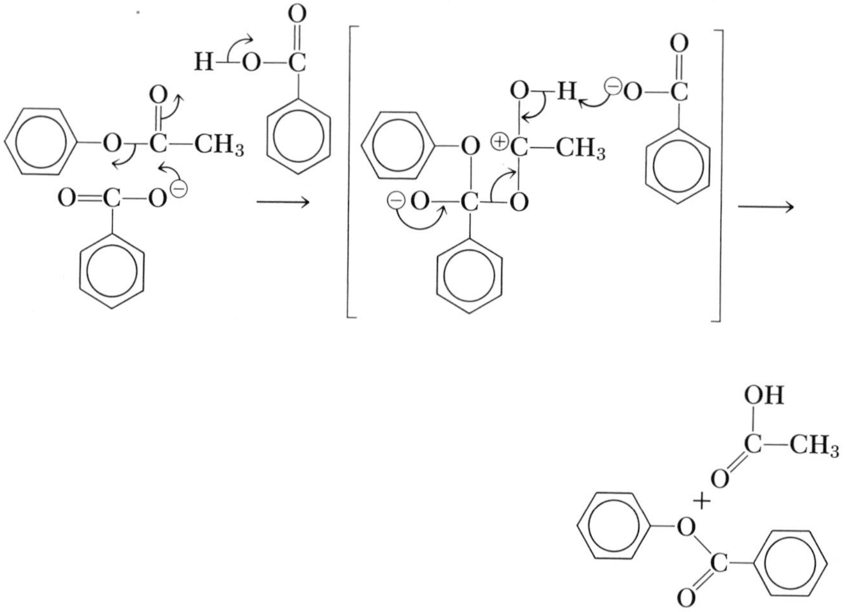

An alternative procedure for obtaining the dianhydride precursor involves using the monoacid chloride of TMA and an aromatic dihydroxy compound. These are reacted in the presence of an HCl acceptor such as pyridine [23].

Typical Preparations

POLYAMIDE-IMIDES

The amine-terminated amide precursor has been prepared as follows:

A solution containing 32 grams of *m*-phenylenediamine, 75 grams of borax, 10 grams of sodium sulfite, and 1,600 grams of water was stirred vigorously while a solution of 15 grams of isophthaloyl chloride in 1,000 grams of xylene was added rapidly. The mixture was stirred for 2 minutes, and the precipitated polymer was filtered off. A second run was made in the exact same way. The products of the two runs were combined, washed twice with water, and once with acetone, and then dried for 1 hour at 150°C to give a gray powder weighing 48 grams. This material appears to include molecules of various chain lengths, but the average composition was found to correspond to about 0.33 mole of diamine per mole of combined isophthalate and terephthalate. Thus, the average molecule contained seven benzene rings, six amide groups, and two amino groups [15].

The polyamide-imide from *N,N'*-bis(3-aminophenyl)isophthalamide and pyromellitic dianhydride has been prepared as follows:

N,N'-Bis(3-aminophenyl)isophthalamide, in the amount of 3.46 grams, is mixed with 2.18 grams of pyromellitic dianhydride, while blanketing the mixture with nitrogen. A mixed solvent consisting of 13.7 ml of dry dimethylacetamide and 9.0 ml of dry pyridine is added, and the resulting mixture is stirred while the reaction vessel is cooled in an ice bath for a period of 4 hours. The ice bath is then removed, and stirring continued for an additional 7 hours, the mixture reaching room temperature. A viscous solution results. A film of the polymer, on heating to a temperature of 250°C, undergoes dehydration. Conversion may also be effected by the addition of an excess of acetic anhydride to the original polymer solution, causing it to turn yellow and precipitate the product. The alternating copolyamide-imide formed by either of the above means is soluble in concentrated sulfuric acid, in which it exhibits an inherent viscosity of 0.53. The polymer is also soluble in a solution of lithium chloride in dimethylacetamide; an inherent viscosity of 0.97 is determined in this medium. Dry spinning of the latter solution results in the production of fibers [4].

POLYESTER-IMIDES

Preparation of a dianhydride from hydroquinone and trimellitic anhydride, e.g., *p*-phenylene-bis(trimellitate anhydride) has been described as follows:

One mole (192 grams) of trimellitic anhydride and 0.5 mole (97 grams) of hydroquinone diacetate were mixed with 500 cc of chlorinated diphenyl and with stirring heated to 300°C for 3 hours. At the end of this time, a total of 60 grams of acetic acid had distilled over. The reaction mixture was cooled to 80°C and

4 volumes of normal n-heptane added to precipitate the product which was then filtered, washed three times with diethyl ether, and dried under vacuum. A total of 200 grams of product was obtained which, after hydrolysis, had a neutral equivalent of 121 as against a theoretical 123. The yield was 88.9 percent of theory [17].

MODIFICATION AND FORMULATION

Polyamide-Imides

The number of modifications that can be made in the basic amide-imide chain is quite large. The amide linkage appears to be the limiting factor with regard to thermal stability. In one series of tests [3] with a number of polyimide copolymers, the following order of thermal stability was established: imide $>$ ether, sulfide, direct phenyl-phenyl bonds $>$ amide, ester $>$ methylene $>$ isopropylidene. Typical performance characteristics of a number of amide-imide polymers are indicated in Table 7.1. In a separate program, decomposition was found to occur by attack on the carbonyl group with the amide carbonyl being possibly more labile than the imide carbonyl [20].

In addition to selecting specific amine-terminated amides and their chain lengths, it is also possible to produce species from combinations of acid chlorides to obtain special properties. Likewise, any of the commercial dianhydrides (see Chap. 8) may be employed in final synthesis.

TABLE 7.1   Properties of Polyamide-Polyimides [5]

Diamine	Inherent viscosity	Film properties[a]	Weight loss at 325°C, %,[b] after:			
			100 hours	200 hours	300 hours	400 hours
4,4'-Diaminobenzanilide	2.20	Brittle	5.7	8.4	11.9	12.1
4,3'-Diaminobenzanilide	1.55	Flexible	4.3	7.8	10.8	11.9
3,4'-Diaminobenzanilide	2.19	Flexible	2.0	4.2	6.9	9.8
3,3'-Diaminobenzanilide	1.18	Flexible	3.2	6.5	9.8	11.2
3,5'-Diaminobenzanilide	1.29	No film, just crumbs				
Isophthal(4-aminoanilide)	1.46	Flexible	6.9	9.4	14.4	20.4
N,N'-m-Phenylenebis(4-aminobenzamide)	1.48	Flexible	6.0	9.2	12.5	15.6
Isophthal(3-aminoanilide)	1.48	Flexible	6.8	8.1	10.5	13.2
N,N'-Bis(3-aminobenzoyl)-2,4-diaminodiphenyl ether	0.54	Flexible	24.1	31.5	38.6	44.3
N,O-Bis(3-aminobenzoyl)-p-aminophenol	1.22	Flexible	12	17	21	27
Bis(4-aminophenyl) isophthalate	0.93	Flexible (shrunk)	3.6	6.7	10.9	15.0

[a] The samples consisted of films approximately 1 mil thick adhering to aluminum. The film was judged to be flexible if it could be creased without cracking; brittle if it cracked on creasing.
[b] The values at 100-hour intervals were obtained from plots of weight loss vs. time.

TABLE 7.2   Effect of Solvents on Viscosity of Amoco Polymer Type 10 [10]

Solvent	Typical viscosity at 32% solids, poises at 25°C
Dimethylacetamide	14
Dimethylformamide	4
Dimethyl sulfoxide	20
Acetone	Insoluble
Formamide	Insoluble
Dimethylacetamide/acetone (50/50)	3
Dimethylacetamide/xylene (60/40)	10
N-Methylpyrrolidone	63
N-Methylpyrrolidone/dimethylacetamide (66/33)	30
N-Methylpyrrolidone/quinoline (70/30)	95
N-Methylpyrrolidone/acetanilide (70/30)	280

Efforts have been made to improve the thermal stability of the polymers through the use of more highly functional precursors. For example, 3,5,4'-triaminobenzanilide has been used in blend with m-phenylenediamine. However, the resultant polymeric reaction product from the blend of amines and pyromellitic dianhydride crosslinked even with refrigerated storage [6].

The solvents commonly used with the polyamide-imides are dimethyl formamide, pyridine, N-methylpyrrolidone, dimethyl sulfoxide, and the like. Additional thinning of the commercially available solutions may be accomplished by use of up to 40 percent aromatic or ester solvents, and up to 60 percent acetone or MIK, and up to 80 percent cyclohexanone. A typical viscosity curve is shown in Fig. 7.1. Table 7.2 gives solubility data, and Table 7.3 solution stability data. At lower solids contents, the polyamide-imides provide excellent stability in comparison with that offered by the polyimides, as indicated in Fig. 7.2. Solution stability declines as solid content increases.

TABLE 7.3   Stability of 20% Solids Solution Viscosities of Amoco AI Polymer [10]

Time at 100°C, hours	Viscosity, poises at 25°C°	
	DMAC	NMP
0	0.65	1.8
2	0.78	2.0
5	0.85	2.0
20	0.65	1.5

° Brookfield

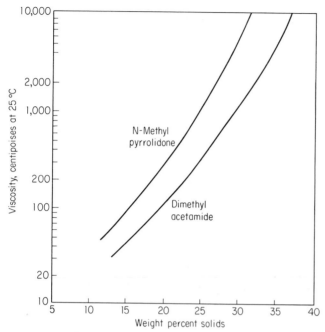

FIG 7.1   *Typical viscosities of solutions of Amoco AI polymer (type 10)*
[10].

Polyester-Imides

As indicated in the previous section, the amide and ester linkages appear approximately equal in terms of thermal stability. Thus, the polyester-imides can be considered generally similar to the polyamide-imides.

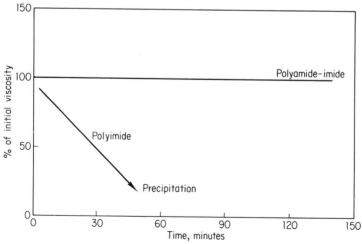

FIG 7.2   *Solution stabilities at 150° C of polyimide and polyamide-imide in amide solvents* [10].

The methods by which they may be modified are comparable to those used for the polyamide-imides. The influence of the diamine component on film strengths is indicated in Table 7.4. The influence of thermal aging on film flexibility at elevated temperature is indicated in Table 7.5.

TABLE 7.4 Physical Properties of the Polyester-Imide Films [18]

Diamine	Tensile strength $\times 10^{-3}$ psi		Tensile modulus $\times 10^{-3}$ psi		% elongation at break	
	23°C	200°C	23°C	200°C	23°C	200°C
H₂N—⟨◯⟩—O—⟨◯⟩—NH₂	15	6.3	440	193	14	23
H₂N—⟨◯⟩—CH₂—⟨◯⟩—NH₂	14.5	6.2	544	191	6	21
H₂N—⟨◯⟩—O—⟨◯⟩—NH₂ ° H₂N—⟨◯⟩—⟨◯⟩—NH₂	22.7	9.9	790	354	6	11

° 50 mole % copolymer.

PHYSICAL PROPERTIES

The commercial polyamide-imide materials from Amoco Chemical Corporation are supplied as light yellow powders with a specific gravity of 1.4. Their principal use is in solution coatings for electrical insulation applications. Some laminate data have been developed, as reported in the section Thermal Properties.

Westinghouse Electric Corporation has assigned the trade names Aramidyl to their polyamide-imide polymers and Amanim to their films.

Insofar as the principal suggested uses are in the electrical insulation field for higher-temperature duty, the major properties are more properly presented under that section of this chapter. Typical properties of a magnet wire enamel are given in Table 7.6.

THERMAL PROPERTIES

The commercial polyimide film (Kapton H) reveals no definite melting point, whereas experimental polyamide-imide films prepared by Westinghouse Electric Corporation reveal a melting point of about 400°C, with the glass transition temperature being about 265°C [19]. The superiority of the polyimides, in terms of elevated-temperature weight loss, is indicated

Diamine	Dianhydride	Time to failure,° hours	Weight loss at failure time, %
ODA	I	1,000	6.0
MDA	I	750	8.5
2Me-MDA	I	500	6.5
4Me-MDA	I	270	7.0
ODA	PMDA	>1,000	....
MDA	PMDA	160	1.0
Aromatic polyester from iso- and terephthalic acid and hydroquinone		500+	4.5

° Samples tested at 20, 100, 160, 270, 500, 750 and 1,000 hours.
I = dianhydride from hydroquinone and trimellitic anhydride.
ODA = 4,4′-diaminodiphenyl ether.
MDA = 4,4′-diaminodiphenylmethane.
2Me-MDA = 3,3′-Dimethyl-4,4′-diaminodiphenylmethane.
4Me-MDA = 3,3′5,5′-Tetramethyl-4,4′-diaminophenylmethane.
PMDA = Pyromellitic dianhydride.

T A B L E 7.6   Properties of Al 220 Magnet Wire (Standard-build 18-gage Copper Wire) Compared with Heavy-build Magnet Wires [7]

Property	Value		
	Standard Al 220	Heavy Isonel 200/17	Heavy ML
Thermal Properties			
Thermal stability:			
IEEE 57 classification...............	Class 220°C	Class H (180°C)	Class 220°C
Temperature at 20,000 hours life, °C.....	240	215	245
Thermoplastic flow, °C.................	425	360	475
Compression flow, %....................	2.8	34	2.5
Enamel deformation under 500-g load at 250°C			
Heat shock, °C.......................	425	180	425
Passing temperature for 15% prestretch, 3× wrap, 1 hour			
Weight loss after 1 month at 210°C, %......	0.2	18	3.3
Burnout test........................	15 min +	1 min 30 sec	15 min +
Time for twisted pair at 40 amp to fail 120 volts a-c			
Physical properties			
Flexibility	20%, 1×	20%, 1×	20%, 1×
Quick snap..........................	Okay	Okay	Okay
Abrasion resistance:			
Repeated scrape test................	100+	25	20
Unilateral scrape test, grams...........	1,300	1,500	1,200
Low-temperature flexibility	Okay	Okay	Okay
1× wrap at −70°C			

TABLE 7.7 Weight Loss of Aromatic Polymer Films in Air at 325°C [19]

Polymer	Weight loss, %, after:		
	200 hours	400 hours	800 hours
Polyimides			
MPD-PMDA	....	5.6	
DAPE-PMDA	....	6.6	
DAPS-PMDA	....	7.9	
MPD-BTDA	2.7	3.2	3.7
DAPE-BTDA	6.3	11.2	
DAPS-BTDA	2.0	3.3	
DAPE-MPD-BTDA$_2$	4.9	7.1	
DAPE$_3$-MPD-BTDA$_4$	3.7	6.3	14.5
DAPE-MPD$_3$-BTDA$_4$	2.8	3.7	5.1
MPD$_3$-PMDA$_2$-BTDA	1.8	2.7	4.8
MPD$_2$-PMDA-BTDA	1.4	2.3	4.3
MPD$_3$-PMDA-BTDA$_2$	1.6	2.3	3.9
Polyamide-Imides			
(MAB-PPD)-PMDA	....	9.8	
(MPD$_2$-IP)-PMDA	....	10.7	
(MAB$_2$-MPD)-PMDA	....	20.3	
(MAB-PPD)$_{3.4}$-IP$_{2.4}$-PMDA	38.0		
MPD$_{16}$-IP$_9$-TP$_3$-PMDA$_4$	30.0		
(MAB-PPD)-BTDA	2.2	4.4	8.8
(MPD$_2$-IP)-BTDA	10.5	19.5	
DAPE-(MAB-PPD)BTDA$_2$	3.9	6.3	15.0
MPD-(MAB-PPD)$_2$BTDA$_3$	3.9	5.0	

BTDA = benzophenonetetracarboxylic dianhydride.
DAPE = diaminodiphenyl ether.
DAPS = diaminodiphenyl sulfide.
IP = isophthalic acid.
MAB = *m*-aminobenzoic acid.
MPD = *m*-phenylenediamine
PPD = *p*-phenylenediamine.
TP = terephthalic acid.
NOTE: Weight loss of 1-mil film determined from plots of average loss versus aging time.

in Table 7.7. The superiority of the polyimides is evidenced by thermal gravimetric analysis, as shown in Fig. 7.3, and by a comparison of glass transition temperatures, as measured by a power factor, in Fig. 7.4. This superiority is also shown in terms of thermoplastic flow under load, as indicated in Figs. 7.5 and 7.6. Comparison of polyester-imides are given in Figs. 7.7 and 7.8 and Table 7.8.

However, it should be noted that the performance of the polyamide-imide polymers, at somewhat lower temperatures, may be only marginally less than that obtained with the polyimides. This is illustrated on laminate data in Fig. 7.9; in Figs. 7.10 and 7.11, differences in thermal resistance

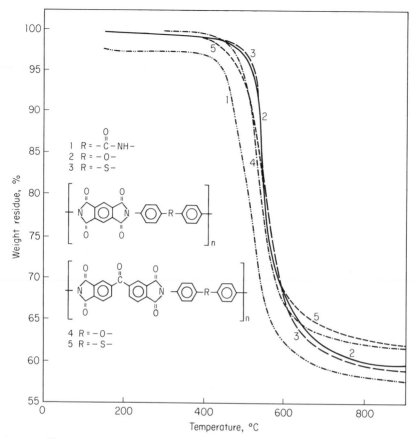

FIG 7.3 *Thermogravimetric analysis for aromatic polyamide-imide and polyimides in nitrogen.* T = 150°C per hour [19].

between two commercial polyamide-imide polymers are indicated. At 250°C, deformation of a polyamide-imide film under 5,000 psi load is only 3 percent [10]. Even though the higher-temperature performance of the polyimides may prove superior, the all-around properties of the polyamide-imides represent a very desirable technological combination.

Polyamide-imide laminates provide strength-retention properties as shown in Table 7.9 and Figs. 7.12 and 7.13. Strengths have been shown to be dependent on processing conditions, and truly optimized values have probably not yet been developed [12]. Bond strengths are better retained with temperature than with conventional varnish systems as shown in Figs. 7.14 and 7.15.

TABLE 7.8 Weight Loss of Polymers Heated at Various Temperatures in Air [23]

Polymer	Type	Weight loss during 100 hours of heating, %					
		260°C	280°C	300°C	325°C	350°C	Total weight loss
(structure)	Ester° imide	1.20	1.38	3.42	7.95	29.0	42.95
(structure)	Amide† imide	6.17	1.58	6.49	10.92	71.8	96.93
(structure)	Ester	3.90	1.39	10.44	22.92	60.4	99.01
(structure)	Imide‡	1.16	0.07	1.38	2.40	12.0	17.01

° General Electric polymer.
† Amoco Chemical Co. AI-10.
‡ Du Pont's H film.

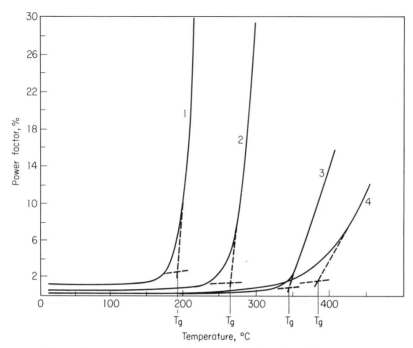

FIG 7.4 *Power factor vs. temperature for aromatic polyamide-imides and polyimides, showing* T_g *[14].* (1) MPD_{16}-IP_9-TP_3-$PMDA_4$; (2) $(MAB$-$PPD)$-$PMDA$; (3) $DAPS$-$PMDA$; (4) $DAPE$-$PMDA$.

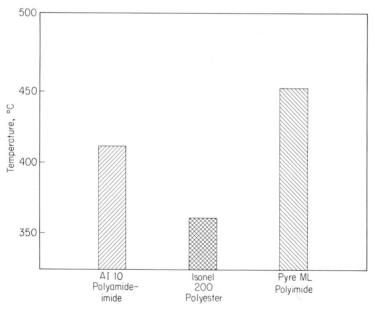

FIG 7.5 *Thermoplastic flow under 1,000-gram load of aromatic polyamide-imide compared with polyimide and polyester [19].*

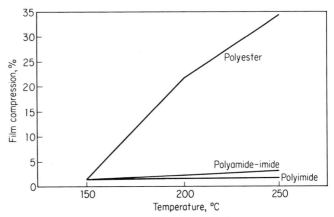

FIG 7.6 *Degree of film flow under 500 grams load at various temperatures for high-temperature films* [13].

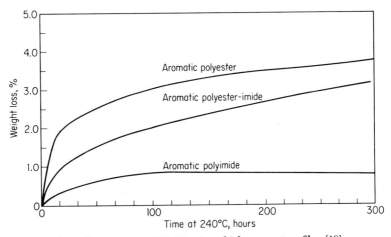

FIG 7.7 *Effect of heat aging at* $240°C$ *in air on high-temperature films* [18].

TABLE 7.9 Typical Flexural Properties of Amoco Polyamide-Imide Laminate (12-ply, 181 A-1100 glass, 33% resin, specific gravity 1.8) [10]

Temperature, °C	Flexural strength, psi	Modulus of elasticity, psi $\times 10^{-6}$
25	60,000	2.7
225	46,000	2.3
275	39,000	2.2

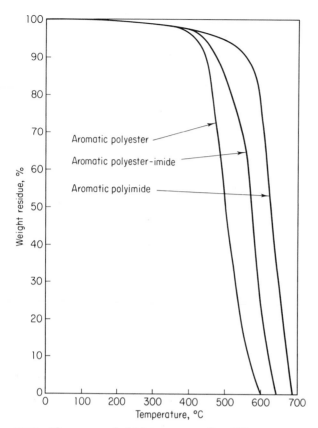

FIG 7.8 *Thermograms for high-temperature films* [18].

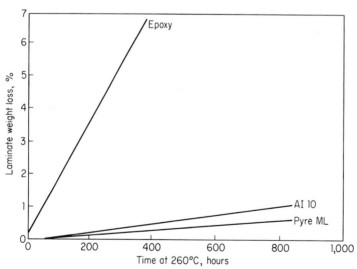

FIG 7.9 *Weight loss of aromatic polyamide-imide, polyimide, and epoxy laminates vs. temperature* [10].

190

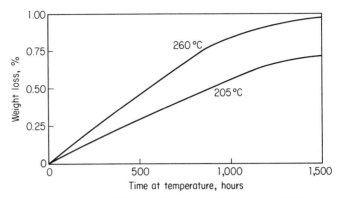

FIG 7.10   *Isothermal weight loss of Amoco AI 10 polymer at 205° C and 260° C [10].*

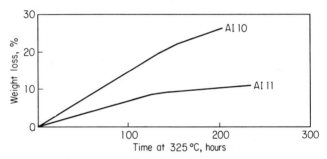

FIG 7.11   *Isothermal weight loss of Amoco AI polymers at 325° C [10].   (**AI 11 was formerly AI 20.**)*

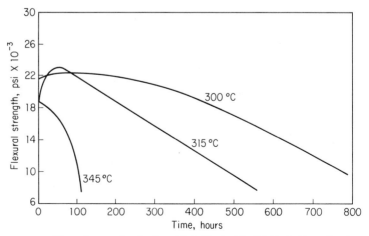

FIG 7.12   *Flexural strength of polyamide-imide (MAB-PPD/PMDA) aged and tested at temperature [14].*

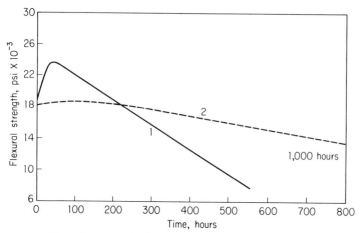

FIG 7.13 *Flexural strength of polyamide-imide and polyimide laminates aged and tested at* 315° C [14]. (1) (*MAB-PPD)-PMDA;* (2) *DAPS-PMDA.*

ELECTRICAL PROPERTIES

Like the polyimides, the polyamide-imides are valuable in electrical applications for a number of reasons [13]:

1. Unusually high dielectric strength
2. Tough, smooth, slippery surfaces highly resistant to abrasion damage
3. High dielectric strength at elevated temperatures under humid conditions and after long-term aging

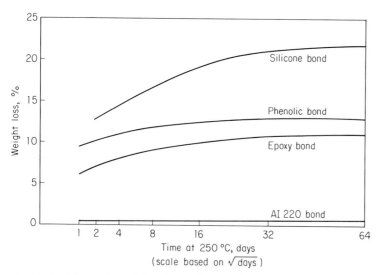

FIG 7.14 *Weight loss (on resin) at* 250° C *of various bonding varnishes used in fiber-glass-served magnet wire* [13].

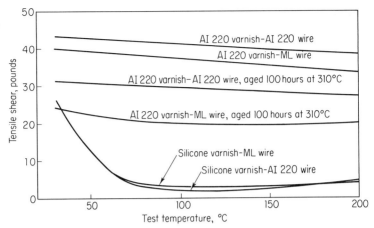

FIG 7.15 *Bond strength vs. temperature for high-temperature magnet wires and impregnating varnishes* [13].

4. Extreme resistance to film deterioration under heat and pressure, which property assures prevention of cut-through failures at wire crossovers

5. High thermal stability and longer thermal life than offered by conventional insulations

6. Excellent windability (magnet wire and coil applications)

7. Excellent chemical resistance

8. Higher overload resistance, thus permitting heavier-duty operation

The wires, additionally, are supplied in a standard-build coating which is intermediate between the single-build and heavy-build grades offered with conventional wire coatings. The standard build offers improved properties over competitive heavy-build magnet wires with a resultant space factor savings.

The polyamide-imide varnishes and magnet wire coatings which are commercially available have demonstrated long-time thermal stability at 220°C. The projected service life of the magnet wire, in comparison with other types, is indicated in Figs. 7.16 and 7.17. Overload performance in comparison with other wires is given in Fig. 7.18.

Cloth coating with a polyamide-imide varnish preserves electrical properties with temperature as indicated in Fig. 7.19. Reinforced thin-wall tubing prepared from the polyamide-imide and glass preserves properties with aging as indicated in Table 7.10. It is noteworthy that the properties improve, at least up to about 20 weeks at 250°C, while declining more or less linearly at higher temperatures. The extrapolated aging data for the tube construction are shown in Fig. 7.20. But even at 300°C, at the end of 42 days aging, the dielectric strength, when tested at room temperature,

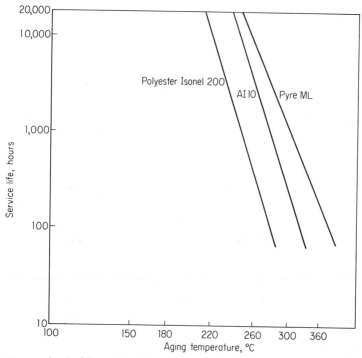

FIG 7.16   *Service life vs. temperature for aromatic polyamide-imide, polyimide, and polyester* [19]. *Temperature at 20,000 hours life: Isonel 200, 215°C; AI10, 240°C; Pyre ML, 245°C.*

is 82 percent of its original value [19]. Twisted pair specimens, aged at 250°C for 40 days, give breakdowns of 7,100 volts as against 8,000 volts initially. Dielectric strength is 4500 volts at room temperature, 4,100 volts at 220°C, and 3,000 volts at 225°C [19]. Effect of temperature or moisture on dielectric strength of polyamide-imide films in comparison to polyester and polyimide films is shown in Fig. 7.21.

Dielectric constant and dissipation factor for the Westinghouse polyamide-imide materials are given in Tables 7.11 and 7.12. Dissipation factor and dielectric constant for temperatures and frequencies for the polyester-imide prepared from oxydianiline and TMA-hydroquinone-TMA are shown in Figs. 7.22 to 7.25. For comparison, the electrical properties of the Isomid polymer and a high-temperature branched polyester are indicated in Table 7.13. Further comparison of properties between the polyester and a polyester-imide is given in [21].

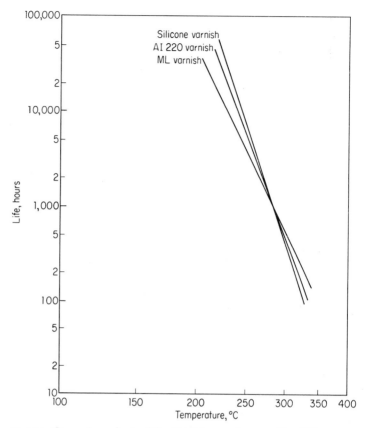

FIG 7.17 *Comparison of aging life of high-temperature varnishes* [13].

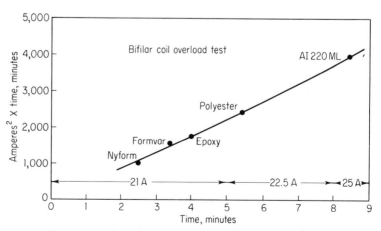

FIG 7.18 *Comparison of magnet wires by bifilar coil overload test* [13].

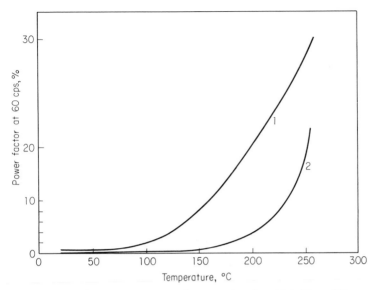

FIG 7.19 *Power factor vs. temperature for aromatic polyamide-imide on* 116 *glass cloth* [3]. (1) 3/1 = *ratio of amide to imide;* (2) 1/2 = *ratio of amide to imide.*

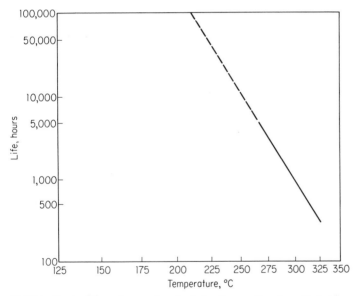

FIG 7.20 *Service life vs. temperature for tube of aromatic polyamide-imide on* 116 *glass cloth (end point of service: 250 volts per mil)* [3].

TABLE 7.10 Dielectric Strength (in volts per mil) of Thin-wall Tubes (0.032-in. Wall Thickness) after Aging [14]

Time, weeks	Aging temperature, °C			
	250	275	300	325
0	912	910	910	830
1	....	....	....	657
2	....	....	....	145
3	....	....	833	
4	....	....	960	
6	....	920	120	
12	....	740		
17	....	640		
19	1040			
20	....	330		
62	533			

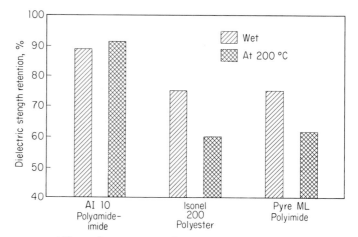

FIG 7.21 *Effects of temperature and moisture on dielectric strength of polyamide-imide films in comparison to polyester and polyimide films* [19].

TABLE 7.11 Dielectric Constant vs. Temperature for Aromatic Films [19]

Temperature, °C	Dielectric constant at 1 kc		
	Amanim	AI 220	Kapton H
25	3.8	3.32	3.40
100	....	3.54	3.28
150	....	2.41	2.53
200	4.5	3.20	2.72

TABLE 7.12 Dissipation Factor of Amanim Film [19]

Temperature, °C	Frequency, cps	Dissipation factor
25	60	0.006
100	60	0.005
200	60	0.020
25	1,000	0.007
200	1,000	0.010
25	100,000	0.016

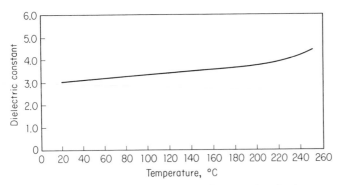

FIG 7.22 *Dielectric constant vs. temperature for aromatic polyester-imide film* [18].

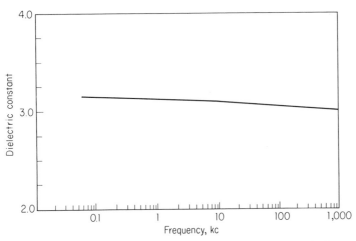

FIG 7.23 *Dielectric constant vs. frequency for aromatic polyesterimide film* [18].

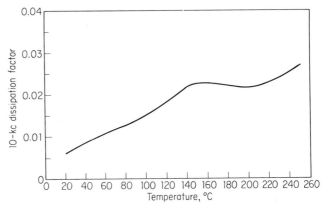

FIG 7.24 *Dissipation factor vs. temperature for aromatic polyester-imide film* [18].

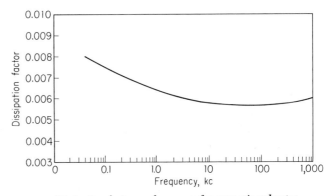

FIG 7.25 *Dissipation factor vs. frequency for aromatic polyester-imide film* [18].

T A B L E 7.13   Electrical Properties of Polyester-Polyimide Varnish in Comparison with High-temperature Polyester Varnish [21]

Property	Isonel 200/17	Isomid
Dielectric strength, volts/mil:		
Dry, at room temperature..........................	4,300	4,400
Wet after 24 hours in H_2O.........................	2,500	2,700
Dielectric strength, thermal stability MIL-W-583C,		
type K, volts/mil:		
Unvarnished:		
Before heat aging	4,300	4,400
After 168 hours at 250°C......................	4,000	4,200
Varnished, Isonel 31, meets MIL-24092, Ships:		
Before heat aging	4,600	4,870
After 168 hours at 250°C (800 volts/mil minimum).........	3,550	3,670
Insulation resistance, twisted pair, 10-minute water boil, megohms..	500,000	500,000
Dissipation factor at 1 kc:		
25°C	0.0068	0.0064
150°C	0.0185	0.0170
Dielectric constant at 1 kc, 25°C...........................	3.50	3.44

199

CHEMICAL RESISTANCE

Dielectric strength of the polyamide-imide magnet wire coating is little affected by humidity, declining only about 10 percent after 16 hours at 100 percent relative humidity. The chemical resistance of the polyamide-imide varnish is exceptionally good as indicated in Table 7.14. It is compatible with conventional varnish solvents and even with chlorinated species, as well as with epoxy resin encapsulation systems. Additionally, as shown in Table 7.15, the varnish is completely suited for use in Freons and in hermetically sealed systems.

When polyamide-imide magnet wire coatings are used in connection with varnishes containing powerful solvents such as dimethylacetamide, dimethyl formamide, and N-methylpyrrolidone, it is recommended that a stress-relieving prebake of at least 200°C be employed to prevent solvent crazing.

PROCESSING

Varnishes

The commercial polyamide-imide varnish may be thinned if required. The solution is then applied by conventional varnish techniques using a step-cure cycle. The effect of cure cycles on properties is shown in Table 7.16.

TABLE 7.14 Chemical Properties of Amoco Polyamide-Imide Standard-build Magnet Wire in Comparison with Heavy-build Wires [7]

Property	Standard AI 220	Heavy Isonel 200/17	Heavy ML
Solvent shock, 15% prestretch 3× wrap in boiling xylol	Okay	Okay	Okay
Solvent resistance, 24 hr immersion followed by cheesecloth wipe:			
Toluol	Okay	Okay	Okay
Xylol	Okay	Okay	Okay
5% H_2SO_4	Okay	Okay	Okay
Perchloroethylene	Okay	Okay	Okay
Ethanol	Okay	Okay	Okay
1% KOH	Okay	Okay	Okay
Methylene chloride	Okay	Fails	Okay
Varnish compatibility, IEEE 57 test methods	Excellent	Good	Excellent
Epoxy encapsulation, softening in curing systems:			
Amine curing agents	None	Severe	None
Anhydride curing agents	None	None	None
Sealed-tube test, moisture added, 1 week at 150°C	Film darkens	Severe degradation	Film cracks

TABLE 7.15 Comparison of Amoco Polyamide-Imide Single-build Magnet Wire with Heavy-build Urethane-modified Formvar [11]

Test	No. 18 AI 220, standard build	No. 18 Urethane-modified Formvar, heavy build
Extractibles, %, in:		
R-12	0.5	0.4
R-22	0.2	0.5
R-502	0.1	0.3
Extractibles, %, in toluol-methanol	0.5	0.8
Blister test in:		
R-12	Okay	Okay
R-22	Okay	Okay
R-502	Okay	Okay
Abrasion resistance in:		
R-12	1,000+	1,000+
R-22	1,000+	100
R-502	8,000+	650
Closed-tube test with R-12, after 100 days at 130°C:		
Wire color	No change	Darkens (black)
Wire flexibility	1×, Okay	10×, fails
Oil color	Sl. darkening	Sl. darkening
Copper appearance	Sl. tarnish	Tarnished
Steel appearance	Sl. tarnish	Tarnished
Closed-tube test with R-22, after 6 weeks at 160°C:		
Wire color	No change	Darkens (maroon)
Wire flexibility	1×, okay	4×, okay; 3×, fails
Oil color	No change	Sl. darkening
Copper appearance	Sl. tarnish	Sl. tarnish
Steel appearance	Tarnished	Sl. tarnish
Closed-tube test with R-502, after 6 weeks at 160°C:		
Wire color	No change	Darkens (maroon)
Wire flexibility	1×, okay	4×, okay; 3×, fails
Oil color	No change	No change
Copper appearance	Tarnished	Tarnished
Steel appearance	Tarnished	Tarnished

TABLE 7.16 Effect of Various Curing Schedules on Properties of Coatings Made from Amoco AI Polymer (Type 10) [10]

Time, minutes	Temperature, °C	Impact resistance, 180 in.-lb	Flexible ⅛-in. mandrel	2% NaOH resistance after 16 hours at 25°C
10	120	Fail	Fail	Fail
30	120	Pass	Pass	Fail
30	150	Pass	Pass	Spots
10	175	Pass	Pass	Pass
2	315	Pass	Pass	Pass

The varnishes are stored in stainless steel or polyethylene-lined containers to prevent corrosion by the polyamic acid.

Laminates

Although polyamide-imide laminates have been produced only experimentally, it is useful to consider their processing requirements, since they have many features in common with the processing of the polyimide laminates.

As indicated in Chap. 8, difficulty has been experienced with the removal of water from the final processing steps of the polyimide polymer. The water can cause reversible reactions, leading to low-molecular-weight polymers. This problem is not as pronounced in the processing of the polyamide-imide laminate, but it still proves potentially troublesome.

In addition to the removal of water, it is also necessary to drive off the solvents from the laminate if dense, nonporous structures are to be developed. Ideally, the solvents should be removed while the polymer is still in the soluble phase in order to obtain adequate wetting and adhesion to the glass fibers of the laminate. Press-cured laminates are superior to the vacuum-bagged laminates in strength and water absorption since the former technique produces a more compacted, less porous composite [24].

However, the normal solvents employed are high-boiling and cannot be removed at temperatures sufficiently low to arrest the ring-closing imidation reaction. Thus, whereas at 35°C the imidation reaction will progress only to 20 percent completion in 4,800 hours, it will advance appreciably in only one hour at 80°C [14]. When temperatures above 100°C are used to remove the solvents, the imidation reaction occurs rapidly and coincidentally. This results in the production of an insoluble, higher-melting polymer which cannot readily wet and provide bond to the fibrous reinforcement.

In view of these requirements, the fundamental approach in preparing the laminates is to remove the water of imidation and the solvents at conveniently low temperature and pressures to permit essentially complete escape. Following this, through the application of increased heat and pressure, the fully reacted polymer is then caused to flow to the extent possible to create the necessary density and bonding in the final laminate. Because of this flow requirement, it has been generally found that optimum resin contents are about 35 percent [14], which is somewhat higher than optimum for other laminating systems (as, for example, with the epoxy resins, where a resin content of about 30 percent provides optimum properties).

The laminating cycle is thus, necessarily, conducted in a number of steps.

With the Amoco polymers, the material is applied for prepregs at 20 to 30 percent solids, preferably from n-methylpyrrolidone. The prepreg

TABLE 7.17   Suggested Postcure Schedule for Amoco Polyamide-Imide Laminate [10]

Time, hours	Temperature, °C
4	200
4	225
4	260
2	300

is dried at 150°C for 10 to 20 minutes. The laminate is pressed, typically, 25 minutes at 600 psi and 200°C plus 5 minutes at 1,500 psi. The press is frequently vented to release volatiles. A satisfactory postcure is indicated in Table 7.17.

The polyamide-imides permit processing at lower temperatures than the polyimides, not only because of their lower water of imidation content, but also because of their more soluble nature and lower glass transition temperature. As the ratio of imide to amide linkages increases, increasing difficulty is encountered in the preparation of satisfactory laminates.

One technique that has been investigated involves the use of an intercoat of a polyamide-imide high in amide links between cured plies of polyimide. This results in an improved structure of increased bond strength, but the elevated-temperature performance is reduced to that expected of the poly-amide-imide [14].

On the basis of glass transition temperatures, obtained from electrical measurements (see Fig. 7.4), it is possible to predict the minimum final laminating temperatures required to produce satisfactory laminates. These predictions have been shown to be valid. Thus, good laminates could be obtained with the (MAB-PPD)-PMDA polymer at temperatures above 265°C, whereas to obtain good laminates with the polyimide, DAPE-PMDA, temperatures above 385°C were required [14].

APPLICATIONS

In addition to the present uses as magnet wire coatings and insulating varnishes, the polyamide-imides are promising binder materials for composite slot liners, phase insulation, slot sticks, and sleeving for high-temperature electrical insulation applications.

REFERENCES

1945

1. Linear Fiber Forming Polymers (to E. I. du Pont de Nemours & Co., Inc.), Brit. 570,858.

1947

2. C. J. Frosch, Linear Polymer Containing Cyclic Imide Groups, U.S. 2,421,024.

1962

3. J. H. Freeman, New Organic Resins and Reinforced Laminates for Service to 300°C, *SPE Trans.* **2**:216–221.
4. C. W. Stephens, Polyamides from N,N'-Bis(3-aminophenyl)-isophthalamide, U.S. 3,049,518.

1963

5. G. M. Bower and L. W. Frost, Aromatic Polyimides, *J. Polymer Sci.*, part A, vol. 1, pp. 3135–3150.
6. Westinghouse Research Center Monthly Letter Report no. 7, AD 603 002, February.

1964

7. Anaconda AI-220, The All Purpose Magnet Wire, Pub. WC-6478, Anaconda Wire and Cable Co.
8. Ester-Imide Resins (to Dr. Beck, GmbH), Brit. 973,377.
9. High Polymers and Processes for Their Production (to Standard Oil Co.), Belg. 650,979. See also, Stephens, Fr. 1,386,617.

1965

10. Amoco Chemicals Corp., Amoco AI Polymers for High Temperature Applications, Bulletins HT-1a, 12 pp., and HT-2, 4 pp.
11. Anaconda AI-220, The Best Choice for Hermetic Motor Applications, Pub. WC-6518, Anaconda Wire and Cable Co.
12. B. A. Bolton, AI Polymer Laminates, SPE RETEC Pacific Northwest Region, Seattle, Wash., July.
13. D. H. DeVries, The New Poly(amido-imide) Magnet Wire and Supporting Insulations for Rotating Equipment Applications, Proceedings of 6th Electrical Insulation Conference (IEEE and NEMA), September.
14. J. H. Freeman et al., Resins and Reinforced Laminates for Continuous Use at 650°F, *SPE Trans.*, April, pp. 75–83.
15. L. W. Frost and G. M. Bower, Linear Polymeric Amide-modified Polyimides and Process of Making Same, U.S. 3,179,635. See also Brit. 935,388 and Fr. 1,283,378 (both to Westinghouse Electric Corp.).
16. D. F. Loncrini, Cupric and Zinc–Bis(Trimellitate) Dianhydrides, U.S. 3,182,074.
17. D. F. Loncrini, Trimellitic Anhydride Derivatives, U.S. 3,182,073.
18. D. F. Loncrini and J. M. Witzel, Novel Polyimides, Proceedings of 6th Electrical Insulation Conference (IEEE and NEMA), September.
19. J. T. Milek, Polyimide Plastics Technology: a State of-the-Art Report, Electronic Properties Information Center, Hughes Aircraft, Culver City, Calif.
20. L. C. Scala and W. M. Hickman, The Behavior of Polypyromellitimide Resins at High Temperature, *J. Appl. Polymer Sci.* **9**:245–266.
21. Single Film Class 180 + Polyester-Polyimide Magnet Wire Enamel Developed: Low Price Forecast, *Insulation*, September.

1966

22. Amoco Chemical Corp. Data Sheet HT-A.
23. D. F. Loncrini, Aromatic Polyesterimides, *J. Polymer Sci.*, part A-1, pp. 1531–1541.

1967

24. B. A. Bolton and R. J. Dieterle, Resins for High Temperature Laminates—Polyamide-Imide, *Plastics Design Process*, January, pp. 13–15.

8

Aromatic Polyimides

The aromatic polyimides are produced essentially in two steps by the reaction of a suitable dianhydride with a diprimary aromatic amine. In the first step of the reaction, a polyamic acid is formed which may be subsequently converted by heat or through the use of suitable catalysts and water acceptors to high-molecular-weight linear polyimides.

A number of versions of the polyimides have been made available as films, varnishes, laminating resins, adhesives, and molding compounds. Initial difficulties were experienced in the development of systems which could be converted to suitably high-molecular-weight polymers without degradation occurring as a result of the release of water during the final processing. These difficulties are being progressively overcome.

The polyimides are among the most promising of the high-temperature plastics, and they have been made available in both linear and crosslinked forms. They provide particularly outstanding elevated-temperature oxidative stability and have already found a secure place in the technology as electrical insulations.

Polyimides have long been known to the polyamide technology, their production arising from the cyclodehydration of amide linkages by proximate carboxyl groups:

$$\underset{\text{Secondary amide}}{RNH\overset{\overset{\text{O}}{\|}}{C}R'} + \underset{\text{Carboxyl acid}}{HO\overset{\overset{\text{O}}{\|}}{C}R''} \longrightarrow \underset{\text{Imide linkage}}{R''-\overset{\overset{\text{O}}{\|}}{C}-NR-\overset{\overset{\text{O}}{\|}}{C}-R'} + \underset{\text{Water}}{H_2O}$$

Thus, when short-chain dicarboxylic acids are employed and higher temperatures are used during the synthesis of polyamides, imidation will occur.

Although linear aromatic polyimide polymers were observed as early as 1908 upon heating 4-aminophthalic anhydride [1], the imidation reaction was generally regarded as undesirable in the early technology. However, with the commercial production of tetraacids and dianhydrides, the reaction assumed new importance: the acid or anhydride could be reacted to produce a linear polyamide chain containing pendant carboxyls in proximity to the secondary amide hydrogens. Thus, the more stable imide link could be introduced into linear polymers by cyclodehydration of the less stable amide link without the occurrence of excessive crosslinking.

Linear, fiber-forming materials from the reaction of tetracarboxylic acids and diamines were reported in 1945 [2]. Ten years later, the specific polymer from hexamethylenediamine and 2,2-bis(3,4-dicarboxyphenyl)propane dianhydride was disclosed [3]. In the same year, it was reported that the polyimides from tetracarboxylic acids could be produced more readily, with fewer side reactions, if the acid were present in ester form [4]. In 1959, it was reported that improved products could be obtained from the diacid-diester, with the esterified carboxyls on nonadjacent carbons, these half esters being produced from the dianhydride [6]. In that year, the polyimide from pyromellitic dianhydride (PMDA) and 1,4-bis(5-amino-1,1-dimethylpentyl)benzene was disclosed [7]. In 1962, the half-ester route was used to produce polyimides from bicyclic tetracarboxylic anhydrides and aliphatic amines [9]. An excellent review of the chemistry of polyimides from both aromatic and aliphatic polyamines and aromatic dianhydrides is given by Sroog [55]. A more general review of the aromatic polyimide technology, together with a comprehensive review of other new linear polymers, through 1964, is given by Jones [45].

In June, 1965, a number of patents covering the aromatic polyimides were issued to E. I. du Pont de Nemours & Company. In these patents,

207

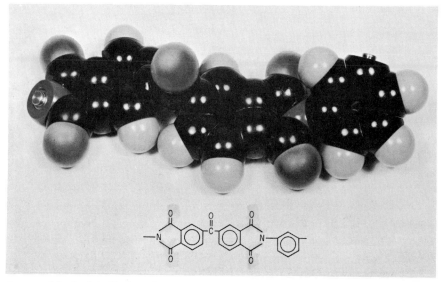

Atom model of polyimide from benzophenonetetracarboxylic acid anhydride and m-*phenyl-enediamine.* (The Epoxylite Corporation.)

polyamic acid prepolymers were produced from the dianhydride directly [36], and were subsequently converted to the polyimides by the use of heat [39], or through treatment with aliphatic [38] or aromatic [43] mono-carboxylic anhydrides and a tertiary amine. Specific compounds described include the polyimide from m-phenylenediamine and p-phenylenediamine [40] and other aromatic diamines [37]. Shawinigan Resins Corporation, in the same month, was granted a patent covering production of a polyimide film from benzophenonetetracarboxyl dianhydride and aromatic diamines [46].

In the early 1960s, the United States Air Force evinced interest in the higher-temperature capabilities of the aromatic polyimides, and research and development contracts were awarded to Westinghouse Electric Company, and Narmco Division of Whittaker Controls.

As a result of the development activity in the late 1950s, the polyimides from PMDA and aromatic diamines were introduced commercially by Du Pont in 1961 as films and electrical-grade varnishes. Specialized adhesive and laminating systems were subsequently offered by Du Pont on an experimental basis. In 1963, Monsanto Plastics Division introduced polyimide laminating systems based on research of its subsidiary, Shawinigan Resin Corporation. Molding compounds were introduced commercially in 1965 by Du Pont.

SYNTHESIS

Chemistry

In theory, high-molecular-weight linear polyimides may be synthesized from any dianhydride and any diprimary amine. Species based on aromatic dianhydrides and aliphatic diamines have been developed, but their properties (i.e., glass transition temperatures below 150°C) are not commercially attractive in view of the cost of the ingredients and the processing. When both precursors are aromatic, polymers of much improved heat resistance are developed. These have attracted the majority of the research. Typical of the precursors are those shown in Table 8.1.

TABLE 8.1 Typical Diamines and Dianhydrides Investigated in Synthesis of Polyimides [55]

Diamines	
m-Phenylenediamine (MPD)	Hexamethylenediamine
p-Phenylenediamine (PPD)	Heptamethylenediamine
2,2-Bis(4-aminophenyl)propane (DDP)	Octamethylenediamine
4,4'-Methylenedianiline (DDM)	Nonamethylenediamine
Benzidine (PP)	Decamethylenediamine
4,4'-Diaminodiphenyl sulfide (PSP)	3-Methylheptamethylenediamine
4,4'-Diaminodiphenyl sulfone (PSO₂P)	4,4-Dimethylheptamethylenediamine
4,4'-Diaminodiphenyl ether (POP)	2,11-Diaminododecane
1,5-Diaminonaphthalene	1,2,-Bis(3-aminopropoxyethane)
3,3'-Dimethylbenzidine	2,2-Dimethylpropylenediamine
3,3'-Dimethoxybenzidine	3-Methoxyhexamethylenediamine
2,4-Bis(β-amino-tert-butyl)toluene	2,5-Dimethylhexamethylenediamine
Bis(4-β-amino-tert-butyl phenyl) ether	2,5-Dimethylheptamethylenediamine
1,4-Bis(2-methyl-4-aminopentyl)benzene	3-Methylheptamethylenediamine
1-Isopropyl-2,4-phenylenediamine	1,4-Diaminocyclohexane
m-Xylylenediamine	1,12-Diaminooctadecane
p-Xylylenediamine	Bis(3-aminopropyl) sulfide
Di(4-aminocyclohexyl)methane	Bis(3-aminopropyl)methylamine

Dianhydrides	
Pyromellitic dianhydride (PMDA)	2,2-Bis(3,4-biscarboxyphenyl)propane dianhydride (PPDA)
2,3,6,7-Naphthalenetetracarboxylic acid dianhydride	3,4-Dicarboxyphenyl sulfone dianhydride
3,3',4,4'-Diphenyltetracarboxylic acid dianhydride	Perylene-3,4,9,10-tetracarboxylic acid dianhydride
1,2,5,6-Naphthalenetetracarboxylic acid dianhydride	Bis(3,4-dicarboxyphenyl) ether dianhydride (PEDA)
2,2',3,3'-Diphenyltetracarboxylic acid dianhydride	Ethylenetetracarboxylic acid dianhydride
Thiophene-2,3,4,5-tetracarboxylic acid anhydride	3,4,3',4'-Benzophenonetetracarboxylic dianhydride (BTDA)

The general procedure is, essentially, to conduct the reaction of the dianhydride and the diamine in two steps: polyamic acid formation followed by imidation.

$$\left[\begin{array}{c} \text{HOOC} \quad \text{COOH} \\ \diagdown \diagup \\ \text{R} \\ \diagup \diagdown \\ \text{HNOC} \quad \text{CONH} \end{array}\right]_n \longrightarrow \left[\begin{array}{c} \text{O} \quad \text{O} \\ \| \quad \| \\ \text{N} \diagdown \text{R} \diagup \text{N} \\ \| \quad \| \\ \text{O} \quad \text{O} \end{array}\right]_n$$

Polyamic acid   Polyimide

The polyamic acid is formed by combining the two ingredients in a solvent which is sufficiently active to permit reaction between the two species. Such solvents should strongly associate with both the polymer and the reactants and (provided imidation has not progressed to too high a degree) should maintain the polyamic acid in solution. Suitable solvents are N,N-dimethylformamide, N,N-dimethylacetamide, dimethyl sulfoxide, N-methyl-2-pyrrolidone, tetramethylurea, etc. Generally, the polyamic acid is obtained at 10 to 15 percent solids, although high-molecular-weight polyamic acids have been obtained at concentrations up to about 40 percent.

The polyamic acid is formed under anhydrous conditions at temperatures of 50°C or below. Higher temperatures generally cause premature imidation with the consequent undesirable release of water, although under suitable synthesis conditions temperatures to 175°C have been employed.

One reactant may be first dissolved and the other slowly added to the solution; both reactants may be separately dissolved and combined, or the reactants may be combined in the dry state and added portionwise to the solvent. It has been shown that the order of addition of ingredients and method used in combining them (which ingredients are in the solution phase initially) will, along with purity of the ingredients, influence the average molecular weights [which may range from 13,000 to 55,000 (degree of polymerization 31 to 131)] and the weight averages (22,500 to 266,000) [56].

The ingredients of the synthesis should be of high purity and used at substantially equal molar amounts. The influence of excess anhydride on the reaction is shown in Fig. 8.1. Slight excess provides highest initial molecular weights. This may be due to the lower solubility of the dianhydride. It should be noted that the anhydride promotes instability, so that with aging at temperature, the molecular weight decreases. Molecular weights may be controlled by the use of a small amount of monofunctional material, such as phthalic anhydride, as a chain stopper. Lower-molecular-weight species may also be developed through the use of amine in excess,

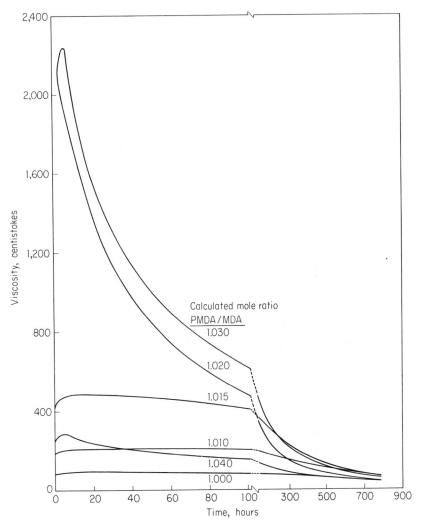

FIG 8.1 *Effect of reactant ratio on viscosity behavior of* 12% *MDA-PMDA in DMAc at* 35°C [24].

but the effect of this on solution stability, and on the properties of the final polymer, is more severe than use of excess anhydride.

In the first step of the synthesis, conversion of the polyamide to polyimide normally should not exceed 50 percent, the tolerable amount depending on the specific reactants and the solvent employed.

After polyamic acid formation, the imide is obtained by heating the films to about 300°C (if thin films are to be produced) or through the use of cyclizing agents at temperatures of 100°C or lower.

Typical of the solvents, concentrations, and the methods of conversion of the intermediates are the data given in Table 8.2. Effect of temperature on the reaction is indicated in Table 8.3. Influence of solvents on viscosity is indicated in Fig. 8.2.

TABLE 8.2 Reaction Conditions and Solvents for Synthesis of
Polyimides [8]

Example	Amount of reactant, grams		Amount of solvent, ml	Conversion
	Diamine	Dianhydride		
1	20.0 DDM	22.0 PMDA	200 DMF	Heat
2	10.35 DDP	10.0 PMDA	60 DMF/P(1/1)	Heat
3	3.0 DDM	3.3 PMDA	50 DMF	Heat
4	9.15 POP	10.0 PMDA	100 DMF/P(3/2)	Heat
5	9.38 PSP	10.0 PMDA	130 DMF/P(1/1)	Heat
6	5.17 DDP	10.1 PMDA	75 DMF/P(3/2)	Heat
	4.22 PP			
7	10.35 DDP	10.0 PMDA	50 DMF	Heat
8	3.0 DDM	3.3 PMDA	50 DMF	Heat
9	10.35 DDP	10.0 PMDA	56 DMF	
10	11.2 PSO_2P	10.0 PMDA	75 DMF/P(2/1)	
11	2.01 PP	2.37 PMDA	50 DMF	P/AA
12	5.17 DDP	10.1 PMDA	75 DMF/P(3/2)	P/AA
	4.22 PP			
13	11.2 PSO_2P	10.0 PMDA	150 DMF	P/AA
14	9.8 PSP	10.0 PMDA	180 DMF	P/AA
15	1.30 POP	2.18 PPDA	30 P	
16	80.0 POP	87.1 PMDA	464 DMA	Heat
17	12.0 POP	13.0 PMDA	191 DMA	Heat
18	0.7 POP	1.09 PEDA	25 DMA	Heat
19	12.4 MPD	25.0 PMDA	145 DMF	Heat
20	6.2 MPD	25.0 PMDA	200 DMF/P(1/1)	Heat
	6.2 PPD			
21	12.4 MPD	25.0 PMDA	175 DMF/P(4/3)	
22	6.2 PPD	12.5 PMDA	120 DMA	P/AA
23	12.4 MPD	25.0 PMDA	145 DMF	P/AA
24	12.4 MPD	10.0 PMDA	200 DMF/B(4/1)	P/AA

Polyamide-Acid Formation

Example	Reactants		Solvent	Conversion step chemicals used
25	MPD	PMDA	DMA	AA/P
26	PP	PMDA	DMF	AA/P/benzene
27	DDP	PMDA	DMF	AA/P
28	MPD	PMDA	DMF	AA/P
	PPD			
29	MPD	PMDA	DMA	AA/P/cyclohexane
30	MPD	PMDA	DMA	AA/P/acetonitrile
31	MPD	PMDA	DMA	AA/P/chloroform

TABLE 8.2 *(Continued)*

Polyamide-Acid Formation

Example	Reactants		Solvent	Conversion step chemicals used
32	MPD	PMDA	DMA	AA/P/benzene
33	MPD	PMDA	DMA	AA/P
34	MPD	PMDA	DMA	AA/P/carbon tetrachloride
35	MPD PP	PMDA	DMA	AA/P/benzene
36	MPD DDM	PMDA	DMF	AA/tetramethylene sulfone
37	PSP	PMDA	DMF	AA/P/cyclohexane
38	PSO₂P	PMDA	DMF	AA/P/cyclohexane
39	MPD	PMDA	DMA/P	AA
40	DDM	PMDA	DMA/P	AA
41	DDM	PMDA	DMA/AA	AA/P/ethyl acetate
42	POP	PMDA	DMA/P	AA
43	PSP	PMDA	P	AA
44	PSP	PMDA	DMA/P	AA
45	PPD	PMDA	DMA	AA/P
46	MPD	PMDA	DMF	AA/P
47	PP	PMDA	DMF	AA/P
48	DDP PP	PMDA	DMF/P	AA/P
49	PSO₂P	PMDA	DMF	AA/P
50	PSP	PMDA	DMF	AA/P

NOTE: Abbreviations for diamines and dianhydrides identified in Table 8.1.
DMF = N,N-dimethylformamide.
DMA = N,N-dimethylacetamide.
P = pyridine.
AA = acetic anhydride.
B = butyrolactone.
NOTES: In examples 7 and 8, 50 mole % of the acid groups in the polyamide-acid solution were converted to the triethylammonium salt.
In examples 9 and 10, stoichiometric amounts of acetic anhydride/pyridine were added to the polyamide-acid solutions to convert 30 mole % of the polyamide-acid groups to the corresponding polyimide before final conversion by heating.
In example 21, stoichiometric amounts of acetic anhydride/pyridine were added to the polyamide-acid solutions to convert 30 mole % of the polyamide-acid groups to the corresponding polyimide before final conversion by heating.
In examples 27 through 34 the acid groups in the polyamide-acid were converted to the triethylammonium salt.

In a kinetics study, it was found that the initial reaction occurs by nucleophilic attack of the amino group to give the polyamic acid [33]. Equilibrium was reached after 78 mole percent of anhydride was consumed. The remaining free amine reacted to form a nylon-type salt through the available carboxylic acid groups. The overall course of the reaction was determined to be as follows:

During the course of the reaction, the presence of minor amounts of isoimide linkages have been detected [40]. They presumably arise as follows [53].

Isoimide

TABLE 8.3 Effect of Temperature of Polymerization on Inherent Viscosity of Polyamic Acid* [Reaction of bis(4-aminophenyl) ether and pyromellitic dianhydride] [54]

Solvent	Bis(4-aminophenyl) ether		Pyromellitic dianhydride		Solids, %	Temperature, °C	Time at temperature, minutes	Inherent viscosity
	Gram	Moles	Grams	Moles				
Dimethylacetamide	10.00	0.05	10.90	0.05	10.0	25	120	4.05
Dimethylacetamide	10.00	0.05	10.90	0.05	10.0	65	30	3.47
Dimethylacetamide	20.00	0.10	21.80	0.10	10.6	85–88	30	2.44
Dimethylacetamide	20.00	0.10	21.80	0.10	10.7	115–119	15	1.16
Dimethylacetamide	20.00	0.10	21.80†	0.10	10.3	125–128	15	1.00
Dimethylacetamide	20.00	0.10	21.80‡	0.10	15.7	135–137	15	0.59
N-Methyl caprolactam..	10.00	0.05	10.90	0.05	14.2	150–160	2	0.51
N-Methyl caprolactam..	10.00	0.05	10.90	0.05	12.9	175–182	1–2	Only partly soluble
N-Methyl caprolactam..	20.00	0.10	21.80	0.10	15	200	1	Insoluble

° Determined at 0.5% concentration in the particular solvent at 30°C.

† Increment of 0.35 g pyromellitic dianhydride added before determination of inherent viscosity.

‡ Increment of 0.25 g pyromellitic dianhydride and then 0.21 g of bis(4-amino-phenyl) ether added before determination of inherent viscosity.

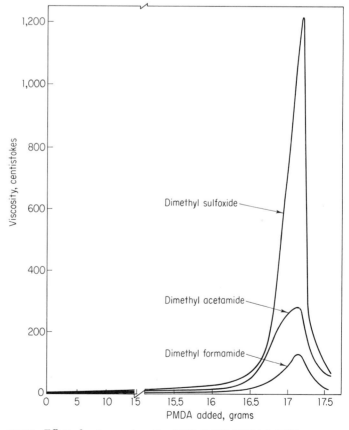

FIG 8.2 *Effect of water on viscosity of* 10% **DAPE-PMDA in DMAc at** 35°C [24].

More troublesome, however, is the influence of water on the reaction, and the tendency of regenerated ingredients to transimidify, resulting in low-molecular-weight polymers.

The polyamic acids have exhibited poor storage stability as a result of water being liberated during the imidation reaction. The influence of water on the viscosity of the polyamic acid is indicated in Fig. 8.3. Stability is in part a function of dilution, dilute solutions decreasing in viscosity more rapidly than concentrated ones, as shown in Fig. 8.4.

Because water is liberated in the conversion of the prepolymer in the final polyimide, difficulties may be encountered in the casting of thicker sections, where the water, before liberation, may split polymeric chains to cause reversion to the acid and the amine species.

Through the use of water acceptors, such as acetic anhydride, and a catalyst, such as pyridine, the water can be effectively removed from the reaction, thus preventing the formation of undesirably low molecular-weight species prior to conversion. Conversion of the polyamic acid film to the imide film may, for example, be accomplished by steeping the film in a 3/2 pyridine/acetic anhydride mixture for 24 hours followed by immersion in dioxane for 2 hours and drying for 1 hour at 130°C plus heating for

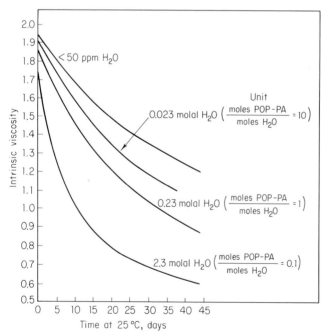

FIG 8.3 *Effect of added water on 0.23 molal POP-PMDA [polyamic acid from bis(4-aminophenyl) ether and PMDA] solution in DMAc* [51].

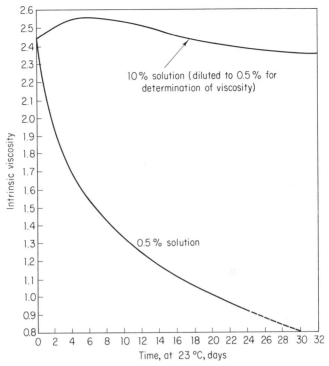

FIG 8.4 *Effect of concentration on stability of POP-PMDA in DMAc at 23°C* [51].

1 minute at 380°C [40]. The anhydride/amine mixture may be added to the solution of the polyamic acid, thereby precipitating the polyimide as a finely divided powder from the reaction mixture [39].

The progress of the imidation reaction has been followed with infrared, giving spectra shown in Figs. 8.5 and 8.6, the spectra indicating the temperature sensitivity of the reaction. Additional data for one system are shown in Table 8.4, with band assignments.

An investigation of the effect of variables in synthesis on polymerization of the aromatic polyimides is given by Dine-Hart [35].

Preparative Procedure

An example from the literature illustrates the synthesis of a typical polyimide:

4,4′-Diaminodiphenylmethane, 200.00 grams (0.101 mole), was dissolved in 150 ml of dimethyl formamide. 22.00 grams (0.101 mole) of pyromellitic dianhydride was added portion-wise with agitation while the solution was externally cooled with circulating water at approximately 15°C. A viscous dope formed and was

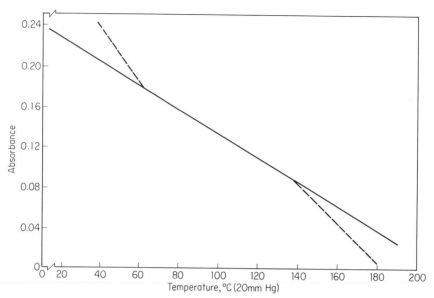

FIG 8.5   *N-H absorbance (at 3.05 μ) as a function of temperature of poly*(m-*phenylene*-3,3,′4,4′-
benzophenonetetracarboxylimide) [46].

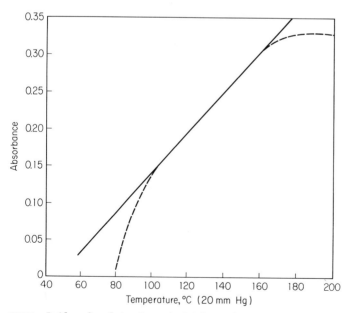

FIG 8.6   *Imide carbonyl absorbance (at 5.6 μ) as a function of temperature*
of poly(m-*phenylene*-3,3,′4,4′-*benzophenonetetracarboxylimide*) [46].

TABLE 8.4 Polymerization of 3,3′,4,4′-Benzophenonetetracarboxylic Dianhydride and m-Phenylenediamine under Various Conditions [49]

Sample no.	Reaction conditions, cumulative		Infrared absorption bands, relative absorbance					Polymer softening temperature, °C	Gel time at 300°C, seconds	Remarks	Solubility in pyridine at 23°C
	Temperature, °C	Time, minutes	3.05 μ N-H	5.65 μ (Imide ring)	5.8 μ (Imide carbonyl)	6.55 μ (Amine H band)	7.35 μ (Imide ring)				
1	23	5	0.244	0.000	0.174	0.284	0.125			No melt	Yes
	45	10	0.244	→	→	0.284	0.125	78–101	120	No melt	Yes
		60	0.229	→	→	0.252	0.125	125	115	Semimelt	Yes
		120	0.229	→	→	0.232	0.143	140–145	110	→	Yes (115°C)
2	65	30	0.168	0.004	0.181	0.237	0.161	160>	110		Yes
3	80	30	0.155	0.004	0.181	0.237	0.161	≈160	≈110		Yes
4	100	30	0.125	0.131	0.301	0.161	0.194	180>	≈75	No melt	Partial
5	120	20	0.114	0.187	0.347	0.132	0.208	180>	≈50		→
6	140	20	0.086	0.237	0.456	0.102	0.347	205>	≈50		No
7	160	20	0.046	0.284	0.456	Weak	0.368	220>	17		→
8	180	20	Weak	0.323	0.456	Weak	0.377	220–235	5		
9	200	20	Weak	0.323	....	Weak	0.377	No melt	No gel point	→	→

further diluted with 50 ml of dimethylformamide to give a casting solution containing 18.1 percent by weight of the polyamide-acid. The intrinsic viscosity was 1.73 (0.5 percent solution in dimethylformamide).

Films were cast with a doctor knife having a 15 ml opening and dried at 120°C for 15 minutes under dry nitrogen in a forced draft oven. The films were fixed over steel plates with magnets, additionally dried for 15 minutes at 120°C under nitrogen, and then heated to 300°C in a hot vacuum oven to convert the polyamide-acid to the polyimide [8].

MODIFICATION AND FORMULATION

In common with most of the other polymers described in this work, the extent to which the basic polyimide polymer can be modified is limited. Principal modifications are achieved before synthesis through the selection of the amine and the anhydride component. The influence, for example, of the diamine on thermal stability of PMDA-based systems is indicated in Figs. 8.7 to 8.10. Methylene and isopropylidene groups between aromatic groups provide particularly poor thermal stability. DTA data indicate that connections at the para positions of the aromatic diamine give higher decomposition temperatures than those connected at the meta positions

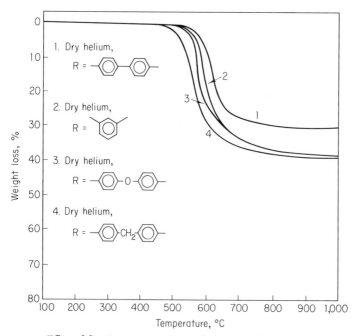

FIG 8.7 *Effect of diamine structure on weight loss of PMDA-polyimide during thermal grammetric analysis* [51].

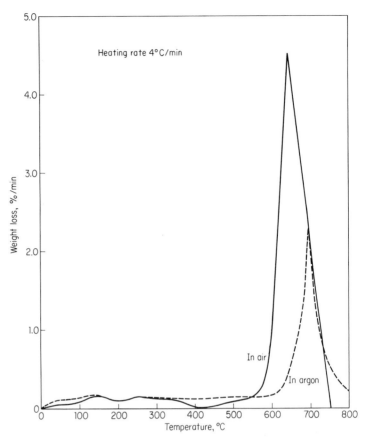

FIG 8.8 *Differential thermal analysis of polyimide from PMDA and* m-*phenylenediamine* [9].

[17]. A comparison of various polyimides from both aromatic and aliphatic diamines, with regard to thermal stability, is given in [50].

The polyimide from PMDA and 4,4′-diaminodiphenyl ether, while slightly less acceptable in terms of heat resistance, compared to the others, is apparently the preferred amine for use with PMDA. The superiority of this amine, for example, in terms of water resistance is shown in Table 8.5.

Polyimides from PMDA and p-phenylenediamine are crystalline. Others are more or less ordered. Films from PMDA and m-phenylenediamine or 4,4′-diaminodiphenyl-methane, -isopropylidene, -sulfide, and -ether normally exhibit a low degree of order as prepared. High-temperature treatment will cause crystallization of films of the latter and of m-phenylenediamine [54].

Attempts have been made to introduce crosslinking agents into the polymer chain by the use of some portion of a more highly functional

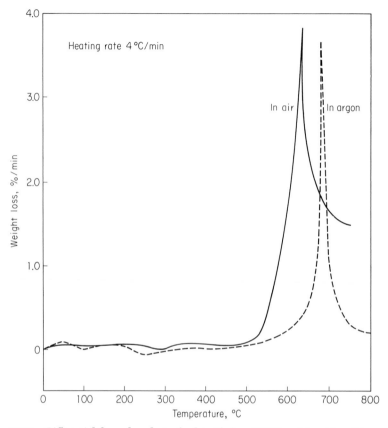

FIG 8.9   *Differential thermal analysis of polyimide from PMDA and benzidene* [9].

TABLE 8.5   Effect of Boiling Water on Flexibility of
Polyimide Films [54]

Diamine component	Period of flexibility retention
benzene ring (meta)	1 week
benzene ring (para)	1 week
diphenyl ether (—O—)	1 year
diphenyl sulfide (—S—)	>3 months

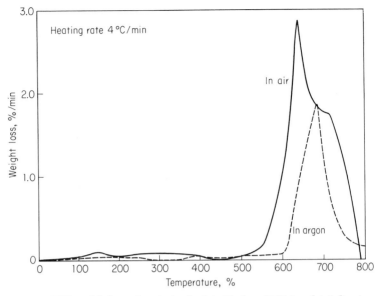

FIG 8.10   *Differential thermal analysis of polyimide from PMDA and 4,4'-diaminodiphenyl ether* [9].

amine.   For example, 3,5,5'-triaminobenzanilide has been used in combination with m-phenylenediamine for this purpose, but no outstanding results were obtained [19].   Likewise, pentaerythritol units have been introduced in an attempt to develop a polyester-type reaction during cure in the hopes of lowering pressure-temperature requirements for laminating operations, but again no significant advantages were obtained [20].   Special thermosetting laminating varnishes of undisclosed composition have been made available experimentally by Du Pont.   The Monsanto material, Skygard 700 laminating varnish, is reported to crosslink with heat [59].

Adhesive formulations may be developed from the solution systems by the use of fillers and stabilizers.   These are generally supplied in B-staged form on glass cloth carriers.   The polyimides, however, do not appear to be improved as readily by the addition of fillers as do, for example, the polybenzimidazoles (see Chap. 9).

Before the conversion of the polyamic acid to the polyimide, the acid may be converted to a silver salt.   When the polyimide is subsequently formed, free-metal particles are thus distributed throughout the system. These have dimensions less than 0.8 micron and as a consequence, do not interfere with transparency but yet will provide for electrical conductivity in the cured polymer [16].   Copper and iron may be incorporated by similar techniques [12].

Vespel molding compounds based on Du Pont's SP polymers have been employed with graphite fillers to provide high-temperature self-lubricating bearings. Special leafing pigments are used with polyimide paints to improve ultraviolet resistance. Carbon-black filler has been used to make electrically conductive heating panels.

Combinations of polyimide films and polytetrafluoroethylene (PTFE) are offered commercially. For example, a polyimide varnish may be used to treat the PTFE to improve abrasion resistance and cut-through resistance without adversely degrading the properties of the PTFE [27].

PHYSICAL PROPERTIES

Films

E. I. du Pont de Nemours & Company offers a polyimide film from pyromellitic dianhydride and diaminodiphenyl ether in thicknesses of 0.5, 1, 2, 3, and 5 mils in widths up to 18 in., available under the registered trade name Kapton H. Its room-temperature properties are very similar to those of Mylar, as indicated in Table 8.6. A typical infrared spectrum is presented in Fig. 8.11. Additional spectral data are given in Figs. 8.12 to 8.14. The film, as supplied, is amber in color, probably caused by a charge-transfer interaction between respective units in the polymer chain. Transparent films have been made, but at some sacrifice in thermal stability.

Additionally, Du Pont offers, on an experimental basis, Kapton film coated on one or both sides with hexafluoropropylene-tetrafluoroethylene copolymer (Kapton HF) and a composite film of Kapton H and poly(tetrafluoroethylene), Kapton HB. The HF film is available in thicknesses of 1.5, 2, 3, 4, 5, and 6 mils. It is sealable by heating at temperatures of 300°C or higher for short times (see Fig. 8.15), as distinct from Kapton H, which

TABLE 8.6 Physical Properties of Kapton H vs. Mylar [24]

Property	Mylar	Kapton H
Ultimate tensile strength, psi	23,000	25,000
Yield point, psi	12,000	14,000
Stress to produce 5% elongation, psi	13,000	13,000
Ultimate elongation, %	100	70
Tensile modulus, psi	550,000	430,000
Pneumatic impact strength, kg-cm/mil (Du Pont test)	6	6
Folding endurance, folds (M.I.T.—½-kg load)	$>10^5$	$\sim 10^4$
Tear strength, g/mil (propagating—Elmendorf)	15	8
Bursting strength, psi (Mullen)	30	75
Density, g/cc	1.4	1.42
Coefficient of friction (kinetic, film-to-film)	0.45	0.42
Area factor, ft²/(lb)(mil)	140	135

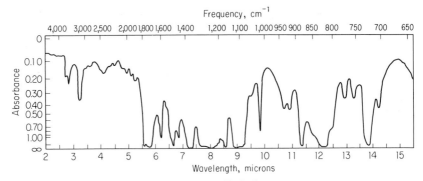

FIG 8.11   *Infrared spectrum of* 1-*mil Kapton H film* [46].

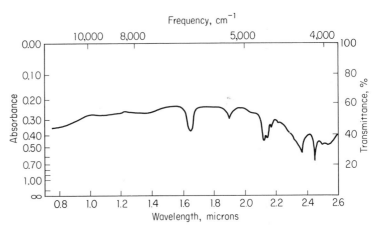

FIG 8.12   *Near-infrared spectrum of PMDA-POP polyimide film,* 15 *mils thick* [51].

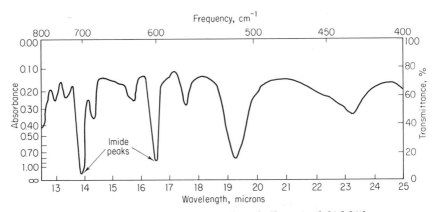

FIG 8.13   *Far-infrared spectrum of PMDA-POP polyimide film,* 0.5 *mil thick* [51].

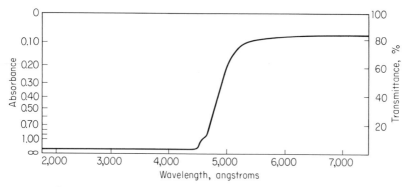

FIG 8.14   *Ultraviolet and visible spectrum of PMDA-POP film 0.5 mil thick* [51].

cannot be heat-sealed.   The Kapton H surface of the single-coated HF film is receptive to most varnishes, but phenolic, polyester, and epoxy varnishes should be avoided for higher-temperature operation, since they can lead to embrittlement and carbonized degradation products.   Silicone and polyimide varnishes are compatible at elevated temperature and do not lead to embrittlement.   Figure 8.16 indicates the effect of varnishes on elongation with aging.   A comparison of properties of PTFE and Kapton type HF are given in Table 8.7.

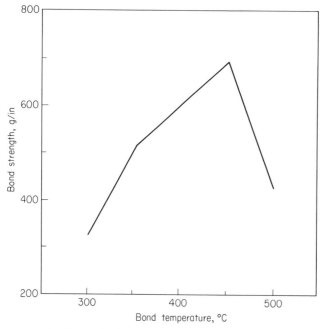

FIG 8.15   *Bond strength of Kapton H film to PTFE as a function of temperature; 10-second dwell at 10 psi pressure* [47].

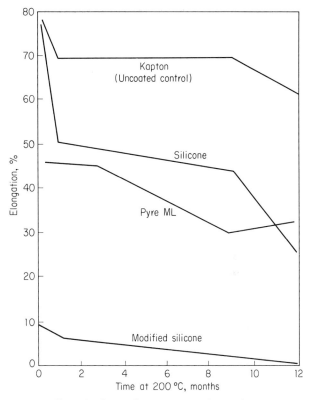

FIG 8.16 *Elongation loss with age at* 200°*C for* 1-*mil Kapton H film with various* 0.5-*mil varnish coatings* [49].

TABLE 8.7 Comparative Properties of Kapton HF and PTFE Films [48]

	Polyimide type HF	PTFE fluorocarbon
Thickness, mils	1.5	1
Tensile strength, psi:		
At 25°C	16,000	3,000
At 200°C	10,000	200
Elongation, %:		
At 25°C	75	300
At 200°C	75	175
Tear propagation, grams (Elmendorf)	20	125
Tear initial, grams (Graves)	800	270
Water-vapor permeability, g/(100 in.^{2})(24 hr) . . .	0.6	0.4

Polyimide films of known molecular weight have been prepared from polyamic acid prepolymers of known molecular weight. The prepolymer films were dehydrated in an acetic anhydride–pyridine bath for one day. This treatment produced no other changes. By plotting the properties against molecular weight and extrapolating to infinite molecular weight, it was possible to obtain ultimate values for these films: tensile strength, 25,000 psi; elongation, 250 percent; tear strength, 32 g/mil; and impact strength, 9.9 kg-cm/mil [60].

Laminates

A number of polyimide solutions have been developed for laminating operations. Du Pont offers several grades, both thermoplastic and thermosetting, ranging in solids content from about 18 to 45 percent. A higher-solids content laminating resin is supplied by Monsanto Plastics Division, under the designation Skygard 700.

Storage stability of the Skygard 700 solution is indicated in Fig. 8.17, from which it may be seen that the solution is somewhat unstable, tending to thicken with aging. Refrigerated storage is suggested.

Typical properties of the laminating solutions are indicated in Table 8.8.

The properties of the laminate at room temperature are generally lower than experienced with epoxy, polyester, or phenolic laminates. Typically, the flexural strengths are about 60,000 psi; elongations about 2 percent.

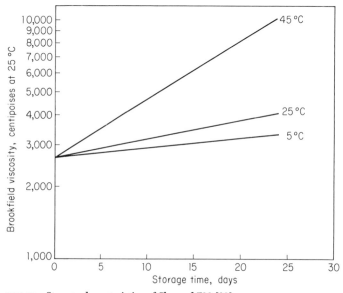

FIG 8.17 *Storage characteristics of Skygard 700* [29].

TABLE 8.8 Typical Properties of Polyimide Solutions

Property	Du Pont		Monsanto Skygard 700
	PI-2101	PI-3301	
Solids, %	20	53	60–64
Viscosity, centipoises ...	500–1,000	6,000–9,000	2,500–7,000
Solvent	NMP/DMF	NMP/xylene	....
Use	Glass cloth laminates	Filament winding	Glass cloth laminates

NMP = *N*-methylpyrrolidone. DMF = *N,N*-dimethylformamide.

In addition to offering solutions for laminating, Du Pont also offers preimpregnated glass cloth (PI-2501) and preimpregnated roving (PI-3301-FGR) for filament winding.

Additional data on composites are presented under the section Thermal Properties.

Among the problems in preparing laminates is the removal of large amounts of solvent associated with low solids (40 to 55°). The best method of fabrication seems to be the vacuum-bag technique because of the facilitated removal of volatiles during fabrication to yield a more compact laminate [61]. Also there is a great need for a coupling agent for the glass fabric which is as thermally stable as the polyimide binder [61].

Adhesives

Polyimide-based adhesives are supplied by Du Pont in solution form. Both thermoplastic, heat-stable systems (PI-1100) and thermosetting solutions (PI-1101) are available at about 18 percent solids. They give, in films, tensile strengths from 11,000 to 13,000 psi and elongations from 8 to 11 percent. Lap shear strengths of typical adhesive joints at room temperature are in the 2,000- to 2,500-psi range, considerably below the values obtained with the better structural adhesives. Peel values (climbing drum) are 20 to 30 psi at 23°C as against values almost twice as high for high-temperature phenolic-epoxy adhesives. Again, the superiority of the polyimides is evidenced only at elevated temperature.

In addition to solution adhesives, special supported tapes have been developed. Typical is Bloomingdale's Rubber FXM 34-B-24, supplied on style 112 glass with Volan A finish. High-solids-content solution adhesives are offered by Shawinigan Resins Corporation.

Varnishes

In addition to Pyre ML varnish, Du Pont has offered a number of insulation varnishes under experimental code numbers, such as RC-5060

(19 percent solids) and RC-B-24951 (45 percent solids). The varnishes are further discussed in the section Electrical Properties.

Structural Coatings

A number of coatings systems for structural metal have been investigated, these involving special pigments. The primary interest is to obtain an organic coating that will withstand high temperatures for aerospace applications.

Magnet Wire Coatings

Du Pont offers Pyre ML magnet wire coating, which is applied by major wire manufacturers. The Pyre ML coatings, together with composite coatings, are described in greater detail under the section Electrical Properties.

Molding Compounds

Special 100 percent solids systems have been successfully molded by Du Pont from their SP-1 polymer and supplied under the trade name Vespel. A 15 percent graphite-filled version is supplied under the designation SP-2. Typical properties at room temperature are given in Table 8.9. Friction and wear properties are indicated in Table 8.10.

Semiconductors

It has been reported that Kapton H, when pyrolyzed in vacuum at temperatures in the range of 800°C, provides a resultant product stable at elevated temperatures and yet having intrinsic resistivities at about 5×10^{-2} ohm-cm at room temperature. This appears to open the way to high-

TABLE 8.9 Properties of SP-1 Polymer at 23°C [32]

Property	Value
Specific gravity	1.41–1.43
Tensile strength, psi	13,500
Elongation, %	6–8
Shear strength, psi	11,900
Compressive strength, psi	24,400
Flexural modulus, psi $\times 10^{-5}$	4.50
Thermal conductivity, Btu-in./(ft^2)(hr)(°F)	2.20
Specific heat, Btu/(lb)(°F)	0.27
Impact strength, ft-lb/in.:	
Unnotched	9.6
Notched	0.7
Hardness, Rockwell H	83–89
Abrasion resistance, 1,000-g load, CS-17 wheel, mg/kc	6.3

TABLE 8.10 Friction and Wear of SP-1 against Carbon Steel*
(No lubrication) [32]

Environment	Pressure P, psi	Velocity V, fpm	Coefficient of friction†	Wear rate, in./1,000 hr
		$PV = 25,000$		
Air	30, 60	834,417	0.17	0.3
Nitrogen	30, 60	834,417	0.10	0.0005
		$PV = 100,000$		
Nitrogen	240	417	0.05	0.002

° Initial surface finish, 8 to 10 microns in rms.
† After break-in.

temperature-resistant organic semiconductors. Inorganic semiconductors, which depend for semiconductivity on trace impurities, are generally not stable above 200°C because of the tendency of the impurities to diffuse and change the semiconducting structure. With the pyrolyzed Kapton H film, however, nonmobile unsaturated valence states are believed to exist, as indicated in Fig. 8.18, which account for the semiconducting properties.

Foams

High-temperature foams have been offered by Du Pont on an experimental basis. These range in density from 2 to 30 pcf and in thicknesses from 5 to 100 mils.

Fibers

Experimental polyimide fibers, showing moderate orientation and medium crystallinity, have been produced; these fibers retain useful properties for 500 hours at 330°C and for 10 hours at 400°C. Fibers had tenacity of about 7.0 grams per denier and flexural and impact strengths comparable to nylon 66 [58].

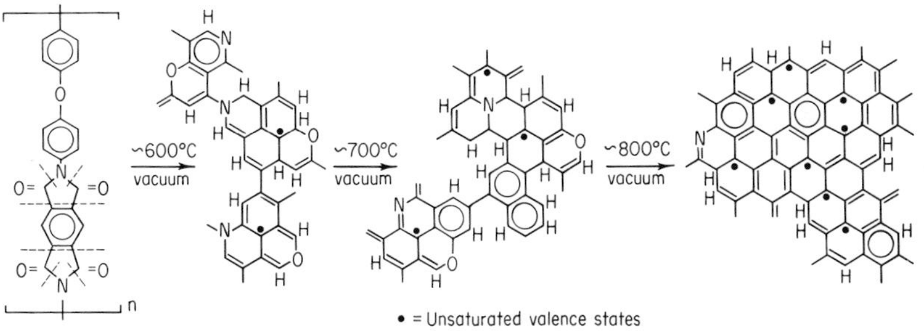

• = Unsaturated valence states

FIG 8.18 *Vacuum pyrolysis of polyimide gives semiconductive residue containing unsaturated valence states* [49].

THERMAL PROPERTIES

The elevated-temperature properties, as previously indicated, are dependent on the precursors used in synthesis. A comparison of the thermal stability of various high-temperature polymers, with commercial polyimides and polyamide-imides, in air at 320°C is given in Fig. 8.19. Except for the silicones, the clear superiority of the polyimides is indicated at all temperatures.

By thermal gravimetric analysis (TGA), Kapton H film is stable in air to approximately 420°C. Above this temperature it volatilizes, and at 485°C the volatilization is almost total within 5 hours. The activation energy for degradation in air is 32 kcal per mole. In vacuum, the polymer is stable to 500°C. Above this temperature (see Fig. 8.20), it volatilizes to leave a residue of approximately 54 percent. The activation energy in vacuum is 74 kcal per mole [14].

As shown in Fig. 8.21, the Kapton H film is little degraded (in terms of weight loss) by aging in air at 400°C as compared with aging in an inert gas. Oxidative stability is also supported by TGA data (Fig. 8.22). The same trend is observed with Skygard 700 (Fig. 8.23). Above 400°C,

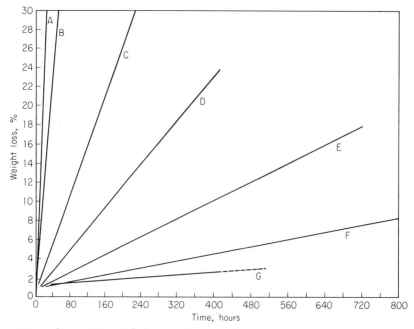

FIG 8.19 *Comparative weight loss as a function of time of thin films of various resins in air at* 320°C [46]. A—*Phenolic;* B—*modified phenolic;* C—*aromatic amide-imides;* D—*aromatic amide-imides;* E—*aromatic polyimides;* F—*aromatic polyimides;* G—*silicone.*

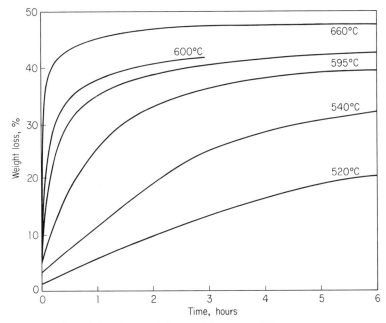

FIG 8.20 *Thermal degradation of Kapton H in vacuum* [46].

oxidative degradation assumes increasing significance as indicated in Fig. 8.24, where data from differential thermal analysis are compared.

The glass transition temperatures of several polyimides have been obtained, giving data as indicated in Table 8.11. The lack of a mechanical glass transition, for the Kapton H film, as against observed softening of the

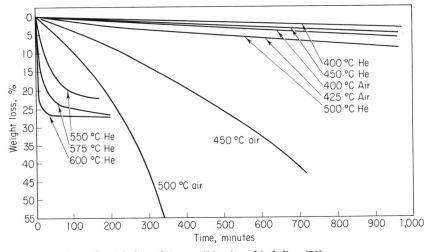

FIG 8.21 *Isothermal weight loss of Kapton H in air and in helium* [51].

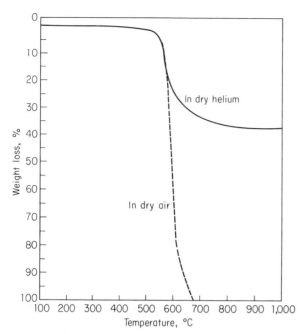

FIG 8.22 *Effect of environment on weight loss of Kapton H film during constant temperature rise of* 3°C *per min* [40].

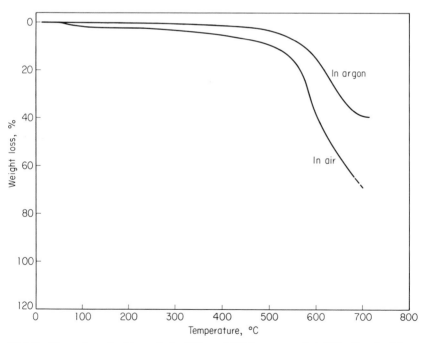

FIG 8.23 *Thermal gravimetric analysis of Skygard 700 in argon and air* [29]. *Sample:* 0.2 *gram; gas flow rate,* 100 *cc per min; temperature rise,* 12°C *per min. Cure conditions of sample:* ½ *hour at* 200°C, 2 *hours at* 250°C, 4 *hours at* 300°C; *ground:* 40–60 *mesh.*

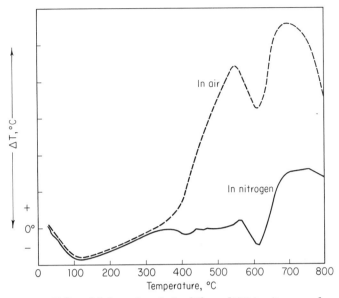

FIG 8.24   *Differential thermal analysis of Skygard 700 in nitrogen and air* [29]. *Sample: 0.200 gram Skygard 700, 60 mesh/0.800 gram Carborundum, 150 mesh. Reference: 1.200 grams Carborundum; gas flow rate, 100 cc per min; rate of rise, 12° C per min.*

other films, has been attributed to some amount of crystallization [34]. On the other hand, studies of the viscoelastic behavior of Kapton H film and Vespel polymers indicated that the elastic modulus of the materials changed very slightly over a wide temperature range and that no sharp molecular transition took place. It was argued that their performance was more characteristic of a crosslinked than of a noncrosslinked system, and it was suggested that crosslinking may occur during the final conversion of the polyamic acid to the polyimide. In this test series, the Kapton H film did not show a sufficient degree of crystallinity for crystallinity to provide an adequate explanation of the performance with temperature [28]. In Table 8.11, it is interesting to note the differences between the electrical and mechanical transition points. The differences can probably be ascribed

TABLE 8.11   Glass Transition Temperature of Polyimide Films [34]

Polymer	T_g by electrical dissipation factor at 1 kc, °C	T_g from modulus-temperature curve, °C
PMDA/bis(4-aminophenyl) ether ...	385	None
PMDA/3,4'-Diaminobenzamide	265	370
BTDA/MPDA	340	240
BTDA/bis(4-aminophenyl) ether ...	345	220

to the different nature of the two measuring methods and to batch differences in the polymer. The electrical measurements reflect very small and rapid responses of the polymer while the 10-second torsional modulus measures a low-frequency, bulk response or a time-dependent viscoelastic response [34].

Kapton H film has been studied by pyrolysis to determine something of the nature of the degradation process [23]. With the untreated film, as supplied, a yellow material appeared as a product in the pyrolysis temperature range of 200 to 250°C. It was concluded that this arose from scission of the residual polyamic acid in the presence of catalytic amounts of water either originally present or formed from cyclodehydration upon heat. Thermal stability could be improved through purification of the film by soaking in solvents, followed by a drying cycle.

Other reactions which might be expected during pyrolysis were thermal cleavage of free carboxyl groups and free-radical degradation as well as additional imidation. The imide links probably decompose by splitting out carbon monoxide by the following route:

to leave a nitrogenous residue.

Typical of the gaseous degradation products of Kapton H film are those indicated in Table 8.12. The gas mixture resulting from pyrolysis of polyimide resin is similar to that found in mine gases, the explosive hazards of which are well known. In addition, traces of hydrogen cyanide and

TABLE 8.12   Mass Spectrometric Analysis of Gaseous
Degradation Products of H Film (Vacuum pyrolysis at 540°C
for 2 hours) [42]

Component	Mole, %
Benzene	0.7
Carbon dioxide	35.1
Carbon monoxide	58.7
Water	1.2
Hydrogen	2.6
Ammonia	Trace
Hydrogen cyanide	1.2
Benzonitrile	0.5

Weight loss on sample 34.6%. Original sample weight 0.4382 g.

ammonia were detected. The calculated low explosive limit for gases from polyimide was found to be 7.7 volume percent. Thus, 2.37 grams of resin pyrolyzed in a 500-cu-in. container would be sufficient to reach the lower explosive limit [57].

In a recent state-of-the-art survey [49], it was found that there was some conflict in the literature regarding weight-loss data and serviceability limits for the polyimides. In view of the variables involved in the synthesis of these new polymers, and in view of the critical nature of processing operations, these variations are not surprising. Variations in properties have been reported, for example, in polyimide enamel magnet wires from spool to spool [44], this being attributed to improper cure. A consideration of the information given in the section on synthesis will indicate the need for careful processing if undegraded, high-molecular-weight polymers are to be obtained.

Films

The thermal properties for Kapton H are given in Table 8.13. From this, it is seen that the service life at 250°C, based on aging time in air to 1 percent elongation, is approximately 10 years. This end point is based on the polymer having an initial elongation of about 28 percent. In common with other high-temperature polymers, there is a gradual decline in physical strength with temperature, as indicated in Figs. 8.25 to 8.27. Performance at cryogenic temperatures appears acceptable. At 4°K,

TABLE 8.13 Thermal Properties of Kapton H vs. Mylar Film [24]

Property	Mylar	Kapton H
Melting point, °C........................	250–265	None
Zero-strength temperature, °C,		
(hot bar, 20 psi, 5 seconds to failure).......	248	815
Coefficient of linear expansion,............	2.7	2.0
cm/(cm)(°C $\times$ 10⁵)	(21 to 49°C)	(-14 to 38°C)
Coefficient of thermal conductivity,		
cal/(cm²)(cm)(sec)(°C $\times$ 10⁴)	3.63	3.5
Flammability	Slow to self-extinguishing	Nonflammable
Cut-through temperature, °C:.............	190	435
Dimensional stability.................200	3.5	0.2
(% shrinkage 250	Melts	0.3
at listed temperature, °C) 300	....	0.5
400	....	3.5
Heat aging........................200	1 year	?
(time to 1% elongation in air 250	Melts	10 years
at listed temperature, °C) 275	....	1 year
300	....	1 month
400	....	1 day

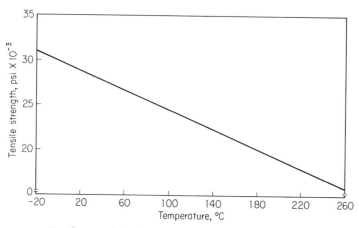

FIG 8.25   *Tensile strength of Kapton H vs. temperature* [22].

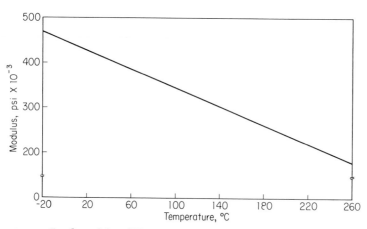

FIG 8.26   *Tensile modulus of Kapton H vs. temperature* [22].

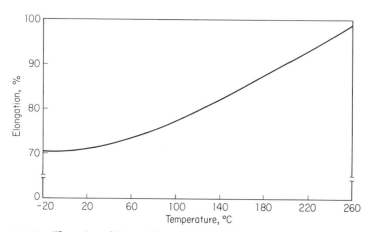

FIG 8.27   *Elongation of Kapton H vs. temperature* [22].

Kapton H film can withstand without breaking a bend around a ¼-in.-diameter mandrel.

Laminates

Typical of the elevated-temperature strength retention of polyimide laminates are the data given in Tables 8.14 and 8.15.   Filament winding data are given in Table 8.16.

Adhesives

The elevated-temperature adhesive properties of polyimide-based systems are indicated in Table 8.17.   Performance at reduced temperature shows improvement over room-temperature values, in accordance with the trend observed with other high-temperature adhesives.   Interestingly enough, the formulated adhesive shown in the table only manifests superiority over the unformulated system on aging at 370°C for periods in excess of 24 hours.

Molding Compounds

Du Pont's SP polymers give deflection temperatures greater than 245°C (10 mils deflection under 264 psi fiber stress), and initial data indicate that

TABLE 8.14   Polyimide Laminate Data vs. Data for Epoxy and Silicone [52]

| Test conditions | Flexural strength, psi $\times$ 10^{-3} | | | |
	PI-2101 181-E-A-1100 glass	PI-2501 181-E-A-1100 glass	Epoxy 181-E-112 glass	Silicone 181-E-112 glass
At 23°C.	43.5	57.1	70	39
After 2-hour water boil.	42.1			
At 288°C after:				
½ hour at 288°C.	33.0	22.7	22	20
100 hours.	31.5	30.1	21	19
200 hours.	27.9	27.5	20	19
500 hours.	21.5	29.9	19	17
1,000 hours	16.6	24.2		
1,500 hours	12.2	24.2		
2,000 hours	13.8	22.0		
At 315°C after:				
½ hour at 315°C.	26.0	10.9		
100 hours.	28.7	18.5		
200 hours.	23.7	26.6		
500 hours.	13.7	22.5		
1,000 hours	2.9	19.1		
At 370°C after:				
½ hour at 370°C.	15.6	12.4		
16 hours.	18.6	21.7		
34 hours.	13.0	24.1		
At 426°C after ½ hour at 426°C. . .	15.6			

TABLE 8.15 Mechanical Properties of Skygard 700 Laminates [31]

Property	Value
Flexural strength, flatwise, psi:	
Standard conditions at 23°C	75,000–85,000
½ hour at 370°C	45,000–60,000
100 hours at 370°C	20,000–35,000
Weight loss after 100 hours at 370°C, %	3.0
Modulus of elasticity, psi $\times$ 10^{-6}:	
Standard conditions at 23°C	3.12
335 hours at 300°C	3.12
Ultimate tensile strength, psi:	
Standard conditions at 23°C	57,000
335 hours at 300°C	42,000
Barcol hardness	70
Flammability	Nonburning
Elongation:	
Standard conditions at 23°C, %	1.90
Tested at 23°C, 335 hours aging at 300°C, %	1.40

Long-term Aging Study at 315°C

Property	500 hours	860 hours	1850 hours
Flexural strength, psi	29,000	20,000	10,950
Flexural modulus, psi $\times$ 16^{-6}	2.61	2.59	2.08
Weight loss, %	2.2	3.4	7.9

TABLE 8.16 NOL Ring Performance Data on Polyimide Prepreg Filament Windings vs. Commercial Systems [29]

Material	Hoop tensile composite strength, psi	
	At 23°C, no age	At 288°C after ½ hour
PI-3301 20 end S-994 (HTS)	185,000	171,700
Epon 828/MNA (epoxy) 20 end E (801)	171,300	111,500
DC-2106/R7145 (silicone) 20 end E (801)	139,800	89,600

Material	Resin content, %	Specific gravity	Horizontal shear strength, psi			
			At 23°C	At 120°C after ½ hour	At 288°C after ½ hour	At 370°C after ⅙ hour
PI-3301 20 end S-994 (HTS)	16.0	1.8	4,600	3,700	1,990	980
Epon 828/MNA 12 end S-994 (HTS)	19.0	1.9	7,800	5,460	1,040	160
DC-2106/R-7145 20 end E (801)	24.2	2.1	3,100	1,400	460	375

Material	Control at 23°C, psi	Horizontal shear strength at 288°C, psi				
		After ½ hour	After 50 hours	After 100 hours	After 200 hours	After 500 hours
PI-3301 20 end S-994 (HTS)	4,600	1,990	3,390	2,310	2,030	1,910
Epon 828/MNA 30 end E (801)	7,870	1,000	560	570	650	Burned out
DC-2106/R-7145 20 end E (801)	3,100	460	1,100	1,260	1,060	940

TABLE 8.16 (*Continued*)

Material	Control at 23°C, psi	Horizontal shear strength at 370°C, psi	
		After 10 minutes	After 16 hours
PI-3301 20 end S-994 (HTS)............	3,090	980	920
Epon 828/MNA 30 end E (801).........	6,580	160	Burned out
DC-2106/R-7145 20 end (801)..........	2,950	375	755

Flexural Strength and Modulus

Test temperature, °C	PI-3301° strength, psi	PI-3301° modulus, psi × 10⁻⁶	Epoxy† strength, psi	Silicone† strength, psi
23............................	90,500	5.3	110,000	50,000
120	75,600	4.95	63,000	27,000
176	....	....	26,000	....
288	33,100	3.85	....	12,000
370	31,400	3.7		

Compressive Strength

Test temperature	PI-3301‡ strength, psi	Epoxy† strength, psi	Silicone† strength, psi
23°C	50,100	60,100	25,000
120°C after ½ hour..................	29,900	....	15,000
288°C after ½ hour..................	22,800	....	5,300
23°C, aged ½ hour at 370°C...........	52,500		
23°C, aged 16 hours at 370°C.........	23,500		

Panel Shear Strength

Test temperature	PI-3301‡ strength, psi	Epoxy† strength, psi	Silicone† strength, psi
23°C	4,020	6,000	3,100
120°C after ½ hour..................	3,370		
288°C after ½ hour..................	1,790	....	1,100
23°C, aged ½ hour at 370°C...........	2,800		
23°C, aged 16 hours at 370°C.........	2,385		

° Resin Content 17.5%, specific gravity 1.84, 20 end S-994 (HTS).
† Literature data.
‡ Resin content 16.2%, specific gravity 1.92, 20 end S-994 (HTS).

they are suited for continuous service at 260°C and for short-time exposures to temperatures as high as 500°C, with these limits being, perhaps, conservative. Weight-loss data under vacuum aging are given in Fig. 8.28. In air, at 400°C, weight loss will be approximately 30 percent after 200 hours.

Thermal expansion rates of SP-1 and SP-2 are given in Table 8.18.

TABLE 8.17 Polyimide Adhesive Data vs. Data for Commercial
High-temperature Adhesives [52]

	Lap shear strength, psi			
	P-1101		PBI	Commercial
Test conditions	Unformulated	Formulated	Formulated	epoxy phenolic
At 23°C................	2,500	2,200	4,000	4,000
At 288°C after:				
1 hour at 288°C.........	1,800	1,400	3,500	2,100
100 hours..............	1,800	1,900	2,500	0
200 hours..............	1,900	1,400	1,100	0
500 hours..............	1,600	1,300	700	
1,000 hours............	1,400	1,400	0	
At 370°C after:				
1 hour at 370°C.........	1,400	600	2,000	900
10 hours..............	1,300	1,100	2,000	0
24 hours..............	1,300	1,200	900	0
60 hours..............	0	1,100	0	

Various properties vs. temperature are shown in Figs. 8.29 to 8.33. Elevated-temperature creep resistance is shown in Fig. 8.34.

Coatings

Experimental coatings have been developed for elevated-temperature service. Typical weight-loss data on such systems, aged on stainless steel,

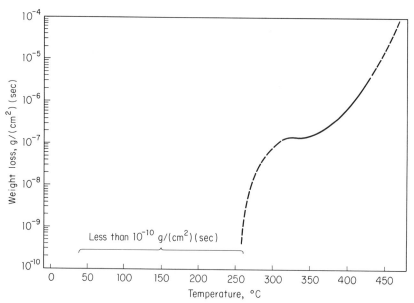

FIG 8.28 *Weight loss of SP-1 polyimide in vacuum as a function of specimen temperature. Ambient pressure, 10^{-7} to 10^{-8} mm Hg* [46].

TABLE 8.18 Coefficient of Linear Thermal Expansion* [21]

Temperature, °C	micro-in./(in.)(°F)
Polyimide	
23–100	24.2
23–200	26.5
23–300	27.4
23–400	30.0
Graphite-filled Polyimide	
23–250	21.6
23–400	22.5

° Values given here are for one direction. This property is an isotropic, and values in the other direction are 15 to 25% higher for unfilled polyimide and 40 to 50% higher for graphite-filled polyimide.

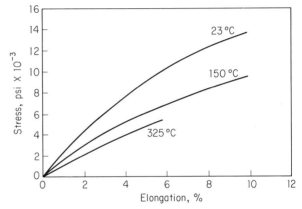

FIG 8.29 *Stress-strain curves of SP-1 based on original cross section using a strain rate of 0.2 in. per min* [19].

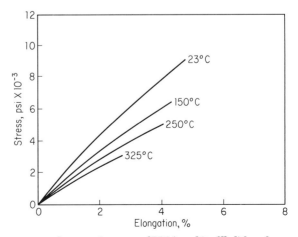

FIG 8.30 *Stress-strain curves of SP-2 (graphite-filled) based on original cross section using a strain rate of 0.2 in. per min* [19].

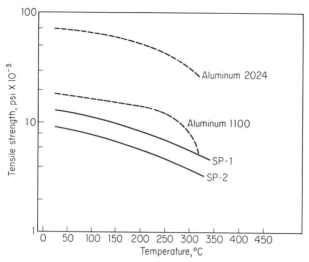

FIG 8.31   *Tensile strength vs. temperature of SP polymers compared with aluminum* [19].

are given in Table 8.19. A summary of properties of selected systems is given in Table 8.20.

The thermal properties of electrical-grade varnishes and magnet wire coatings are indicated under the section Electrical Properties.

PHYSICAL-CHEMICAL PROPERTIES

The polyimides, generally, are somewhat more water-sensitive than most other linear polymers. For example, the water uptake at 50 percent rela-

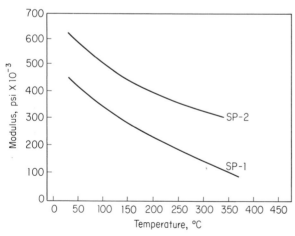

FIG 8.32   *Flexural modulus vs. temperature of SP polymers* [19].

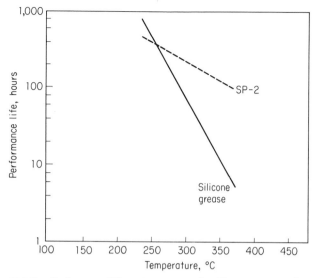

FIG 8.33 *Performance life vs. temperature for silicone grease and SP-2 lubricated ball bearings* [19].

tive humidity is about six times that of Mylar. However, Kapton H film has preserved 75 percent of its elongation and 90 percent of the impact value after 15 days in boiling water. The SP polymer will pick up about 3 percent water at equilibrium in boiling water with a loss of about 50 percent of original strength.

Typical of the chemical resistance of Kapton H film are the data given in Table 8.21. Chemical resistance data of the SP polymer are given in Table 8.22. Pyre ML treated cloth gives chemical resistance as indicated in Table 8.23, and the magnet wire as shown in Table 8.24. The influence

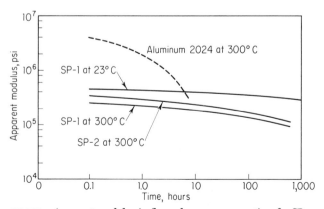

FIG 8.34 *Apparent modulus in flexural creep vs. creep time for SP polymers and aluminum* [19].

TABLE 8.19 Weight Loss of High-temperature Polyimide Coatings
on Stainless Steel [49]

Specimen	Temperature, °C	Time, hours	Weight loss, %
Du Pont RCW62480 polyimide + nonleafing Al pigment, pigment/binder ratio = 200/100, DMAC solvent......	426	1	−2.69
		3	0.77
		5	8.20
		10	15.0
		25	20.1
		50	6.02(?)
		100	29.7
	537	1	13.96
		3	15.45
		5	20.68
		10	14.48
		25	8.25
		50	9.36
Polypyromellitimide PPMI + nonleafing Al pigment, pigment/binder ratio = 200/100, DMAC solvent......	426	100	8.67
		1	−6.19
		3	−6.25
		5	−6.46
		10	−8.68
		25	34.7
		50	34.7
		100	50.2
	537	1	27.4
		3	32.87
		5	39.5
		10	37.8
		25	27.9
		50	17.9
Du Pont RCW62480 + leafing Al pigment, pigment/binder ratio = 200/100, DMAC solvent......	426	100	25.2
		1	9.04
		3	10.49
		5	17.11
		10	20.39
		25	28.8
		50	12.8(?)
		100	35.2
	537	1	11.32
		3	13.09
		5	14.63
		10	15.8
		25	8.42
		50	11.83
		100	14.48

TABLE 8.20 Summary of High-temperature Evaluations of Single-Coat Polyimide Systems on Stainless Steel and Aluminum [48]

Resin (Du Pont formula)	Pigment	Pigment/binder ratio	Appearance after exposure		
			At 426°C	At 482°C	At 537°C
			On Stainless Steel		
RCW62480	N.L.Al°	200/100	After 25 hours†	At 25 hours†	Fair adhesion after 25 hours†
RCW62480	N.L.Al°	100/100	Powder only after 5 hours	At 25 hours†	At 25 hours†
RCW62480	N.L.Al°	50/100	Powder only after 5 hours	At 25 hours†	At 25 hours†
PPMI	N.L.Al°	200/100	After 25 hours†	At 25 hours†	Adhesion fair after 25 hours
PPMI	N.L.Al°	50/100	After 25 hours†	At 25 hours†	Failure after 1 hour
RCW62480	Leafing Al	200/100	After 25 hours†	At 25 hours†	Coating integrity poor, failure after 25 hours
RCW62480	Leafing Al	100/100	Adhesion poor after 25 hours	Adhesion poor after 25 hours	Coating integrity poor, failure after 25 hours
RCW62480	Leafing Al	50/100	Adhesion poor after 5 hours	Adhesion failure after 25 hours	Adhesion failure after 1 hour
PPMI	Leafing Al	200/100	After 25 hours†	At 25 hours†	At 25 hours†
RCW62480	SrCrO4	200/100	Complete failure at 1 hour	Complete failure at 1 hour	Complete failure at 1 hour
RCW62480	SrCrO4	100/100	Complete failure at 2 hours	Complete failure at 1 hour	Complete failure at 1 hour
RCW62480	SrCrO4	50/100	Complete failure at 5 hours	Complete failure at 1 hour	Complete failure at 1 hour
PPMI	SrCrO4	50/100	Vehicle gone after 2 hours	Failure at 1 hour	Failure at 1 hour
RCW62480	Black	100/100	Complete failure at 1 hour	Failure at 1 hour	Failure at 1 hour
PPMI	Black	50/100	Complete failure at 1 hour	Failure at 1 hour	Failure at 1 hour
			On Aluminum		
RCW62480	N.L.Al°	100/100	Adhesion poor after 5 hours	Discoloration after 25 hours	Coating gone after 10 hours
PPMI	N.L.Al°	200/100	Excellent after 25 hours	Discoloration after 25 hours	Coating gone after 25 hours
PPMI	Leafing Al	200/100	Excellent after 25 hours	Discoloration after 25 hours	At 25 hours†
PPMI	SrCrO4	50/100	Failure at 2 hours	Failure at 1 hour	Failure at 1 hour
RCW62480	Black	100/100	Complete failure at 1 hour	Complete failure after 1 hour	Complete failure at 1 hour
PPMI	Black	25/100	Complete failure at 2 hours	Complete failure after 1 hour	Complete failure at 1 hour

° N.L. = nonleafing.
† Adhesion good, but some aluminum can be scraped off.

TABLE 8.21 Chemical Resistance of Kapton H [49]

| Property | Typical values | | | Test condition | Test (ASTM unless otherwise noted) |
	Tensile strength, % retained	Elongation, % retained	Modulus, % retained		
Chemical resistance to:				Days immersed at 23°C:	
Benzene	100	82	100	365	
Toluene	94	66	97	365	
Methanol	100	73	140	365	
Acetone	67	62	160	365	
10% sodium hydroxide		Degrades		5	
Glacial acetic acid	85	62	102	36 days at 110°C	
p-Cresol	100	77	102	22 days at 200°C	
Arochlor	100	53	142	365 days at 200°C	
Transformer oil	100	100	100	180 days at 150°C	
Water:					
pH 1	65	30	100	14 days at 100°C	
pH 4.2	65	30	100	14 days at 100°C	
pH 7.0	65	30	100	70 days at 100°C	
pH 8.9	65	20	100	14 days at 100°C	
pH 10.0	60	10	100	4 days at 100°C	
Fungus resistance	Inert			12 months	Soil burial
Moisture absorption	1.3%			50% relative humidity at 23.5°C	Constant-environment room
	2.9%			Immersion for 24 hours at 23.5°C	D 570–59T
Hygroscopic coefficient	2.2×10^{-5} in./(in.)(% relative humidity)			20–80% relative humidity at 23°C	
Permeability:					
Gas, cc/(100 in.³) (24 hr) (atm/mil)				23°C	D 1434–58
Carbon dioxide	45				
Hydrogen	250				
Nitrogen	6				
Oxygen	25				
Helium	415				
Water vapor, gm/(100 in.³) (24 hr) (mil)	5.4			23°C	E 96–53T

TABLE 8.22 Chemical Resistance of Unfilled SP Polymer [46]

Chemical	Temperature, °C	Time, hours	Tensile strength, % retained
Nitric acid, 15%	23	720	66
Nitric acid, 70%	23	120	37
Hydrochloric acid, 38%	23	120	71
UDMH vapor	23	113	48
UDMH liquid	23	78	42
Aerozine 50 vapor	23	120	67
Sodium hydroxide, 5%	23	120	56
Skydrol 500A	23	233	100
	180	24	88
N₂O₄ vapor	23	120	60
	23	720	43
o-Dichlorobenzene + 1% tricresyl phosphate	172	720	100
Water	100	400	48
	100	1,000	44

TABLE 8.23   Chemical Resistance of Pyre ML Coated Fabrics [49]

Solvent	Condition	Exposure period
Acetone	No change	4 weeks
Methyl ethyl ketone		
Formaldehyde		
Methanol		
Ethanol		
Ethyl acetate		
Skydrol		
Carbon disulfide		
Carbon tetrachloride		
Chloroform		
Perchlorethylene		
o-Dichlorobenzene		
Benzene		
Toluene		
Hexane		
Naphtha		
Xylene		
Dimethylformamide		1 day
Dimethylacetamide		
N-Methylpyrrolidone		
γ-Butyrolactone		
Freon-22		4 hours
NaOH, 5%, aq.	Somewhat stiffened	4 weeks
NaOH, 1%, aq.	Slight stiffening	
NH_3, 5%, aq.	Slight stiffening	
H_2SO_4, conc., 96%	Coating dissolved	1 day
HNO_3, conc., 70%	Coating embrittled, deteriorated	
HCl, conc., 37%	Coating became cloudy, softened	3 weeks
H_2SO_4, 5%, aq.	Somewhat stiffened	
HNO_3, 5%, aq.	Slight discoloration, no softening	
HCl, 5%, aq.	Slight stiffening	4 weeks
H_2SO_4, 1%, aq.	Slight stiffening	
HNO_3, 1%, aq.	No softening, slight discoloration	
HCl, 1%, aq.	No softening, slight discoloration	

of chemicals on bond-strength retention of adhesive joints is shown in Table 8.25. Ozone resistance is relatively good (50 percent strength retention after exposure to air with 2 percent ozone for 3,700 hours) [18]. Polyimide films, however, embrittle after constant exposure to sunlight for 6 months, limiting their usefulness in coating applications for exterior members. Hydrazine readily attacks both the film and the molded Vespel compositions.

Radiation resistance of the polyimides is exceptional, as indicated in Tables 8.26 and 8.27, and in Fig. 8.35. In a series of tests of magnet wire insulation, polyimides proved superior to all the other wires tested—polyester, polyvinyl formal, polyurethane, nylon, and epoxy [47].

TABLE 8.24   Comparative Chemical Resistance of No. 18 AWG Magnet
Wires [49]

Chemical properties	Standard AI 220	Heavy Isonel 200/17	Heavy Pyre ML
Solvent shock, 15% prestretch 3× wrap in boiling xylol	Okay	Okay	Okay
Solvent resistance, 24 hr immersion followed by cheesecloth wipe:			
Toluol	Okay	Okay	Okay
Xylol	Okay	Okay	Okay
5% H_2SO_4	Okay	Okay	Okay
Perchloroethylene	Okay	Okay	Okay
Ethanol	Okay	Okay	Okay
1% KOH	Okay	Okay	Okay
Methylene chloride	Okay	Fails	Okay
Hermetic data:			
Scrape abrasion under liquid, R-22, strokes to failure	1,000+	225	90
Soxhlet extraction in toluol-methanol, %	0.5	1.4	0.5
Soxhlet extraction in R-22, %	0.2	0.3	0.3
Blister test in R-22	Okay	Blisters	Okay

TABLE 8.25   Comparative Lap Shear Strengths of Adhesives after
Exposure to Test Fluids [52]

Exposure time, days	Fluid	Lap shear strength at 25°C, psi			
		PI-1101		PBI formulated	Commercial epoxy-phenolic
		Unformulated	Formulated		
7	70°C, water	1,400	1,300	1,900	2,600
30	43°C at 100% relative humidity	1,500	1,600	1,900	2,900
30	35°C, 5% salt spray	200	600	1,900	3,200
7	JP-4 jet fuel	2,300	2,300	3,900	>4,000
7	Hydraulicoil	2,200	2,300	3,900	>4,000

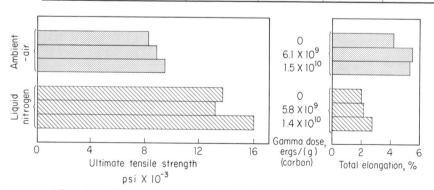

FIG 8.35   *Effect of radiation resistance on Vespel SP polyimide* [48].

TABLE 8.26 Radiation Resistance of Kapton H vs. Mylar [24]

Gamma Radiation
Kapton H remained flexible (180° bend), although slightly darkened, after exposure to 5×10^9 reps (4.16×10^9 rads) at Savannah River. Under this type of radiation, Mylar polyester film fails at levels of 10^8 reps.

Electrons from Van de Graaff Generator
Exposures of 100 minutes in air at 10 watt/cm^2 (6×10^9 rads) in the Van de Graaff generator caused approximately 50% decrease in elongation of Kapton H. Mylar endures 2×10^8 rads.

Brookhaven Pile (Neutrons and Gamma)
Exposure to mixed neutrons and gamma rays in the Brookhaven pile at 175°C is summarized below:

Temperature, °C	Flux, neutrons/(cm²)(sec)	Total exposure	Condition of Kapton H
175	5×10^{12}	8.3×10^{18} neutrons/cm^2 (5×10^9 rads)	Darkened
175	5×10^{12}	1.7×10^{19} neutrons/cm^2 (10^{10} rads)	Dark, tough

This exposure is equivalent to 0.005 pile-year. (One pile-year is 10^{13} neutrons/sec for 365 days.)

TABLE 8.27 Effect of Radiation on Polypyromellitimide Films [54]

Exposure Van de Graaff, 2-Mev. Electrons

Polymer film	Thickness, mils	Number of passes	Dose, megarads	Remarks
DDM-PI°	2.0	8,000	10,000	Retains toughness, good electrical properties
Mylar	2.0–3.0	200	240	Creasable
	1.0–3.0	500	600	Brittle, yellow
Polystyrene	1.2	500	600	Yellow, extremely brittle
Polyethylene (branched)	6–10	200	240	Very weak,
	6–10			sticky gum

Thermal Neutron Degradation

Polymer	Thickness, mils	Exposure, days	Temperature, °C	Flux 10³ neutrons/(cm²)(sec)	Remarks
POP-PP†	2–2.7	40	50–75	0.4	Slightly darkened, brittle in spots
		40	175	0.5	Darkened, tough
		80	175	0.5	Darkened, brittle
Polystyrene	1.2	10	50–75	0.4	Yellow, very brittle
Polyethylene	3.0	10	50–75	0.4	Sticky, rubbery
(branched)	3.0	40	50–75	0.4	Brown varnish
Mylar	3.0	10	50–75	0.4	Failed
	3.0	20	175	0.5	Yellow, brittle

° Polypyromellitimide from bis(4-aminophenyl)methane.
† Polyimide from bis(4-aminophenyl) ether and pyromellitic dianhydride.

ELECTRICAL PROPERTIES

The polyimides are exceptionally good elevated-temperature electrical insulating materials, probably the best organic materials available in the present technology. Arc resistance, however, is somewhat less than desirable, owing to a tendency to carbon tracking. Corona resistance is superior to that of the unfilled fluorocarbons and uncrosslinked polyethylenes.

The electrical properties of the polyimide varnishes give projected service lives as indicated in Fig. 8.36. From this, the service life at Class 180 hot spot would be well in excess of normal design requirements, with long-time service possible at even higher temperatures. The polyimide insulation is potentially suitable for duty at temperatures well above those encountered except in the most exotic electrical applications. When used as a coating for glass fabric for insulating applications, properties are as shown in Figs. 8.37 and 8.38. Units employing the polyimide varnishes, coated cloths, and Pyre ML insulated magnet wire have successfully withstood 28-day cycles of operation at Class 220 alternated with 100 percent relative humidity exposures as indicated in Table 8.28.

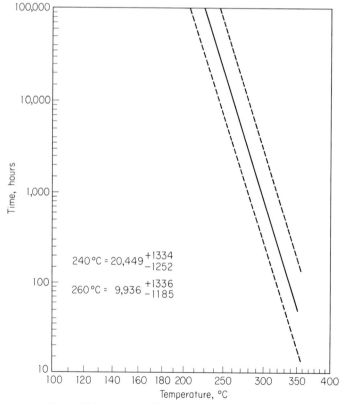

$$240\,^{\circ}C = 20{,}449\,^{+1334}_{-1252}$$

$$260\,^{\circ}C = 9{,}936\,^{+1336}_{-1185}$$

FIG 8.36 *Thermal life of unvarnished Pyre ML magnet wire* [10].

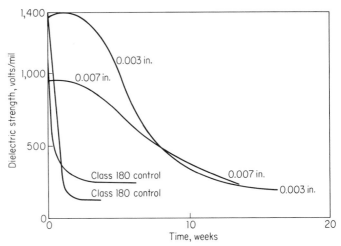

FIG 8.37 *Effect of aging time at* $300°C$ *on dielectric strength of Pyre ML coated glass fabric* [10].

High-temperature insulation system used in generator armature is based on aromatic polyimides. Slot-cell insulation is Pyre ML coated glass fabric, and magnet wire is covered with Pyre ML insulating varnish. The polyimide is noted for its unusual thermal stability, permitting smaller-sized electrical units with efficiency similar to that of larger ones. Electrical properties are essentially uniform at temperatures up to $250°C$. (E. I. du Pont de Nemours & Co., Inc.)

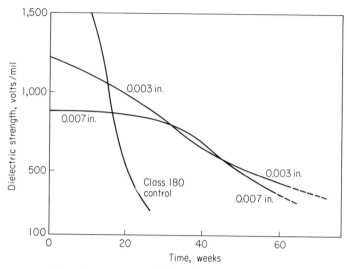

FIG 8.38 *Effect of aging time at 250°C on dielectric strength of Pyre ML coated glass fabric* [10].

TABLE 8.28 Motor Insulation and High-temperature Test Results [11]

Type of motor............. Random-wound 3-hp 3-phase open motor
Wire .... Heavy Pyre ML
Slot liners................ 2 layers 10-mil Pyre ML coated glass
Mid-sticks .... 62-mil Du Pont polyimide MK coated glass laminate
Wedges .... 2 layers of 62-mil MK coated glass laminates
End turn insulation......... 7-mil Pyre ML coated glass
Tying cord................ Glass
Varnish .... Polymer MK
Test cycle for first 28 cycles... 8 hours reversal running at 220°C with 13½ reversals per minute
8 hours not running at 100% relative humidity
8 hours not running at room temperature and humidity

TABLE 8.29 Electrical Properties of Laminate Made with P-3301 Tested at 9,375 Mc [52]

Conditioning	Test temperature, °C	Dielectric constant	Loss tangent
None	23	3.94	0.0143
	120	3.98	0.0165
	288	4.02	0.0187
	370	4.06	0.0194
	23	3.90	0.0122
Aged 16 hours at 370°C..........	23	4.01	0.0197
Aged 32 hours at 370°C..........	23	3.93	0.0197

Electrical properties of laminates are shown in Tables 8.29 and 8.30. Electrical properties of Kapton H film are compared with those of Mylar in Table 8.31. Dielectric properties of the film vs. frequency are shown in Fig. 8.39. Figures 8.40 through 8.44 indicate performance vs. temperature.

TABLE 8.30   Electrical Properties of Skygard 700 Laminates [31]

Property	Value
Dielectric strength:	
Short-time, parallel to laminate, volts	55,000
Step-by-step, parallel to laminate, volts	38,000
Short-time, volts/mil	179
Stepwise, volts/mil	140
Dielectric constant at 10^3 cps	4.10
Dissipation factor at 10^3 cps	0.00445
Insulation resistance, megohms	1.9×10^7
Volume resistivity, ohm-cm	2.47×10^{15}
Surface resistivity, ohms	3.35×10^{14}

TABLE 8.31   Electrical Properties of Kapton H Compared with Mylar [24]

Property	Temperature, °C	Mylar	Kapton H
Dielectric strength (1 mil),	25	7,000	7,000
volts/mil at 60 cps	150	5,000	6,000
Dielectric constant at 10^3 cps	25	3.1	3.5
	200	.....	3.0
Dissipation factor at 10^3 cps	25	0.0047	0.003
	200	0.01	0.002
Volume resistivity, ohm-cm	25	10^{18}	10^{18}
	200	5×10^{11}	10^{14}
Surface resistivity, ohms, at 1 kv, 50% relative humidity	25	10^{16}	10^{16}

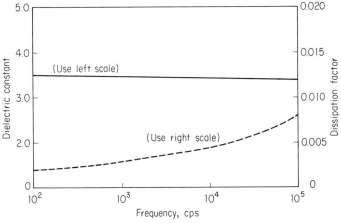

FIG 8.39   *Dielectric constant and dissipation factor of Kapton H vs. frequency* [22].

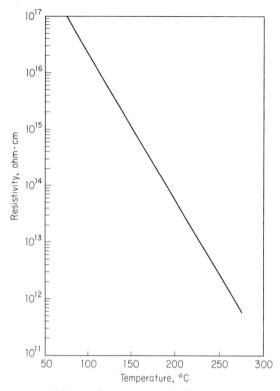

FIG 8.40   *Volume resistivity at* 125 *volts dc of Kapton H vs. temperature* [22].

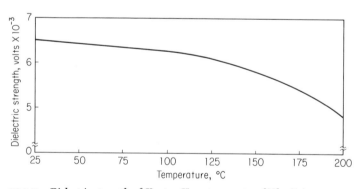

FIG 8.41   *Dielectric strength of Kapton H vs. temperature* [22].   *¼-in.-diameter electrodes,* 500 *volts per sec; rate of rise:* 1*-mil film.*

Figures 8.45 and 8.46 indicate the effect of thermal aging on these properties; Table 8.32 shows life under corona attack.

The SP polymer provides a dielectric strength of about 400 volts per mil in ⅛-in.-thick sections.   In 1 mil thickness, the strength declines from

7,500 to about 5,000 volts as temperature increases to 260°C. At 300°C, the dielectric strength is about 90 percent of original value at temperature after 80 hours aging. Dissipation factor vs. frequency and temperature is given in Table 8.33. Values at lower temperatures are shown in Fig. 8.47.

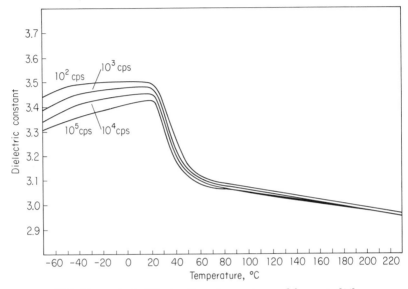

FIG 8.42 *Dielectric constant of Kapton H. vs. temperature and frequency* [14].

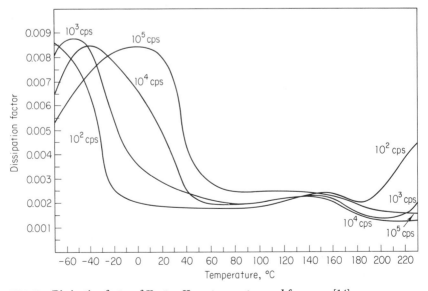

FIG 8.43 *Dissipation factor of Kapton H. vs. temperature and frequency* [14].

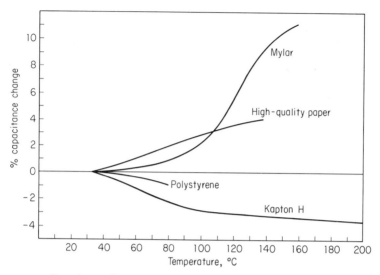

FIG 8.44 *Capacitance change at 10^3 cps vs. temperature for insulating films* [14].

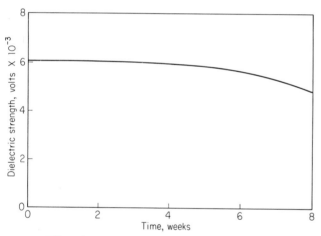

FIG 8.45 *Effect of thermal aging at 300°C on dielectric strength of 1-mil Kapton H* [14].

PROCESSING

The polyimide varnishes may be applied as magnet wire coatings with conventional equipment, using stainless steel or polyethylene dies. The coated wire, after winding, is heated to 175 to 200°C for 1 hour to prevent crazing during subsequent varnish treatment.

When used as an insulating varnish, the commercial material may be thinned with toluene or xylene. Parts are then dipped at 50°C and given a high-temperature step cure to flash off the solvents and provide final

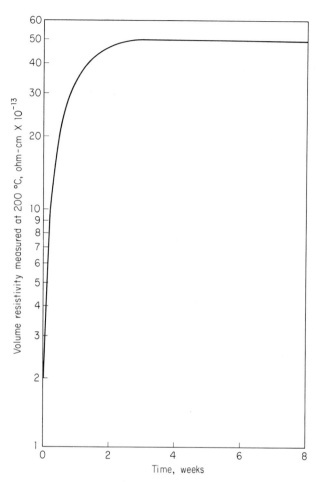

FIG 8.46 *Effect of thermal aging at* $300°C$ *on volume resistivity of 1-mil Kapton H* [10].

TABLE 8.32 Life Test of Insulation Systems [22]

Material	Relative life under corona attack°
Butyl rubber	0.3
Cast polycarbonate resin	0.7
Cast oil-modified phenolic resin	0.9
Epoxy varnish on woven glass	0.9
Mylar	1.0
Cast epoxy resin	1.0
Kapton H film	1.1
Polyethylene (Irrathene)	1.7
Oil-modified asphaltic varnish on woven glass	2.2
Teflon loaded with carbon black	4.6
Silicone rubber	500+
Mica	500+

° The relative listing is based on the life of Mylar, which is 20 hours.

TABLE 8.33 Dissipation Factor of SP-1 Polymer vs. Temperature and Frequency [49]

Temperature, °C	Frequency, cps	Dissipation factor (ASTM D-150)	Temperature, °C	Frequency, cps	Dissipation factor (ASTM D-150)
23	10^2	0.0015	215	10^3	0.0010
	10^3	0.0017		10^4	0.0010
	10^4	0.0035		10^5	0.0010
	10^5	0.0052	250	10^2	0.0197
50	10^2	0.0012		10^3	0.0089
	10^3	0.0014		10^4	0.0016
	10^4	0.0020		10^5	0.0010
	10^5	0.0052	255	10^2	0.0370
100	10^2	0.0011		10^3	0.0046
	10^3	0.0013		10^4	0.0012
	10^4	0.0013		10^5	0.0013
	10^5	0.0015	260	10^3	0.0173
150	10^2	0.0010		10^4	0.0024
	10^3	0.0011		10^5	0.0011
	10^4	0.0011	264	10^2	0.0815
	10^5	0.0015		10^3	0.0103
205	10^2	0.0012		10^4	0.0017
				10^5	0.0010

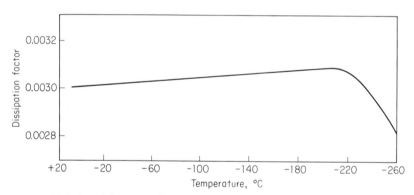

FIG 8.47 *Variation of dissipation factor with temperature for SP polymer at* 10^3 *cycles* [46].

cure. It is essential to use stainless steel equipment in view of the corrosive action of polyamic acids.

When making moldings, heat and pressure techniques are employed which are similar to those used in powdered metallurgy [16]. Presently, the technique is complicated and expensive, and molding powders are not available. Molded bars of the polyimide are supplied by Du Pont. These may be subsequently finished by machining. It has been reported that solid polymeric masses may be obtained during synthesis by removing solvents at about 140°C after ingredients are combined, and subsequently heating the prepolymer in stages, under diminished pressure, to a final temperature of 325°C [5].

Typical processing cycles for wet layup laminates with the low solids materials employ vacuum-bag application techniques, using an initial cure for 4 hours at 175°C followed by a 10-hour postcure at 315°C. The higher solids materials are applied under higher pressures and usually B-staged for about an hour at 120°C to obtain proper flow control before pressing. The laminate is then exposed for 1 to 2 minutes at 315°C and 10 to 25 psi, followed by 30 minutes at 250 psi. This is followed by a postcure, such as illustrated in Table 8.34.

B-staged prepreg filament windings from the low-solids-content resin are usually handled on a mandrel heated to about 65°C with a cure of 4 hours at 175°C followed by a 10-hour postcure at 315°C. A more detailed discussion of laminating techniques applicable to the polyimides is given in Chap. 7.

APPLICATIONS

Polyimide wire enamels, of the Pyre ML type, are offered as magnet wire coatings by several magnet wire suppliers. Combinations of the Pyre ML with other magnet wire coatings are also offered.

Polyimide varnishes, together with polyimide-impregnated cloths, are useful for high-temperature motors, making possible continuous operation, in conjunction with polyimide-coated magnet wire, to Class 220.

Kapton H film is also employed as motor insulation and has been suggested for use in capacitors, where it provides, like polystyrene, a negative coefficient of capacitance. The capacitance at 100 cps changes about -4 percent at 200°C as compared with a change of $+10$ percent at 160°C with Mylar.

The SP-type polymers are potentially useful in high-temperature bearing applications, as gasketing, and in structural applications. Their initial use was for the manufacture of diamond grinding wheels.

T A B L E 8.34   Typical Cure Cycle for Skygard 700 Laminate [31]

2 hours at 200°C
2 hours at 225°C
2 hours at 250°C
2 hours at 300°C
2 hours at 325°C
2 hours at 350°C
4 hours at 372°C

The high-temperature adhesives and laminates are of potential interest in the aerospace industry; and the electrical varnishes, magnet wire coatings, and molding compounds are already seeing service in that industry.

REFERENCES

1908

1. M. T. Bogert and R. R. Renshaw, 4-Amino-o-phthalic Acid and Some of Its Derivatives, *J. Am. Chem. Soc.* **30**:1135–1144.

1945

2. Linear Fiber-forming Polymers (to E. I. du Pont de Nemours & Co., Inc.), Brit. 570,858.

1955

3. W. M. Edwards and I. M. Robinson, Polyimides of Pyromellitic Acid, U.S. 2,710,853.
4. W. F. Gresham and M. A. Naylor, Polyimide Intermediates, U.S. 2,712,543.

1956

5. W. F. Gresham and M. A. Naylor, Novel Polyimides, U.S. 2,731,447.

1959

6. W. M. Edwards and I. M. Robinson, Diamine Salts of Pyromellitic Acid Diester, U.S. 2,880,230.
7. W. M. Edwards and I. M. Robinson, Polyimide Composition, U.S. 2,900,369.

1960

8. Polyimides and Methods of Making Same (to E. I. du Pont de Nemours & Co., Inc.), Australian 58424.

1962

9. S. Chow and J. M. Whelan, Jr., Method for Producing Polyimides from Diamines and Di-acid Di-ester Derivatives of Dianhydrides, U.S. 3,037,966.
10. J. I. Jones, F. W. Ochynski, and F. A. Ruckley, Pyromellitimides: a New Class of Thermally Stable Polymers, *Chem. Ind. (London)*, pp. 1686–1688.
11. F. E. Schweitzer et al., An Evaluation of Insulation Systems Based on Polymer ML, 4th Insulation Conference (AIEE & NEMA), Washington, D.C.

1963

12. R. J. Angelo, Electrically Conductive Polymeric Compositions, U.S. 3,073,785.
13. G. M. Bower and L. W. Frost, Aromatic Polyimides, *J. Polymer Sci.*, part A, vol. 1, pp. 3135–3150.
14. S. D. Bruck, Thermal Degradation of an Aromatic Polypyromellitimide in Air and Vacuum, AD 447 961.

15. W. M. Edwards and A. L. Endrey, Moldable Polyimides, Belg. 627,626.
16. A. L. Endrey, Electrically Conductive Polymeric Compositions, U.S. 3,073,784.
17. S. Nishizaki and A. Fukami, Differential Thermal Analysis of Linear Polyimides, *Kogyo Kagaku Zasshi* 66(3):382.
18. W. E. Tatum et al., H-Film: Du Pont's New Polyimide Film, 5th Electrical Insulation Conference (AIEE & NEMA), Chicago.
19. Westinghouse Monthly Letter Report no. 7, AD 608 002, February.
20. Westinghouse Monthly Letter Report no. 11, AD 608 000, August.

1964

21. M. J. Devine and A. E. Kroll, Aromatic Polyimide Compositions for Solid Lubrication, *J. Am. Soc. Lubrication Engrs.*, June, pp. 225–230.
22. J. C. Devins et al., Research of Dielectric Materials, AD 602 438.
23. S. D. Druck, The Effect of Impurities on the Thermal Degradation of Poly[N,N'-(p,p'-oxydiphenylene)] Pyromellitimide, ACS Symposium, Chicago, September.
24. E. I. du Pont de Nemours & Co., Inc., Sales Letter, Film Department, on H-Film.
25. Experimental PI-1200, Technical Data Sheet, E. I. du Pont de Nemours & Co., Inc., September 29.
26. L. W. Frost and I. Kesse, Spontaneous Degradation of Aromatic Polypyromellitamic Acids, *J. Appl. Polymer Sci.* 8:1039–1051.
27. J. R. Learn and M. P. Seegers, Teflon–Pyre ML Wire Insulation System, 13th Symposium on Technical Progress in Communications Wire and Cables, Atlantic City, N.J., December.
28. A. D. Mair, M. C. Shen, and A. V. Tobolsky, High Temperature Polymers: H-Film and SP-Polymer, AD 604 010.
29. PI-3001 FGR, Experimental Polyimide Prepreg Fiber Glass Roving for Filament Wound Constructions, du Pont Fabric and Finishes Department. Bulletin A-36183, February.
30. C. R. Ruffing and E. J. Traynor, A Technique for Bonding New, Thermally Stable Aromatic Polymers to Metal Surfaces, SAMPE Symposium, Los Angeles, May.
31. Skygard 700, High Heat Resistant Resin, Monosanto Plastics Division, Bulletin 5042, December.
32. S. W. Todd and F. A. Wolff, Moldable Polyimide, *Machine Design*, Apr. 23, pp. 230–232.
33. W. Wrasidlo, P. M. Hergenrother, and H. H. Levine, Kinetics and Mechanism of Poly(imides), I, ACS Meeting, Philadelphia, April.

1965

34. S. Cooper, D. Mair, and A. V. Tobolsky, Polyimides, AD 463,880.
35. R. A. Dine-Hart, The Preparation and Fabrication of Aromatic Polyimides, AD 482 530.
36. W. M. Edwards, Polyamide-Acids, Compositions Thereof and Process for Their Preparation, U.S. 3,179,614.
37. W. M. Edwards, Aromatic Polyimides and Process for Preparing Them, U.S. 3,179,634.
38. A. L. Endrey, Process for Preparing Polyimides by Treating Polyamide-Acids with Lower Fatty Monocarboxylic Acid Anhydrides, U.S. 3,179,630.
39. A. L. Endrey, Aromatic Polyimide Particles from Polycyclic Diamines, U.S. 3,179,631.
40. A. L. Endrey, Aromatic Polyimides from Meta-Phenylene Diamine and Para-Phenylene Diamine, U.S. 3,179,633.
41. J. H. Freeman et al., Resins and Reinforced Plastic Laminates for Continuous Use at 650°F, *SPE Trans.*, April.
42. J. F. Heacock and C. E. Berr, Polyimides—New High Temperature Polymers: H-Film, a Polypyromellitimide Film, *SPE Trans.*, April, pp. 105–110.
43. W. E. Hendrix, Process for Preparing Polyimides by Treating Polyamide-Acids with Aromatic Monocarboxylic Acid Anhydrides, U.S. 3,179,632.

44. M. W. Jawitz, Evaluation of Various Cure Tests for Polyimide Enamel Coated Magnet Wire, *Insulation*, August.
45. J. I. Jones, Annual Reports on the Progress of Applied Chemistry for 1964.
46. Lavin et al., Polyamides from Benzophenonetetracarboxylic Acids and a Primary Diamine, U.S. 3,190,856.
47. D. L. McClenahan, Gamma Radiation Effects on Magnet Wire, Proceedings of 6th Electrical Insulation Conference (IEEE and NEMA), September.
48. B. W. Melvin and D. J. Parish, Where and How Polyimide Film Is Used in Electrical Insulation, *Insulation*, September, pp. 120–123.
49. J. T. Milek, Polyimide Plastics Technology: a State-of-the-Art Report, Electronics Properties Information Center, Hughes Aircraft Co., Culver City, Calif.
50. S. Nishizaki, Synthesis and Pyrolysis of Polyimides Having Naphthalene Nuclei in the Main Chain, *Kogyo Kagaku Zasshi* **68:**1756.
51. D. J. Parish and B. W. Melvin, Kapton Polyimide Film in Rotating Machinery, Proceedings of 6th Electrical Insulation Conference (IEEE and NEMA), September.
52. Polyimide High Temperature Binder Solutions, E. I. du Pont de Nemours & Co., Inc., Bulletin 1/22.
53. Pyrolytic Polyimide Is Semiconductor, *C&E News*, July 26.
54. C. E. Sroog et al., Aromatic Polypyromellitimides from Aromatic Polyamic Acids, *J. Polymer Sci.*, part A, vol. 3, pp. 1373–1390.
55. C. E. Sroog, Polyimides, IUPAC Macromolecular Symposium, Prague, September.
56. M. L. Wallach, Aromatic Polyamic Acids: Fundamental Structural Studies, ACS Symposium, Detroit, April.
57. B. L. Weigand and J. E. Hanna, Evaluation of the Explosive Hazard of Gases Generated by Transformer Potting Materials When Subjected to Electrical Overloads, Proceedings of 6th Electrical Insulation Conference (IEEE and NEMA), September.

1966

58. R. S. Irwin and W. Sweeny, Polyimide Fibers, ACS Winter Meeting, Phoenix, Ariz. January.
59. I. Serlin, E. Lavin, and A. H. Markhart, Laminating Techniques with a Crosslinking Polyimide Resin, 23rd Annual Conference, Western Section, SPI, Palm Springs, Calif., April.

1967

60. M. L. Wallach, Structure-Property Relations of Polyimide Films, ACS Spring Meeting, Miami Beach, Fla., April.
61. J. R. Courtright, Resins for High Temperature Laminates—Polyimides, *Plastics Design Process.*, January, pp. 10–12.

9

Polybenzimidazoles

Polybenzimidazoles were first synthesized in the late 1950s, and the thermal stability of the polymeric aromatic-based compounds was established in 1960.

The polymeric materials are produced by reacting a diprimary aromatic amine with a diphenyl ester or other derivative of an aromatic dibasic acid. In this manner, a relatively low molecular-weight prepolymer is developed. The prepolymer may be employed as a hot melt, or may be dissolved in a suitable solvent. Final processing, during which high-molecular-weight, linear thermoplastic molecules are developed, occurs at elevated temperature under pressure.

The polybenzimidazoles are employed in high-temperature-resistant laminate and adhesive formulations. They provide flat properties to about 250°C or so and offer good stability after aging. At temperatures above 250°C, oxidative degradation interferes with long-time stability in air, strength properties gradually declining with time. However, for nearly 1,000 hours at 315°C, these laminates maintain strengths greater than 30 percent of initial ultimate strength.

Polybenzimidazoles generally require fairly long and complicated processing cycles, with high temperatures and inert atmospheres being required for the development of ultimate properties.

The difficult processing conditions are not outside the technology of the aerospace industry, where primary use is envisioned, but might pose economic disadvantages in civilian applications.

The thermal stability of the benzimidazoles, first synthesized in the late nineteenth century, has long been recognized. Essentially, the benzimidazole is formed by the reaction of a 1,2-aromatic diamine with a carboxyl group. The reaction may be written as follows:

| o-Phenylenediamine | Formic acid | Amide intermediate | Water |

| Amide intermediate | Benzimidazole | Water |

The first of the polybenzimidazoles (abbreviated PBI in the trade) were synthesized from aromatic bis-o-diamines and aliphatic dicarboxylic acids or their derivatives in the late 1950s by K. C. Brinker and I. M. Robinson and claimed in the patent literature by E. I. du Pont de Nemours in 1959 [1].

A year later, Dr. C. S. Marvel, then of the University of Illinois, announced at a symposium sponsored by the St. Louis Chapter of the American Chemical Society a new class of linear polymers from 3,3'-diaminobenzidine and diphenyl isophthalate. These polymers, with molecular weights from 55,000 to 90,000, gave melting points above 770°C, were stable in nitrogen to 600°C, and did not decompose completely even at 900°C [2].

The announcement generated considerable interest, and Dr. Marvel, having transferred to the University of Arizona, continued research on the polymers. Subsequently, a research and development contract was awarded by the Air Force to Narmco Research and Development Division of Whittaker Corporation, which developed specific fully aromatic systems for high-temperature aerospace adhesive and laminating applications. As research continued, an additional Air Force contract was awarded to the Celanese Corporation of America for the development of fibers and fibrous structures from the aromatic polybenzimidazoles.

A review of the PBI materials was issued in July, 1966, by Plastecs Technical Evaluation Center [32].

SYNTHESIS

Chemistry

The initial work with the aromatic polybenzimidazoles involved reaction of an aromatic tetraamine with a diphenyl ester of an aromatic dicarboxylic acid, in particular, the reaction of 3,3'-diaminobenzidine and the phenyl ester of isophthalic acid [3]:

Generalized Synthesis of Polybenzimidazole

$$H_2N-\text{(ring)}-\text{(ring)}-NH_2 + \phi O_2C-\text{(ring)}-CO_2\phi \longrightarrow$$

$$H_2N \qquad NH_2$$

3,3'-Diaminobenzidine   Diphenyl isophthalate

$$\left[HN-\text{(ring)}-\text{(ring)}-NH \atop N \qquad N \right]_n + \phi OH$$

Polybenzimidazole   Phenol

Subsequent work extended to the synthesis of a number of polymers from other acid derivatives, the parent acids being shown in Table 9.1 [5]. Oxalic and malonic acids gave cyclic amides. Succinic and glutaric gave high-molecular-weight products which were unstable above 450°C. Instability was experienced with the polymers from maleic and fumaric acid

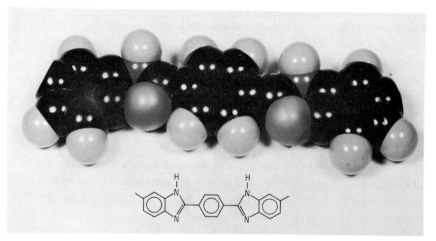

Atom model of polybenzimidazole from terephthalyl chloride and diaminobenzidine. (The Epoxylite Corporation.)

esters at 300°C. With the exception of 4,5-imidazole dicarboxylic acid esters, the remaining compounds shown in Table 9.1 provided relatively poor thermal stability or gave crosslinking with heating above 350°C as evidenced by insolubility. The polymer from 4,5-imidazoledicarboxylic acid esters provided thermal stability equivalent to that obtained with phthalic acid esters.

Attempts were made to improve the thermal stability of the polybenzimidazoles through the use of 1,3-dianilino-4,6-diaminobenzene, in which the resultant polymer contained aryl groups rather than hydrogens [8]:

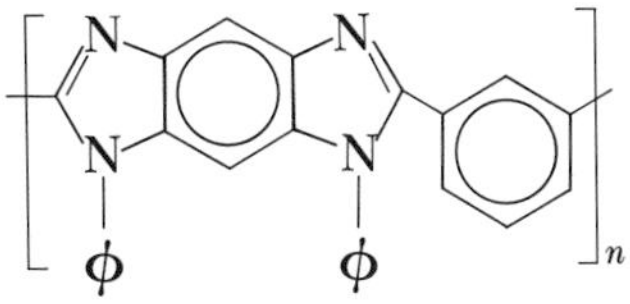

This system was somewhat less thermally stable than the unphenylated products, upon thermogravimetric analysis at a heating rate of 150°C per hour; however, isothermal aging in air at 315, 370, and 425°C showed the N-phenyl-substituted material to be significantly more stable [34].

From this and similar work, 3,3'-diaminobenzidine and isophthalic or blends of isophthalic and terephthalic acid derivatives were selected as most promising. In early work, it was found that the diphenyl esters provided optimum molecular-weight products. The acids themselves tended to decarboxylate; the acid chlorides reacted too rapidly; and the methyl esters resulted in methylation of amine groups.

The overall reaction of the amine with the acid ester is as indicated above; however, the actual reaction is considerably more complex, and it has been suggested that it progresses stepwise as follows [17]:

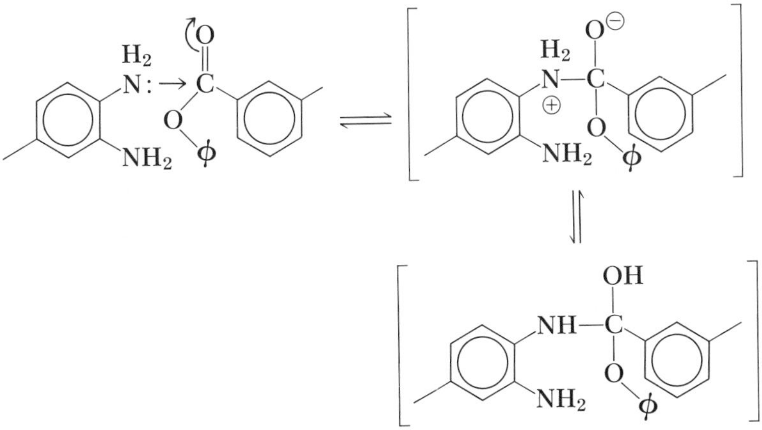

Step 1   Aldol-type Condensation

Schiff base, *anti*

Step 2   Aldol-type Dehydration

The Schiff base, which probably exists in equilibrium with the benzimidazoline structure,

TABLE 9.1   Acids Used in Early Studies of Synthesis of PBI

Isophthalic acid	
Terephthalic acid	
Oxalic acid	
Malonic acid	
Succinic acid	
Glutaric acid	
Maleic acid	
Fumaric acid	

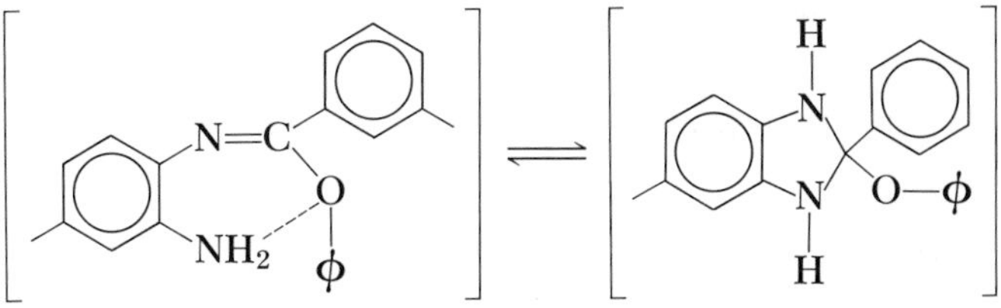

Schiff base, *syn*   Benzimidazoline

can exist in two isomeric forms, of which the *syn* form is capable of intra-molecular hydrogen bonding and hence is favored energetically. Formation of the *syn* isomer automatically causes the polymer to be linear because of intramolecular reaction in the final, irreversible step shown below:

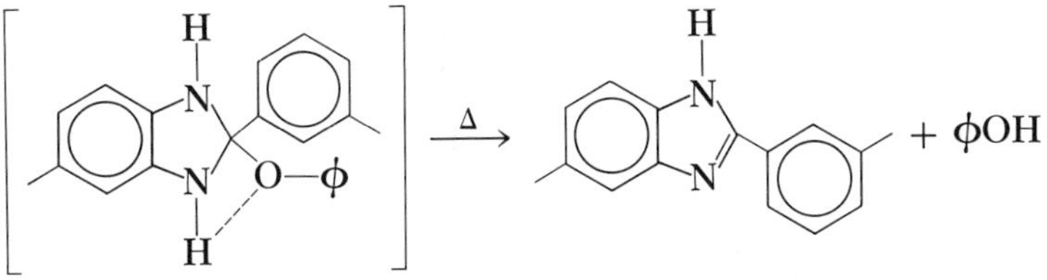

Step 3   Ring Closure

TABLE 9.1   (*continued*)

2,6-Naphthalenedicarboxylic acid	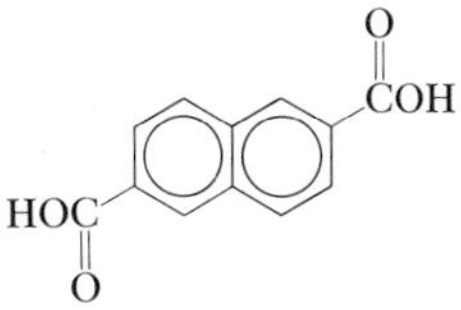
Perfluoroglutaric acid	$HOC(CF_2)_3COH$ (each C double-bonded to O)
Perfluorosuberic acid	$HOC(CF_2)_6COH$ (each C double-bonded to O)
1,1'-Ferrocenedicarboxylic acid	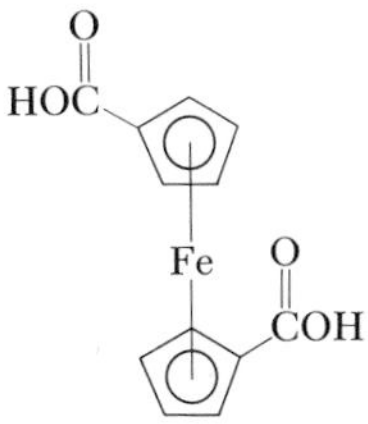
4,5-Imidazoledicarboxylic acid	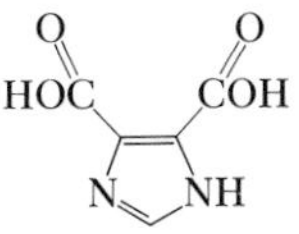

The proposed mechanism shown above has been criticized, based on model studies which indicate that phenol is evolved before complete dehydration [21]. Accordingly, the following mechanism was proposed:

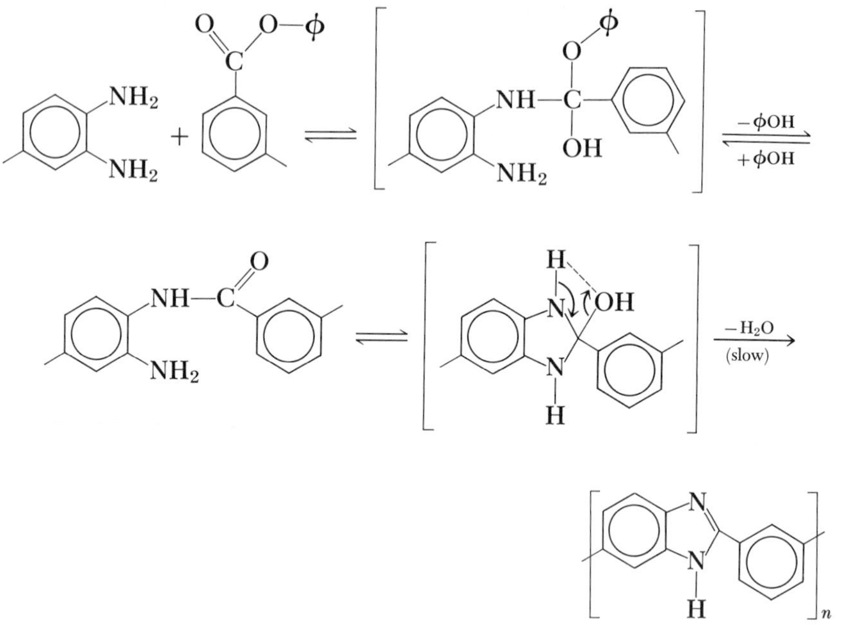

In melt polymerizations conducted at 260°C, it is suggested that the polymeric material at the prepolymer stage has, therefore, both benzimidazole and hydroxybenzimidazolene structures:

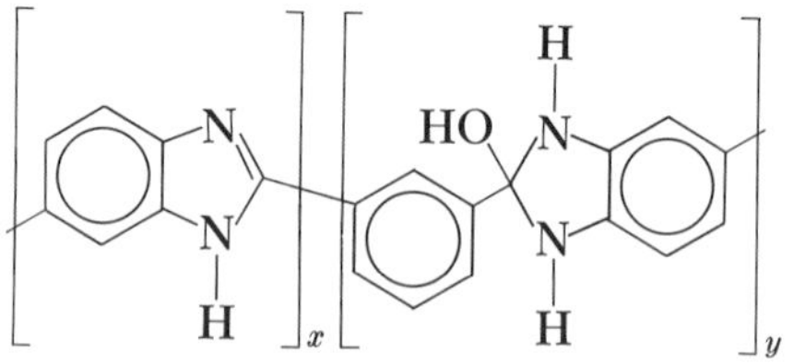

x/y ratio 0.25/1

Heating to 400°C then results in the final conversion.

Rather persuasive evidence for this latter mechanism is also developed by Conley [18].

In any event, if equal molar quantities of reactants are employed, the reaction will continue, with heating, to produce high-molecular-weight polymers soluble only in formic or sulfuric acids. These cannot conveniently be further processed. Accordingly, the reaction may be interrupted at some intermediate stage to produce soluble, lower-melting compounds which can be applied in the liquid phase. Alternatively, through use of an excess of amine, an amine-terminated prepolymer may be produced which is then combined with an acid-terminated prepolymer, with the remainder of the polymerization being subsequently conducted either from solution or as a hot melt.

During the final polymerization, there will be the evolution of considerable volume of volatiles, which must be removed from the polymerizing structure. As is indicated by the suggested reaction mechanisms, the steps prior to final ring closure involve equilibrium reactions. Thus, at high pressures, low molecular-weight polymers may be developed as a result of entrapped volatiles. Early work indicated that this occurs in practice, and that porous laminates provide better strength properties than do the more dense structures. The porosity is undesirable from the standpoint of humidity and water resistance as well as from the standpoint of oxidation resistance.

In order to minimize the release of volatiles during final processing, it is desirable to carry the prepolymer to the highest practical molecular weight. Other approaches may also be employed. Use of isophthalamide in place of the diphenyl ester, for example, gives ammonia as a volatile [27]. By a combination of techniques, systems with volatile contents as low as 4 percent have been developed [24], as compared to theoretical volatile content of 42 percent from the reaction of diphenyl isophthalate and 3,3'-diaminobenzidine.

In the synthesis of the polybenzimidazoles, the tetraamine 3,3'-diaminobenzidine is preferred, even though the material provides difficulties in production and purification. Preparation involves the intermediate diacetylbenzidine from benzidine; this is then converted to 3,3'-dinitrobenzidine and then to the desired tetraamine [5]. The amine is purified by water

Polybenzimidazole polymer before final cure. (Narmco Materials Division, Whittaker Corp.)

Processing equipment for synthesis of polybenzimidazole. (Narmco
Materials Division, Whittaker Corp.)

recrystallization in combination with activated charcoal. The process
requires large volumes of water and results in about 40 percent loss of the
amine. The pure product is a white solid melting at 178 to 180°C. During
synthesis, it is necessary to exclude oxygen to prevent formation of insoluble,
crosslinked products.

Because of the sensitivity of the tetraamine to oxidation, it may be
desirable to use the tetrahydrochloride of the amine. Polyphosphoric acid
has proved both a suitable catalyst and a solvent [7]. In these cases, it was
found that the diphenyl ester and the acid dichloride failed to yield the
polymer because of decomposition of the acid component in the polyphosphoric acid. On the other hand, the free acid, the dimethyl ester, the
diamide and dinitrile all gave satisfactory results, with the dimethyl ester
and the diamide proving superior [9].

Preparative Procedure

A typical synthesis procedure for polybenzimidazole from the literature
is as follows:

The phenyl ester was prepared by reacting phthaloyl chloride with phenol. The reaction was completed at 130°C. The melting point was 77 to 78°C after recrystallization from methanol. A mixture of 3.188 grams (0.01 mole) of diphenyl phthalate and 2.140 grams (0.01 mole) of 3,3'-diaminobenzidine was melted under nitrogen at 250°C and then heated at 270 to 280°C for ½ hour and 300°C for 1½ hour. Vacuum was then applied for ½ hour at 300°C. After powdering and reheating for 3½ hours at 0.1 mm Hg while the temperature was allowed to rise from 300 to 400°C, a polymer with an inherent viscosity of 1.60 (0.2 percent formic acid, 25°C) was obtained.

Anal. calcd. for $(C_{20}H_{12}N_4)_n$: C, 77.92%; H, 3.90%; N, 18.18%.

Found: C, 76.43%; H, 3.98%; N, 17.95% [5].

MODIFICATION AND FORMULATION

The basic polymer from isophthalic acid ester and 3,3'-diaminobenzidine, poly[2,2'-(m-phenylene)-5,5'-bibenzimidazole], may be modified by the selection of other precursors.

In place of the benzidine, 1,2,4,5-tetraaminobenzene may be used. Various acid precursors are also possible, these, along with the amines, influencing solubility as shown in Table 9.2. Likewise, blends of acid esters

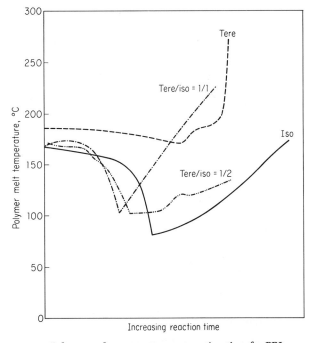

FIG 9.1 *Polymer melt temperature vs. reaction time for PBI systems based on iso- and terephthalate diphenyl esters* [9].

TABLE 9.2 Influence of Reactants on Crystallinity and Solubility [3]

| Reactants | | Crystallinity | Solubility, % | | |
Tetraamine	Diphenyl ester		HCO_2H	DMSO	DMF
3,3′-DAB	(para-phenylene structure)	+	2–3	0.5–1	Insoluble
3,3′-DAB	(methyl-phenylene structure)	0	5–6	Soluble	Part insoluble
3,3′-DAB	(biphenylene structure)	+	Part soluble	Insoluble	Insoluble
3,3′-DAB	(dimethyl diphenyl structure)	0	Soluble	Soluble	Soluble
3,3′-DAB	(pyridine structure)	+	10–15	Soluble	Part soluble
3,3′-DAB	(furan structure)	+	3–4	Soluble	Soluble
1,2,4,5-TAB	(para-phenylene structure)	+	2–3	Insoluble	Insoluble
1,2,4,5-TAB	(meta-phenylene structure)	+	5–6	Insoluble	Insoluble
1,2,4,5-TAB	$-(CH_2)_4-$	+	Soluble	Part soluble	Insoluble

Soluble = >20% concentration.
+ Crystallinity detected.
0 Crystallinity undetected.

have been suggested, these influencing rigidity and crystallinity, as evidenced in Fig. 9.1 by a rapid increase in melt temperature vs. reaction time for the more rigid and crystalline terephthalic ester system as compared with the isophthalic ester system. Infrared spectra of the two systems are given in Figs. 9.2 and 9.3.

By selection of suitable blends of precursor acid esters, systems with optimized properties may be developed. Softening-point and thermal stability data for a variety of PBI systems are shown in Table 9.3. Mixed polymers containing PBI have been prepared such as polyamide-PBI materials [8] and polyester-PBI [10].

Fundamentally, the problem involved is trading off solubility and processing convenience for improved elevated-temperature performance.

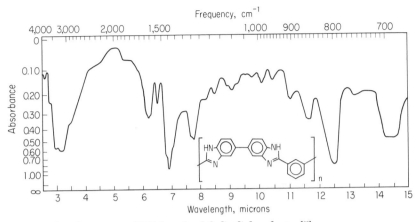

FIG 9.2   *Infrared spectrum of PBI from isophthalic diphenyl ester* [5].

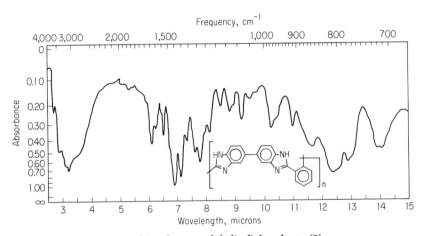

FIG 9.3   *Infrared spectrum of PBI from terephthalic diphenyl ester* [5].

Sophisticated compromises are often required. For example, aromatic polybenzimidazoles have been prepared from 3,3′-4,4′-tetraaminodiphenyl ether and diphenyl isophthalate, from 3,3′-diaminobenzidine and diphenyl oxybibenzoate, and from a combination of the two amines and the latter phenyl ester [19]. The materials containing aromatic ether links from both the amine and the acid proved to be 100 percent soluble in dimethylacetamide, dimethyl sulfoxide, formic acid, and sulfuric acid [19]. Increasing the amount of aromatic ether links, to provide improved solubility, has the effect of reducing the thermal stability of the systems. Improved solubility has also been reported with the polymer from 3,3′-diaminobenzidine and bis(p-carboxylphenyl)methylphosphine oxide [22], and with the polymer from 3,3′-4,4′-tetraaminodiphenylmethane and 4,4′-carbphenoxyphenyl ether [20].

TABLE 9.3 Softening Point and Thermal Stability [11]

Structure		Softening point, °C	Weight loss in nitrogen			
Parent tetramine	Parent diacid		400°	500°	550°	600°
Tetraminobenzene	Terephthalic acid	....	2.8	1.0	1.9	4.0
	Isophthalic acid	....	0.7	0.3	1.4	1.4
3,3'-Diaminobenzidine	Terephthalic acid	....	1.0	0.	1.7	1.0
	Isophthalic acid	....	0.6	0.4	1.3	2.2
	2,5-Pyridinedicarboxylic acid	....	0.2	0.5	1.4	2.7
	2,5-Furanedicarboxylic acid	480 d.	1.4	2.6	2.8	2.0
	2,7-Naphthalenedicarboxylic acid	....	0.4	0.8	1.2	3.7
	4,4'-Biphenyldicarboxylic acid	....	0.3	0.8	0.3	2.1
Bis-3,4-diamino-phenylmethane	Isophthalic acid	380–90	....	5.16	15.45	31.30
	Terephthalic acid	400–10	....	3.44	7.95	15.35
3,3'-Diaminobenzidine	Bis-4-carboxyphenyl ether	460–70	....	5.44	7.41	10.20
Bis-3,4-diamino-phenylmethane	Bis-4-carboxyphenyl ether	350–70	....	3.40	7.24	16.20
Bis-3,4-diamino-phenyl ether..........	Bis-4-carboxyphenylmethyl-phosphine oxide	380–400	....	27.50	39.80	47.85
Bis-3,4-diaminophenylmethane	1,4-phenylenediboric acid	500	....	2.64	7.16	12.80
3,3'-Diaminobenzidine	2,6-Naphthalenedicarboxylic acid	....	....	5.0	10	15
	2,3-Naphthalenedicarboxylic acid	....	....	25	20	35 (700°)
3,3'-Diaminobenzidine	2,7-Naphthalenedicarboxylic acid	....	....	25	30	40 (700°)
	4,5-Imidazoledicarboxylic acid	....	5	5	7–10	
	Ferrocenedicarboxylic acid	....	....	25	25	30
	Maleic acid	....	....	20	....	25
	3,3'-Biphenyldicarboxylic acid					
	2,2'-Biphenyldicarboxylic acid	....	....	20	....	25
3,3'-Diaminobenzidine	Perfluorosuberic acid	....	....	30	....	35
	Perfluoroglutaric acid	....	....	40	....	50

A PBI-type polymer where the carbon at position 2 of the benzimidazole ring has been replaced with a boron atom has been prepared [20]. This polymer is reported to have increased solubility over PBI and to be quite thermally stable.

Some inclusive work has been accomplished on the use of more highly functional reactants (e.g., trimesate) to accomplish crosslinking [12]. Although the desired linear species forms first, synthesis difficulties have been encountered with this approach.

Solvents

Because the commercial polybenzimidazoles are primarily used in laminating and adhesive formulations, it is convenient to apply them from solutions, although hot-melt application is also practical to obtain high solids contents.

The prepolymers possess only limited solubility in relatively strong solvents, and therefore are not obtainable in high solids solutions. Typical solvents include *N*-methylpyrrolidone, dimethyl acetamide, and dimethyl formamide.

Adhesive Formulation

Some measure of greater sophistication can be employed in the development of polybenzimidazole adhesives.

Polymers, for example, from diphenyl isophthalate exhibit thermoplastic behavior at temperatures of about 370°C, but the problem can be overcome by the use of a blend of diphenyl isophthalate and terephthalate in the synthesis [23].

The polymers are sensitive to oxidation on high-temperature aging. This is particularly pronounced with adhesive systems in contact with ferrous metals (Table 9.4). Accordingly, antioxidants may be added. Arsenic-based compounds are preferred (e.g., arsenic thioarsenate). The effect of the additive on a formulated adhesive system is indicated in Table 9.5.

In addition to antioxidants, the adhesive systems contain selected fillers (powdered aluminum is commonly used) to provide lower shrinkage and to reduce the coefficient of thermal expansion of the polymer. The formulated adhesive is then applied to a glass cloth or other carrier, the selection of which is critical in terms of finish and pattern.

TABLE 9.4 Tensile Shear Strength of Polybenzimidazole Adhesives.
Effect of Substrate on Heat Aging at 370°C Tested at Room Temperature [4]

112–112 Carrier   2024–T3 Aluminum
                                                           17–7 PH Stainless Steel

Cure: 1 hour at 343°C and 200 psi
Postcure: 23 to 400°C in 2 hours + 6 hours at 400°C and 1 micron pressure

100 parts MD-105 Aluminum Powder/100 parts Resin

Time at 370°C, hours	Aluminum failure			Steel failure		
	psi°	% cohesive	% adhesive	psi°	% cohesive	% adhesive
Control	1,450†	95	5	3,360	95	5
1	1,390	90	10	1,920	40	60
3	1,387	90	10	1,696	45	55
5	1,444	85	15	828	35	65
7	1,160	80	20	374	10	90
10	1,198	80	20	Failed in oven		

° Data are averages of triplicate specimen.
† The low value at room temperature on aluminum appears to have been due to weakening of the metal as a result of the curing and postcuring conditions.

TABLE 9.5   Influence of AsAsS$_4$ on Tensile Shear Strength of PBI Adhesives [4]

112–112 E Glass Carrier	17–7 PH Stainless Steel
	100 phr MD-105 Aluminum
	20 phr AsAsS$_4$

Cure: 1 hour at 315°C and 200 psi
Postcure: 23 to 400°C in 2 hours + 6 hours at 400°C and 5 microns pressure

Temperature, °C	Time, hours	psi,° arsenic added	psi,° no arsenic
23	. . . .	3,310°	
288	1	3,185	2,570
288	50	2,685	1,205
288	100	1,910	310
288	200	1,200	0
370	1	2,875	3,675
370	5	2,245	2,555
370	10	2,000	401

° Data are averages of duplicate tests.

PHYSICAL PROPERTIES

Except for preliminary properties of polybenzimidazole fibers [6, 28, 30] and equally preliminary properties on nonoptimized moldings produced under a pressure of 9,000 psi and at a temperature of 370°C, the reported values for the polybenzimidazoles have been in terms of adhesive and composite data.

Properties of Composites

Room-temperature strength properties of 125-mil laminates, prepared by a hot-melt technique and having resin contents of about 40 percent, are as follows: ultimate flexural strengths 90,000 to 115,000 psi; ultimate compressive strengths 55,000 to 65,000 psi; ultimate tensile strengths 75,000 to 85,000 psi. Moduli for all three properties range from 4.5 to 5.5 million psi. Interlaminar shear values are about 5,000 psi. Under 60 percent of ultimate load, elongations from 0.02 to 0.03 in. per in. with no failure after 1,000 hours of loading have been obtained on creep tests at room temperature.

It is helpful, at this point, to indicate the problems involved in the generation of optimum laminating data. This serves to suggest, to some extent, the importance of the "extraneous" considerations over and beyond the properties of the polymer per se, which confront the research worker in developing applications for new polymers. These problem areas may equal or exceed those of polymer development.

In the laminating technology, for example, the following variables will affect the cured properties:

1. Type and pattern of reinforcement
2. Type of reinforcement surface finish and aging history
3. Number of plies of reinforcement
4. Specimen thickness and resin content
5. Presence or absence of voids and other defects in the matrix material
6. Processing and cure cycle
7. Postcure conditions
8. Test variables

A brief discussion of each will serve to indicate the nature of the problems inherent in the development of workable new polymeric systems.

TYPE AND PATTERN OF REINFORCEMENT

The reinforcement for polybenzimidazole laminates may be glass, graphite, carbon, or organic fibers. Each may present a different problem with regard to wettability and adhesion and may, therefore, require considerable developmental work to obtain optimized systems.

Further, the pattern of cloth or the pattern of filament winding may influence rather sharply the interlaminar shear strength and the tensile and flexural strength properties. Some patterns, additionally, may produce planes of structural weakness in the laminate during volatile removal.

TYPE OF REINFORCEMENT SURFACE FINISH AND AGING HISTORY

The surface finishes available to the technology are optimized to the requirements of the commercial matrix systems. Thus, broadly, finishes are available for polyester, phenolic, and epoxy resin systems. It is not likely that such finishes will prove optimum for a given new polymer, nor is it likely that finishes optimized for temperatures below 260°C will be inherently suited for temperatures above 260°C.

Further, there is considerable evidence that the storage or aging history of some of the surface finishes will influence cured properties of the composite rather markedly, particularly with regard to humidity resistance.

This area is further complicated by the fact that the actual function of the surface treatments is poorly understood and a subject of some controversy within the field. A completely satisfactory theoretical base does not exist for the selection of suitable materials, thus leading to a time-consuming empirical approach to the problem.

NUMBER OF PLIES OF REINFORCEMENT

In general, initial experimental data with new polymers are generated from small-size samples and from laminates with only a very few plies of reinforcement. Satisfactory scale-up factors must then be considered. Extensive test data, therefore, are required before the development of a sufficiently sophisticated technology to provide readily interpretable design values for the engineer.

SPECIMEN THICKNESS AND RESIN CONTENT

As indicated in the previous paragraph, actual values reported for laminates will vary depending on the thickness of the sample and its configuration. Additionally, the amount of reinforcement in relationship to the amount of matrix material will profoundly influence results. With glass fiber reinforcement, for example, it is probable that the type of glass and glass content more nearly governs the flexural and tensile strengths, whereas the matrix materials influence the compressive and shear strengths.

PRESENCE OR ABSENCE OF VOIDS IN THE MATRIX MATERIAL

Closely related to the resin content is the presence or absence of voids and other defects in the composite structure. Ideally, the composite should be dense and void-free. In practice, this seldom if ever occurs. Voids in the composite structure represent areas of inherent weakness, capable of initiating stress buildups leading to premature failure.

Suitably located voids can interfere with stress-transfer mechanisms to the reinforcing fibers, thereby severely reducing flexural and tensile strengths.

Additionally, voids and passageways in the laminate permit the entrance of atmospheric contaminants. This is particularly undesirable when systems are designed for elevated-temperature service. The easy entrance of oxygen will accelerate the degradation. Moisture may enter the laminate to act as a lubricant and sharply reduce the room-temperature strength values. The adverse effect of moisture can be partly offset by choice of glass surface finish as shown in Table 9.6.

With the polybenzimidazole polymers, the problem of porosity is compounded, as indicated in the discussion on the synthesis of the materials, by the need to remove volatiles to achieve highest possible molecular weights in the cured system. The process of removing volatiles, however, may often lead to the presence of voids and passageways.

Some work has been expended in sealing polybenzimidazole laminates, since the porous, higher-molecular-weight matrices provide superior performance to the more dense matrices. Such sealing operations, while

TABLE 9.6 Effect of Surface Finish of Glass on Wet-strength Retention of PBI Laminates [4]

Volan A		A-1100		Heat-cleaned	
Flexural strength, psi	Modulus, psi $\times$ 10^{-6}	Flexural strength, psi	Modulus, psi $\times$ 10^{-6}	Flexural strength, psi	Modulus, psi $\times$ 10^{-6}
No Water Boil					
88,640	2.99	90,840	2.96	85,560	2.67
88,760	3.00	80,030	2.94	77,140	2.26
89,260	3.16	92,070	3.11	78,850	2.53
Average 88,880	3.05	87,640	3.00	80,150	2.47
2-hour Water Boil					
67,400	2.66	68,100	2.50	35,020	1.44
66,200	2.62	72,140	2.52	28,060	1.54
76,530	3.00	67,010	2.57	35,910	1.62
Average 70,040	2.76	69,080	2.53	32,990	1.53

Resin contents: Volan A   25.2%.
            A-1100   25.5%.
            Heat-cleaned 33.6%.

improving resistance to oxidation and moisture, are not entirely satisfactory since they do not correct the fundamental weakness of the system.

PROCESSING AND CURE CYCLE

The processing and cure cycle will determine the density and the resin content of the laminates. Additionally, when polymers are being conducted more or less gently through various steps to prevent premature degradation, the processing cycle will be critical in terms of the chemical composition of the cured polymer.

POSTCURE CONDITIONS

The time and temperature of postcure is likely to be critical in terms of ultimate properties. With the polybenzimidazoles, some improvement may result when the laminate is exposed to air during the final postcure to promote some amount of crosslinking, although to prevent degradation the majority of the postcure should be conducted in an inert atmosphere.

TEST VARIABLES

There are a number of variables in test procedures which will result in different values from one laboratory to another. Additionally, with some tests, difficulties are experienced with the surface conditioning of samples and with the proper gripping of the specimens in the test devices. These variables can lead to a scatter of data not inherent in the polymeric system.

Properties of Adhesives

Best strength properties are obtained with polybenzimidazole adhesives when they are employed in connection with a primer and are supplied as supported adhesives, carried on glass cloth.

Optimized adhesive formulations provide lap shear strengths, at room temperature, on stainless steel of about 3,000 psi when the primer is the parent polymer in solution. Using a polyimide primer (see Chap. 8), about a 35 percent improvement in initial strengths may be obtained.

Peel resistance is quite good, values by the climbing-drum procedure being 15 to 30 in.-lb per 3 in.-width, this being obtained with tape weighing 0.2 psf. With the same weight tape, flatwise tensile testing of honeycomb bonds gives failure at 450 to 500 psi, with failure occurring core to skin.

As with laminates, the testing of adhesives introduces a number of extraneous variables. For example, the honeycomb sandwich tests will give values which vary with the thickness or weight of the adhesive. This is so because the joint is primarily stressed in tension and shear through the adhesive fillet. Low values, also, may be more dependent on density in testing honeycomb than with lap shear testing, and the filleting action of the adhesive will be of considerable significance.

THERMAL PROPERTIES

The polybenzimidazoles are of chief interest because of their potential suitability in higher-temperature applications.

A typical thermogram for poly[2,2'-(m-phenylene)-5,5'-bibenzimidazole] is presented in Fig. 9.4. In the same figure, performance of a phenolic resin is given for comparison.

In a series of studies designed to investigate the degradation mechanism, it was determined that the aromatic polybenzimidazoles do not liberate volatiles other than water at temperatures below 550°C. Above that temperature, the heterocyclic ring is subjected to degradation, leaving a char based on the aromatic portions of the molecule. On the basis of experimental evidence, the mechanism for thermal degradation indicated in Table 9.7 was advanced on a tentative basis [26].

While early work has shown that polybenzimidazoles prepared from aliphatic diacids are not useful for high-temperature uses, recent work has shown that these polymers have very desirable physical properties at cryogenic and room temperatures [35].

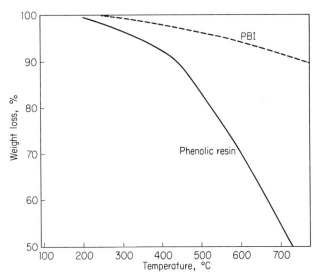

FIG 9.4   *Typical thermogram for PBI and phenolic resin* [24].

Composites

With the laminates, strength properties are preserved to quite high temperatures on short-time aging.   This is illustrated in Figs. 9.5 to 9.7. Compressive strengths drop more rapidly than either tensile or flexural strengths, as might be expected from the dependence of compressive

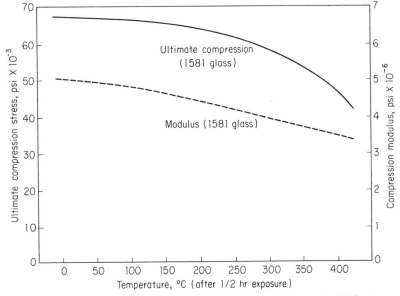

FIG 9.5   *Ultimate compressive strength and modulus vs. temperature for PBI laminate* [14].   *Laminate: 0.125 in. thick tested parallel to warp.*

TABLE 9.7 Postulated Mechanisms for Thermal Degradation of
Poly-2,2'-(m-phenylene)-5,5'-bibenzimidazole [26]

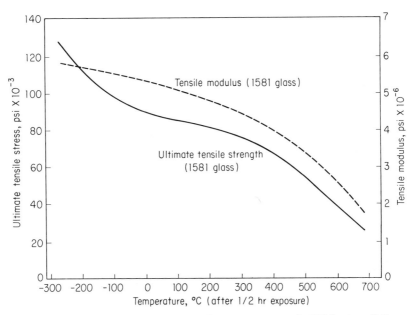

FIG 9.6 *Ultimate tensile strength and modulus vs. temperature for PBI laminate* [14]. *Laminate: 0.125 in. thick tested parallel to warp.*

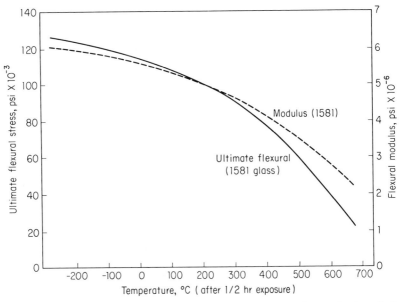

FIG 9.7 *Ultimate flexural strength and modulus vs. temperature for PBI laminate* [14]. *Laminate: 0.125 in. thick tested parallel to warp.*

TABLE 9.8   Weight Loss of Heat-aged Polybenzimidazole/1581-994S Glass Laminates [29]

Aging conditions	Original weight, grams°	Weight loss, %	Resin weight loss, %†
200 hours at 260°C	7.410	1.01	5.35
110 hours at 315°C	7.409	1.71	9.04
25 hours at 370°C	7.265	2.66	14.1
50 hours at 370°C	7.265	9.10	48.2

° Average of five specimens.

† Based on 18.9% resin content of non-heat-aged specimen.

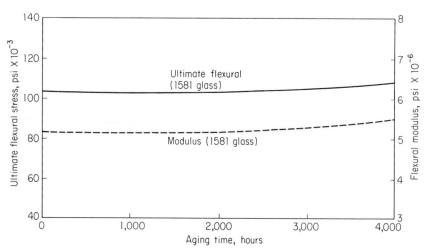

FIG 9.8   *Performance of PBI laminate vs. aging time at* 175°C [24]. *Specimen: 0.125 in. thick tested parallel to warp.*

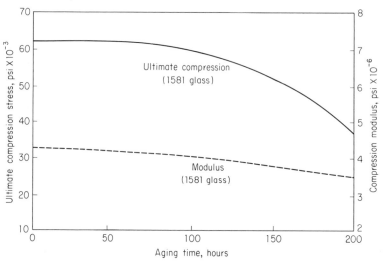

FIG 9.9   *Ultimate compressive strength and modulus of PBI laminate vs. time at* 260°C [14]. *Laminate: 0.125 in. thick tested parallel to warp.*

288

strengths on the basic property of the polymer.   With longer-time aging, some thermal instability is encountered at temperatures of 260°C and above (Table 9.8).   This is attributed to oxidative degradation.   At 175°C, strength properties are virtually flat with time (Fig. 9.8).   Typical values for 260°C aging are given in Figs. 9.9 to 9.11.   Compressive strengths

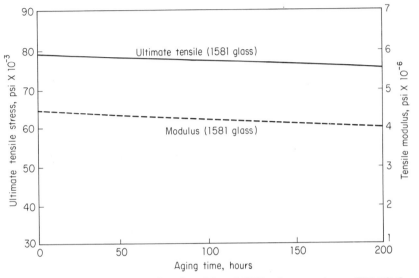

FIG 9.10   *Ultimate tensile strength and modulus of PBI laminate vs. time at* 260°C [14]. *Laminate:* 0.125 *in. thick tested parallel to warp.*

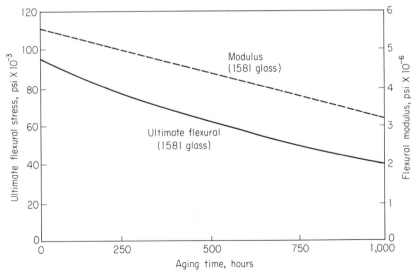

FIG 9.11   *Ultimate flexural strength and modulus of PBI laminate vs. time at* 260°C [14]. *Laminate:* 0.125 *in. thick tested parallel to warp.*

break rather sharply after the first 100 hours of aging. Tensile strengths are relatively flat. Flexural strengths decline slowly. At 315°C, the degradation is accelerated, as indicated by Figs. 9.12 to 9.14.

Creep resistance at 315°C is adequate, since failure under 30 percent load at that temperature appears to be caused by oxidative degradation prior

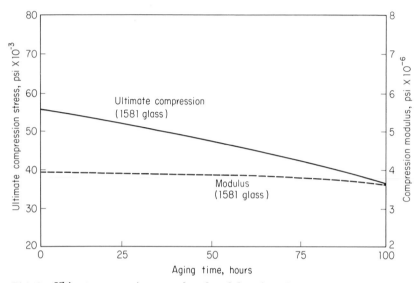

FIG 9.12 *Ultimate compressive strength and modulus of PBI laminate vs. time at* 315°C [14]. *Laminate:* 0.125 *in. thick tested parallel to warp.*

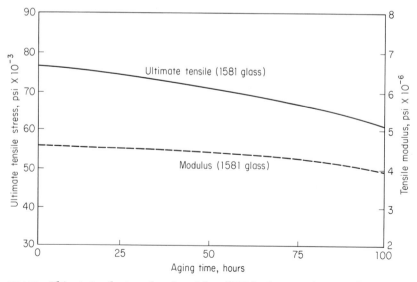

FIG 9.13 *Ultimate tensile strength and modulus of PBI laminate vs. time at* 315°C [14]. *Laminate:* 0.125 *in. thick tested parallel to warp.*

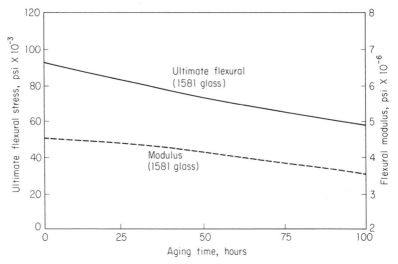

FIG 9.14 *Ultimate flexural strength and modulus of PBI laminate vs. time at* 315°C
[14]. *Laminate: 0.125 in. thick tested parallel to warp.*

to failure in creep. Edgewise compressive strengths, with temperature,
are flat, as shown in Fig. 9.15 for short-time exposures. Interlaminar shear
data are given in Table 9.9, and thermal expansion data in Table 9.10.

As might be expected, performance of laminates at cryogenic temperatures is somewhat better than at room temperature. Typically, at − 196°C,
ultimate flexural strength is 181,118 psi with a modulus of 7 million;
at −253°C, values are 176,361 and 6.59 million psi. This is in comparison

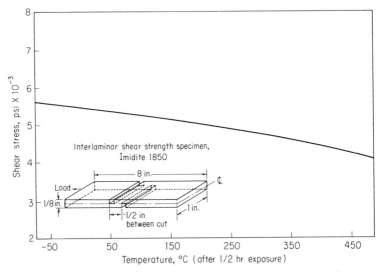

FIG 9.15 *Interlaminar shear strength of PBI laminate vs. temperature* [14].

TABLE 9.9   Interlaminar Shear Properties of Polybenzimid-
azole/1581-994S glass laminates [29]

Test temperature, °C	Ultimate strength, psi
−55	6,810
25	6,275
120	6,290
205	5,460
260	5,975
315	5,470
370	5,300
425	4,645

At temperature after 30 minutes exposure.

TABLE 9.10   Coefficient of Thermal Expansion of
Polybenzimidazole/1581-994S Glass Laminates [29]

Range, °C	Coefficient, $in./(in.)(°C) \times 10^6$
−73 to 93, heating	1.32
93 to −73, cooling	1.36
93 to 425, heating	1.74
440 to 315, cooling	1.97
315 to 205, cooling	1.64
205 to 93, cooling	1.44

with the control laminate giving values of 137,290 and 5.36 million psi at 23°C.

Adhesives

The strength retention of polybenzimidazole adhesives for short times at high temperatures is quite good. The percent loss in properties with temperature is, in fact, about in the range experienced with stainless steel, as shown in Fig. 9.16. Shear strength values, with temperature, are indicated in Fig. 9.17. At 175°C, values improve with aging (Fig. 9.18)—at 4,000 hours, the values are 3,370 psi as against 2,685 originally [23]. At 205°C, values are relatively constant—after 4,000 hours, 2,900 psi vs. 2,570 originally. At 260°C, strength loss sets in after about 250 hours (Fig. 9.19). At 370°C, the values begin to decline after about 6 hours, as shown in Fig. 9.20. Creep properties are quite good with temperature, as indicated in Table 9.11. Fatigue strengths at room and elevated temperatures are indicated in Figs. 9.21 to 9.23; peel strengths in Figs. 9.24 and 9.25. At cryogenic temperatures, lap shear strengths are improved over those at room temperature, as shown in Table 9.12, as are fatigue strengths (Fig. 9.26).

The influence of substrate type on strength vs. temperature is indicated in Fig. 9.27. The polybenzimidazole adhesives are compared with other high-temperature adhesives systems in Fig. 9.28.

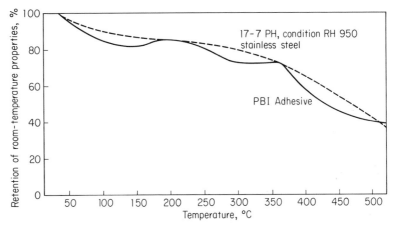

FIG 9.16 *Percent retention of room temperature properties of 17-7 PH, condition RH 950 stainless steel and PBI adhesive as a function of temperature* [23].

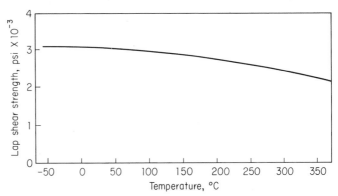

FIG 9.17 *Lap shear strength of PBI adhesive on stainless steel adherends vs. temperature* [14].

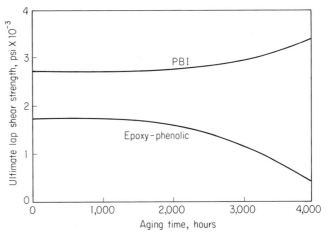

FIG 9.18 *Performance of PBI and epoxy-phenolic adhesive vs. aging time at 175°C* [16].

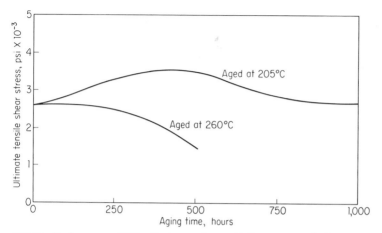

FIG 9.19   *Performance of PBI adhesive vs. time at high temperature* [14].
Substrate: corrosion-resistant steel, 15-7 *Mo.   Specimen:* 0.050 × 1.0 × 7.0 *in.*
with an ½-in. overlap.

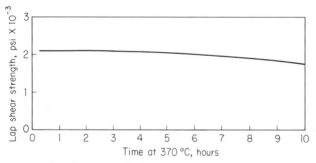

FIG 9.20   *Lap shear strength of PBI adhesive on stainless steel*
adherends vs. time at 370° *C* [14].

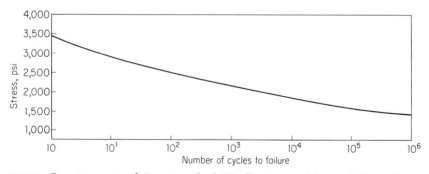

FIG 9.21   *Room-temperature fatigue strength of PBI adhesive on stainless steel adherends*
[25].   *Loading rate:* 1,500 *cpm; ultimate static shear strength:* 3,443 *psi.*

TABLE 9.11   Creep Rupture Test Results of PBI Adhesive on Stainless Steel Adherends after 192 Hours at 1,600 and 800 Psi [25]

Time to failure	Test temperature, °C	Initial° deflection, inches	Total† deflection, inches	Type of failure % adhesive	% cohesive
No failure	77 (1,600 psi)	None	None		
No failure	150 (800 psi)	None	None		
No failure	260 (800 psi)	None	None		
12–15 hours	370 (800 psi)	None	None	Resin burned out	
0 minutes 8 minutes 31 minutes 33 minutes 12 minutes	480 (800 psi)	None	None	.... Resin burned out	100 ↓

° Read optically immediately after applying load to specimen.
† Read optically at 192 hours after applying load to specimen.

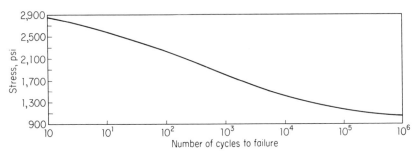

FIG 9.22   *Fatigue strength of PBI adhesive on stainless steel adherends at 260° C [25]. Loading rate: 1,500 cpm; ultimate static shear strength: 2,830 psi.*

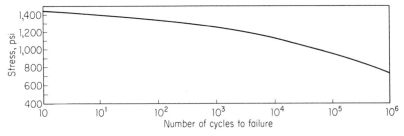

FIG 9.23   *Fatigue strength of PBI adhesive on stainless steel adherends at 370° C [25]. Loading rate: 1,500 cpm; ultimate static shear strength: 1,440 psi.*

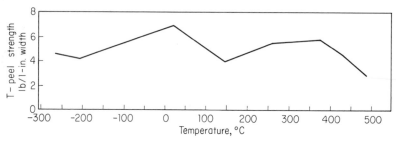

FIG 9.24 *T-peel strength of PBI adhesive on stainless steel vs. temperature after* 10-*minute soak* [25].

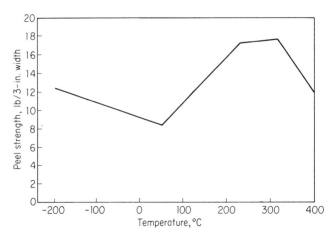

FIG 9.25 *Climbing-drum peel strength of PBI adhesive on stainless steel vs. temperature after* 10-*minute soak* [25].

TABLE 9.12 Tensile Shear Strength of PBI Adhesive on Stainless Steel Adherends at Cryogenic Temperatures [23]

Test temperature, °C	Tensile shear strength, psi
−196	4,900
	4,980
	4,500
	5,140
	Average 4,820
−253	5,640°
	5,740
	Average 5,690

° Metal failure in pin grip hole, despite spot-welded doubler.

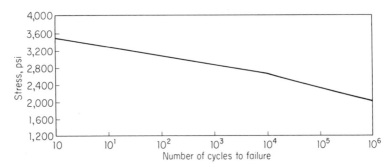

FIG 9.26 *Fatigue strength of PBI adhesive on stainless steel adherends at −196°C* [25]. *Loading rate: 1,500 cpm; ultimate static shear strength: 3,484 psi.*

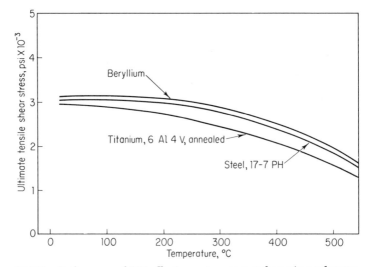

FIG 9.27 *Performance of PBI adhesive vs. temperature for various substrates* [14].

PHYSICAL-CHEMICAL PROPERTIES

The overall chemical resistance of the polybenzimidazoles has not been established, the testing being done on laminates and adhesives, where variables other than polymeric structure are of significance.

Humidity resistance of the laminates is lower than would be normally expected, with water pickup being relatively high. These conditions, how-ever, are a function of the porosity of the laminate rather than inherent properties of the matrix. Porosity permits entrance of water which, in addition to attacking the reinforcement and resin-reinforcement adhesion at the interface, acts as a lubricant to prevent mechanical stress transfer to the reinforcing fibers upon initial bond failure.

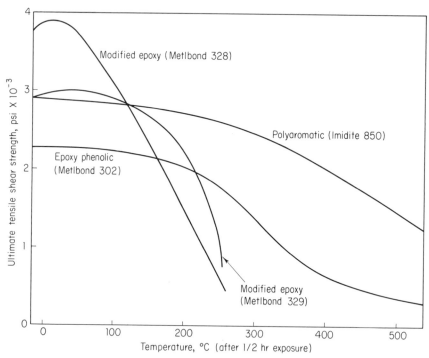

FIG 9.28 *Comparison of elevated-temperature performance of high-temperature adhesives* [13].

TABLE 9.13 Tensile Shear Strength at Room Temperature of PBI
Adhesive on Various Adherends as a Function of Environmental Exposure [25]

	Stainless steel PH 15–7		Beryllium 2219-T81		Titanium, 6Al, 4V	
Environment and exposure time	psi	Standard deviation	psi	Standard deviation	psi	Standard deviation
Salt spray, 30-day duration.........	2,978	94.6	1,700	170.3	1,913	141.0
95–100% humidity, 30-day duration	2,518	141.9	1,575	81.7	992	91.2
Distilled water, 30-day duration.....	2,510	172.0	1,332	348.3	1,774	225.8
JP-4 fuel, 7-day duration...........	3,178	94.6	1,824	189.2	2,200	142
Control at room temperature.......	3,240	236.5	2,034	94.6	2,450	133.3

TABLE 9.14 Resistance of Polybenzimidazole Adhesive to
Exposure to Fluids per MIL-A-5090D [13]

Fluid	Time	% retention of strength
Boiling water......	2 hours	70
JP-4	7 days	100
Anti-icing	7 days	100
Hydrocarbon	7 days	100
Hydraulic	7 days	100

The adhesives provide quite good resistance to the standard military specification fluids, as indicated in Tables 9.13 and 9.14. Boiling water resistance is lower, as might be expected from the previous discussion, but can be significantly improved by selection of the proper finish for the glass carrier. Bonds are unaffected by hydrocarbon fuels and oils.

ELECTRICAL PROPERTIES

The electrical properties of polybenzimidazole laminates are in the range expected of competitive thermosetting plastics but are quite flat with temperature (Fig. 9.29). The values are reported for short-time exposures. It might be expected that the values would be preserved with aging somewhat better than the physical strength properties.

PROCESSING

As has been indicated previously, processing of the polybenzimidazoles is somewhat more complicated than with the standard laminating and adhesive systems. During the conversion of the prepolymer to the final polymer, oxidative degradation may occur, making desirable the use of vacuum or an inert atmosphere for cure. Further, because of the release of volatiles, pressure is required to obtain a dense, void-free structure.

Use of pressure, however, to produce a void-free matrix leads to an internal pressure buildup which inhibits further condensation because of

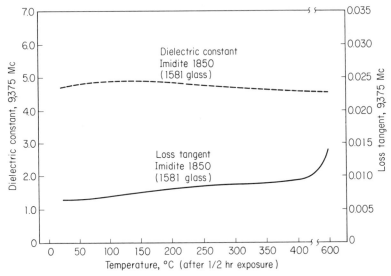

FIG 9.29 *Dielectric constant and loss tangent of PBI laminate at* 9,375 Mc *vs. temperature* [14]. *Laminate:* 0.500 *in. thick; resin content:* 17% *by weight.*

Laminating material preimpregnated with polybenzimidazole. (Narmco Materials Division, Whittaker Corp.)

equilibrium conditions. Consequently, though the void-free laminate or adhesive bond is theoretically optimum, it may not, in practice, be so.

Typical processing of a preimpregnated laminate involves exposing the layup to 120°C, with pressure gradually increasing from contact to 200 psi. The temperature is then increased to 370°C and held for 3 hours. The laminate is then cooled to 100°C, removed from the press, and then post-cured under dry nitrogen or vacuum, according to the following schedule:

24 hours at 315°C
24 hours at 345°C
24 hours at 370°C
24 hours at 400°C
8 hours at 425°C

Following this cycle, an additional cure of 3 hours at 370°C in air is recommended for ultimate properties.

Processing of supported tape adhesives involves a cure of 1 hour at 220°C plus 1 hour at 315°C, with a pressure of 200 psi being applied during both temperatures. Following this, a postcure in dry nitrogen is employed. The temperature is increased from 23 to 370°C slowly (45-minute heat-up) and maintained for 1 hour. The effect of cure temperature on properties is shown in Fig. 9.30. A detailed discussion of fabrication techniques for beryllium sandwiches using polybenzimidazole adhesive is given by Yoshino [31].

More recent work [33] shows that as little as 10 psi applied pressure when curing gives as good results as 200 psi for small-area (0.5-sq.-in.) lap shear specimens. The same work shows that although PBI is a good high-temperature adhesive for steel and beryllium, only half the strength of lap bonds can be obtained with titanium as with the other two metals. In any case, after heat aging at 370°C, all bond strength was lost after 50 hours for all three metals.

Tapes and preimpregnated laminates or rovings may be obtained by the

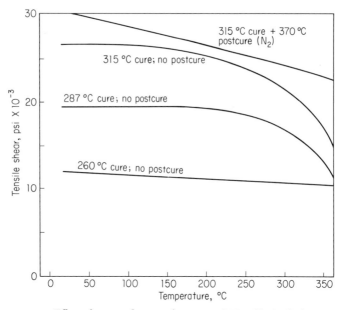

Effect of cure cycle on performance of PBI adhesive [24].

Sonic fatigue test panels for Supersonic transport using experimental polybenzimidazole adhesive. (Narmco Materials Division, Whittaker Corp.)

hot melt technique, which is suitable when higher solids contents are required. Alternatively, the structure may be manufactured using multiple coats of the solution system. Typically, the solution of the prepolymer is applied to the fabric in a series of coatings, each followed by a drying cycle of about 120°C for 30 minutes. When the thickness is obtained to yield the desired resin content, the coating is cured overnight at 160°C under vacuum.

APPLICATIONS

The envisioned applications for the polybenzimidazoles are as high-temperature adhesives and laminating resins for the aerospace industry. They may be employed as secondary structural members in supersonic aircraft and as adhesives for honeycomb bonding in similar applications. The civilian potential of the materials has not been investigated in detail.

REFERENCES

1959

1. K. C. Brinker and I. M. Robinson, Linear Polybenzimidazoles, U.S. 2,895,948.

1960

2. Polymer Resists Heat, C&E News, Nov. 28.

1961

3. H. Vogel and C. S. Marvel, Polybenzimidazoles, I, J. Polymer Sci. 50:511.

1962

4. H. H. Levine, Polybenzimidazole Resins for High Temperature Reinforced Plastics and Adhesives, Symposium sponsored by Air Force Materials Center, Dayton, Ohio, December.

1963

5. H. Vogel and C. S. Marvel, Polybenzimidazoles, II, J. Polymer Sci., part A, vol. 1, pp. 1531–1541.

1964

6. T. C. Bohrer et al., Research and Development of Manufacturing Methods for PBI Fibers and Fibrous Structures of PBI Yarns, Interim Progress Report, AD 457 983.
7. Y. Iwakura, K. Uno, and Y. Imai, Polybenzimidazole, Japan 17,085.
8. Y. Iwakura, K. Uno, and Y. Imai, Polybenzimidazoles, II: Poly(alkylenebenzimidazoles), Makromol. Chem. 77:338–340.
9. Y. Iwakura, K. Uno, and Y. Imai, Polyphenylenebenzimidazoles, J. Polymer Sci., part A, vol. 2, pp. 2605–2615.

10. V. V. Korshak, T. M. Frunze, and A. A. Izyneev, Application of Polycyclization Method to the Synthesis of Polymers Containing Ester and Amide Groups Besides Benzimidazole Rings, *Izv. Akad. Nauk SSSR Ser. Khim.* 1964(11):2104–2106.
11. V. V. Korshak and Ye. S. Kronganz, Advances in the Synthesis of Heat-resistant Polymers, *Usp. Khim.* 33(12):1409. (English translation: AD 482 302.)
12. H. H. Levine, C. B. Delano, and K. J. Kjoiller, Polybenzimidazoles, II: Condensation of Various Diphenyl Esters with 3,3′-Diaminobenzidine, Effect of Structure, ACS Meeting, Philadelphia, April.
13. J. J. Licari, High Temperature Adhesives, *Prod. Eng.*, Dec. 7.
14. Narmco Imidite 850 and 1850 Data Sheets and R. Poet paper Imidite, Narmco Materials Division, Whittaker Corp.
15. L. Plummer and C. S. Marvel, Polybenzimidazoles, III, *J. Polymer Sci.*, part A, vol 2, pp. 2559–2569.
16. L. Suffredini and J. McCann, Heat Resistant and Structural Adhesives, Narmco Materials Division, Whittaker Corp., Costa Mesa, Calif., February 19.
17. W. Wrasidlo and H. H. Levine, Polybenzimidazoles, I: Reaction Mechanisms and Kinetics, *J. Polymer Sci.*, part A, vol. 2, pp. 4795–4808.

1965

18. R. T. Conley, Stability of Condensation Polymers in Oxygen Containing Atmospheres, Proceedings of Symposium on High Temperature Polymers: Synthesis and Degradation, Western Regional Meeting, ACS, Los Angeles, November.
19. R. T. Foster and C. S. Marvel, Polybenzimidazoles, IV: Polybenzimidazoles Containing Aryl Ether Linkages, *J. Polymer Sci.*, part A, vol. 3, pp. 417–421.
20. T. M. Frunze et al., The Preparation of Certain Polybenzimidazoles, Containing Phosphorus, Boron, and Oxygen Atoms in the Chain, *Vysokomolekul. Soedin.*, 7(2):285–289. (English translation: AD 482 739.)
21. D. N. Gray and G. P. Shulman, The Mechanism of Polybenzimidazole Formation by Condensation of Aromatic Tetraamines and Esters, ACS Symposium, Atlantic City, N.J., September.
22. V. V. Korshak et al., Synthesis and Investigation of Properties of Certain Homogeneous and Mixed Polybenzimidazoles, *Vysokomolekul. Soedin.*, 6(7):1251–1255. (English translation: AD 615 865.)
23. S. Litvak, Research on Polybenzimidazole Structural Adhesives for Bonding Stainless Steel, Beryllium, and Titanium Alloys, Symposium on Structural Adhesive Bonding, vol. II, Stevens Institute of Technology, September.
24. R. Poet, The Nature and Application of Heterocyclic Polyaromatic Linear Polymers, Narmco Materials Division, Whittaker Corp., Costa Mesa, Calif.
25. T. J. Reinhart, Jr., and R. Hidde, Mechanical Properties of Imidite Adhesives, Symposium on Structural Adhesives Bonding, vol. II, Stevens Institute of Technology, September.
26. G. P. Shulman and H. W. Lochte, Thermal Degradation of Poly-2,2′-(m-phenylene)-5,5′-bibenzimidazoles, ACS Symposium, Atlantic City, N.J., September.
27. T. J. Aponyi, Progress in High Temperature Resins, 23rd Annual Conference, Western Section, SPI, Palm Springs, Calif., April.
28. A. B. Conciatori, E. C. Chenevey, and T. C. Bohrer, Polymerization and Spinning of PBI, ACS Winter Meeting, Phoenix, Ariz., January.
29. H. A. Mackay, Evaluation of Polybenzimidazole Glass-fabric Laminates, *Mod. Plastics*, January.
30. R. W. Singleton, H. D. Noether, and J. F. Tracy, Relation of the Critical Properties of PBI Fiber to Fiber Microstructure, ACS Winter Meeting, Phoenix, Ariz., January.
31. S. Y. Yoshino, Development of Fabrication Methods for PBI Adhesive Beryllium Sandwich Structures, NAA S&ID Division. Report SID 66-281, April.

1966

32. J. R. Hill and D. W. Levi, Polybenzimidazoles: a Review, Plastec Report 28.
33. J. R. Hill, Process Development of PBI Adhesives, *Adhesives Age*, August, p. 32.
34. H. H. Levine and R. D. Stacy, AFML-TR-65-350, Contract AF33(615)2283, January.

1967

35. D. Trischler, J. Kjoller, and H. Levine, ACS Spring Meeting, Miami Beach, Fla., April.

10

Research Polymers

Primarily in response to the requirements of the aerospace industry for plastics capable of continuous or short-time operation at increasingly higher temperatures, much recent chemical research has been expended on the development of new high-molecular-weight, thermally stable polymers.

In the present technology, the most promising high-temperature polymers are aromatic-based systems containing repeating heterocyclic units in the chain. In their ultimate form, these are ladder polymers which resist chain scission by two chemical bonds within each segmental unit. These have proved more tractable than the completely inorganic systems, and the best of them have given high-temperature performance equal to or better than that offered by the polymeric inorganics.

The new aromatic-based systems are, however, not without problems. They are inherently expensive; their chemistry is incompletely understood; and they pose unique processing problems.

As the temperature resistance of the new polymers is improved, they become increasingly insoluble and infusible. Thus, in order to permit their use as molding compounds, coatings, adhesives, and composite matrices, it is necessary to interrupt the synthesis at some point less than complete insolubility and infusibility.

Final conversion is then subsequently conducted—essentially after the material has been applied. This final conversion is accomplished by the release of small molecules produced by the condensation reactions involved. If useful articles are to be manufactured, these volatiles usually must be removed from the polymer. Removal of volatiles from films, fibers, and coatings poses fewer problems than from adhesives and laminates and fewer still than from moldings. However, even with films, because of reversible reactions leading to lower-molecular-weight polymers, difficulties are encountered.

More remains to be done than has been accomplished to date. But the initial work, which inevitably falls short of perfection, constitutes an impressive monument to the present technology.

As is evident from the preceding chapters, recent developments in linear polymers have been concentrated on the aromatic species. The same concentration is evident in the experimental polymers now under investigation.

Most of the recent new linear polymers have been produced by condensation techniques. This fact, like the interest in aromatics, is because of concentration on developing more thermally stable species. Addition polymers as a general rule decompose by low-energy pathways, by the so-called "unzippering" route, and thereby possess inherently limited thermal stability. The condensation polymers, on the other hand, decompose at higher temperatures by much slower reactions involving splitting of small molecules or by fragmentation to relatively stable free radicals which react further at a slow rate. Aliphatic-based polymers seldom evidence thermal stability at temperatures above 350°C, whereas the fully aromatic ones are generally stable to 550°C or higher [29]. Systems based on fused rings, such as naphthalenes, generally give stabilities somewhat less than those based on simple benzene rings.

In the search for thermal stability, design of the polymeric aromatic backbone is of some consequence. Ideally, the linear species should be a high-melting polymer resistant to pyrolysis and to oxidation.

To produce high-melting species, areas of crystallinity are helpful, as are substituents which provide increased rigidity. However, these two aspects are somewhat opposed: crystallinity being favored by regularity of the molecules and strong hydrogen bonding, assisted by secondary bonding by van der Waals forces; rigidity being enhanced by bulky substituents which, in the present technology, cannot always be stereospecifically located to produce maximum regularity. Generally, then, rigidity is obtained with unsubstituted ring structures, hydrogen bonding is accomplished through the use of polar linkages in the chain [28], and van der Waals forces arise from chain packing.

Resistance to pyrolysis may be improved by avoiding ethylene links which can split out hydrogen to give unsaturation, $-CH_2-CH_2- \xrightarrow{\Delta} -CH=CH- + H_2$, and subsequent degradation. Aliphatic unsaturation is particularly vulnerable to oxidative attack, as are aliphatic tertiary hydrogens in general. These species can decompose to H_2 and ROO, etc., to initiate the chain of radical reactions leading, if not to low-molecular-weight species, then to progressive crosslinking and embrittlement to the detriment of physical strengths. Other thermally unstable groups should be avoided, such as pendant carboxyls which can decarboxylate at higher temperatures, and the hydrogen content should be minimized. This, however, can be done only at the expense of the intermolecular forces.

Perhaps from the standpoint of thermal stability within the organic family, polyphenylene would offer maximum properties. It generally is obtained only with difficulty, however, and as low-molecular-weight species at best. Polyphenylene polymers $(n = 100)$ have been synthesized as follows [29]:

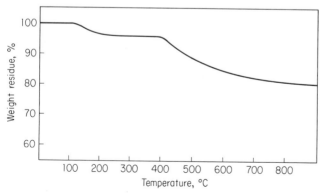

1,3-Cyclohexadiene   Poly-1,3-cyclohexadiene   Polydibromocyclohexane   Polyphenylene

Such polymers offer thermal gravimetric analysis (TGA) data as shown in Fig. 10.1. Poly-p-phenylene is infusible up to 530°C, sustaining extended heating at 230 to 240°C without change [1]. With polyphenylene, insolubility and general intractibility have been experienced, so that useful systems have not been developed. Perfluoropolyphenylene with low degrees of polymerization (11 phenyl rings) has been obtained from 1,4-diiodoperfluorobenzene with powdered copper [2, 3]. Polymers with weights up to 15,000 have been produced from pentafluorophenyl Grignard [64]. These and polymers from 1,2 or 1,3-dibromotetrafluorobenzene are soluble. The melting points of the polymers are above 360°C in some cases, but the very soluble meta-linked polymers [68] are quite low melting. The higher-weight polyperfluorophenylenes have good thermal stability in vacuum up

FIG 10.1   *Thermogram for dehydrogenated poly-1,3-cyclohexadiene* [29].

to 600°C, but in air decomposition begins below 400°C and then increases rapidly with increasing temperature. The hydrocarbon polyphenylenes are more resistant to oxidation up to 500°C; however, if the polyperfluorophenylenes are pretreated at 400°C for one hour, their oxidative stability compares favorably with that of the polyphenylenes. Polyperfluorophenylenes may also be prepared from chloroperfluorotoluene; but only low-molecular-weight materials result, with melting points below 300°C, and, like most aromatic fluorocarbon polymers, they become insoluble upon heating at 300°C. Low-molecular-weight polymers have been obtained from monomers such as *o*- and *m*-terphenyl. These have improved solubility, but during the synthesis, considerable cyclization occurs to produce fused-ring and branched polymers [38]. The materials may have some utility if methods can be found for curing them to crosslinked networks, but as strictly linear polymers, they have no present utility.

Polyphenylenes with a hetero atom in the chain between every fifth and sixth ring have been prepared [72]. These materials are made from bistetracyclones and *p*- or *m*-diethynylbenzene.

Bistetracyclone

p-Ethynylbenzene

Modified polyphenylene

The intermediate Diels-Alder polymer loses carbon dioxide to give the polyphenylene. These polymers are soluble in toluene or chloroform but do not give observable transitions below 300°C. When the hetero atom is oxygen or sulfur, the break in the TGA curve comes at 550°C in air. When heated to just below the decomposition temperatures, the polymers become insoluble, most likely by crosslinking.

It might be reasoned that strictly inorganic polymers would offer greater promise than carbon-based compounds, since bond energy considerations favor them over carbon-to-carbon species. Attempts to prepare such materials have not been outstandingly successful. Many rearrange on heating to small ring compounds; hydrolytic instability and excessive cross-linking are encountered; high bond energies are outweighed by formation of kinetically unfavorable decomposition pathways; and many have proved quite intractable to current polymer fabrication and processing techniques [17]. In fact, the majority of the totally inorganic polymers do not exhibit exceptional thermal stability as compared to carbon-based species.

Polymetal phosphenates, for example, with molecular weights of greater

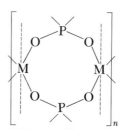

Polymetal phosphenates

than 10,000 melt at about 250°C and decompose by crosslinking at higher temperatures [39]. Polyborphosphane resins show some improvement when the short-chain linear polymers are crosslinked with organic species; such resins decompose slowly between 400 and 625°C [50]. Poly-*m*-carboran-

$$\left[\begin{array}{c} \text{CH}_3 \\ | \\ \text{Si}-\text{CB}_{10}\text{H}_{10}\text{C}-\text{Si}-\text{O} \\ | \\ \text{CH}_3 \end{array} \begin{array}{c} \text{CH}_3 \\ | \\ \\ | \\ \text{CH}_3 \end{array}\right]_n$$

Poly-*m*-carboranylenesiloxane

ylene siloxanes melt at about 210°C, and at 500°C undergo an irreversible rearrangement [53]. The most successful of the polymeric inorganics (aside from glass) are the silicone resins; but these do not provide the thermal stability of some of the new linear aromatic polymers.

Actually, many of the so-called "inorganic polymers" are merely inorganic chains containing organic units or substituents. Phosphonitrilic polymers are a typical example [43]. These are based on the so-called "inorganic rubbers," with the chlorine replaced by organic groups to improve hydro-lytic stability. One such material, containing methylol groups and curable by conventional phenolic curing agents, is available in research quantities from El Monte Chemical Company. It provides continuous heat resistance to above 260°C. United States Rubber has produced, experimentally, thermoplastic polymers, wherein the chlorine is replaced by phenoxy and ethoxy groups [48]. Similar high-molecular-weight linear polymers have been produced by researchers at American Cyanamid, including ethoxy-, methoxy-, trifluoroethoxy-, and phenoxypolyphosphonitrilic derivatives, and several analogous amino derivatives [34]. These linear polymers have molecular weights between 1 and 2 million. A review of resins from phosphonitrilic chlorides is given by Banigan [36].

When organic substituents are used, they may serve to improve processability of the inorganic polymer, but the general effect is to impose their own limits on thermal stability [17].

Nearer to the polymers discussed in this book are the disiloxane benzimidazoles [7]:

Poly(disiloxanebenzimidazole)

and the benzimidazoles containing the carborane link in the backbone. In the latter polymer, low-molecular-weight species have been produced [44]. These materials, by TGA, exhibit 4 percent weight loss at 400°C, followed by a 4 percent weight gain to 560°C, and then an 18 percent loss to 900°C. The limited oxidation, indicated by the weight gain, appears to be a surface phenomenon. The increased thermal stability over the polybenzimidazoles is attributed to the inductive effect of the carborane group on stabilizing the imidazole ring [44].

Similarly, chain carbon atoms may be replaced in the organic polymers, as is done with polybenzborimidazolenes [11]:

Polybenzborimidazolene

Still another class of semiorganic polymers are those called *coordination* polymers. These contain a number of electron donor atoms (nitrogen, sulfur, oxygen) which are coordinated with metals such as beryllium, copper, or nickel. Again, the polymers are generally intractable and obtained only in lower molecular weights [17].

In summary, then, the organic aromatic-based polymers still provide the best thermal stability practically obtainable in the present polymer technology.

In addition to selecting proper polymeric backbones, considerable research has been expended to obtain so-called "ladder polymers," which may be illustrated by the semiorganic polyphenylsilsesquioxanes:

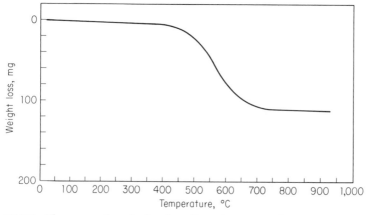

Polyphenylsilsesquioxane

These materials provide TGA data as shown in Figs. 10.2 to 10.4.

There has been some hope that improved thermal stability of aromatic species could be obtained through fluorine substituents. However, a thorough review of the present technology indicates that this approach offers little real promise [27]. This is further supported by TGA thermograms of polybenzimidazoles containing aliphatic perfluoro chains which proved no better in thermal stability than analogous aliphatic hydrocarbon bridges [51].

However, aliphatic fluorinated polymers are under active investigation to provide improved elastomers; and typical of these are polythiocarbonyl fluoride, polyaziridines, and copolymers from vinyl monomers and hexafluoroacetone [47].

FIG 10.2 *Thermogram for polyphenylene silsesquioxane in air* [10]. *Weight of sample, 200 mg; weight of residue, 89.5 mg.*

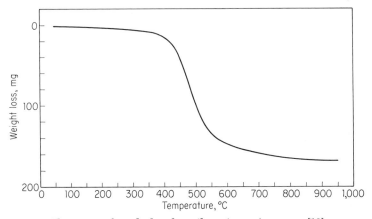

FIG 10.3 *Thermogram for polyphenylene silsesquioxane in vacuum* [10].
Weight of sample, 200 *mg; weight of residue,* 39 *mg.*

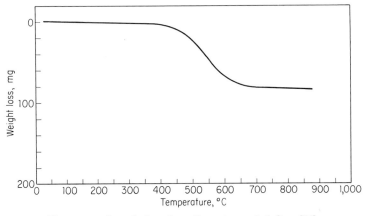

FIG 10.4 *Thermogram for polyphenylene silsesquioxane in helium* [10].
Weight of sample, 200 *mg; weight of residue,* 118 *mg.*

In addition to seeking improved thermal stability, synthesis efforts have
been directed toward improving flexibility and processability of the inherently rigid, difficultly soluble aromatic polymers. Often, for example,
oxygen may be introduced into the polymer chain to reduce brittleness by
providing a rotational point for the polymer. Alternatively, ordered, alternating copolymers may be developed. Examples of these, in the case of
heterocyclics, are shown in Table 10.1. These are prepared by producing
a di- or tetrafunctional block and then condensing this with a monomer or
second block [54]. Films of these often provide improved properties: for
example, structure III (Table 10.1) gives improved retention of flexibility
on aging at 300 and 350°C over both polybenzimidazole and commercial
aromatic polyimide film [54].

TABLE 10.1   Typical Preparative Routes to Ordered
Copolymers [54]

Although beyond the scope of the present work, improved thermal stability, may, theoretically, be accomplished through crosslinking. As indicated in previous chapters, little success has been obtained in this fashion with the linear polymers under discussion. To the contrary, in fact.

TABLE 10.1 (Continued)

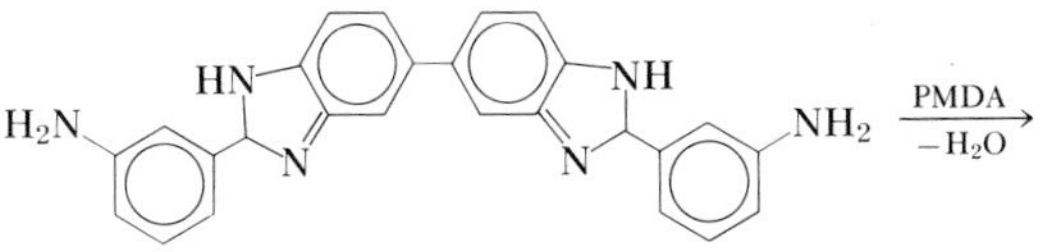

D

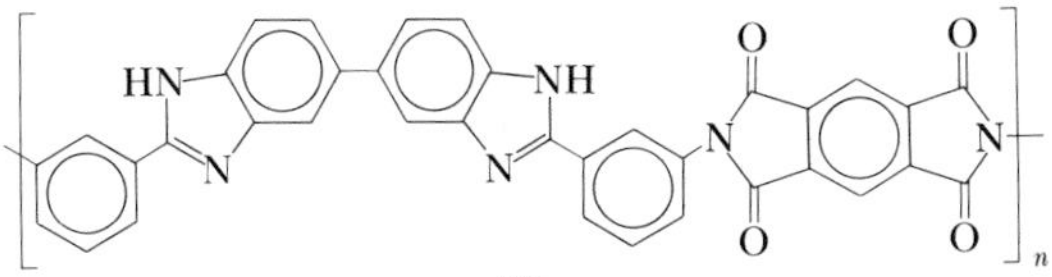

IV

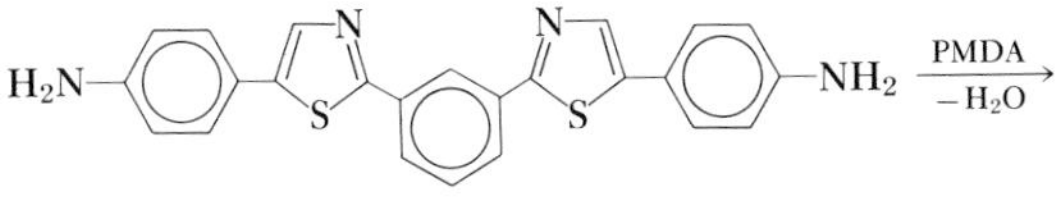

E

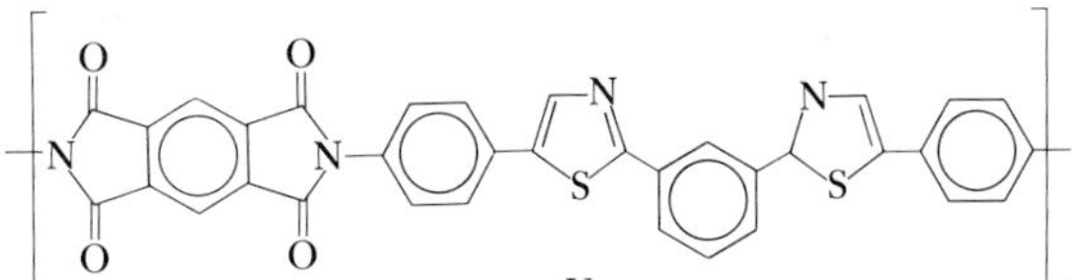

V

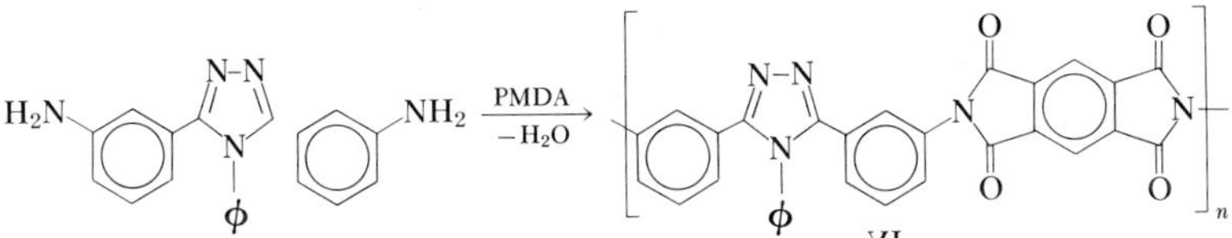

F

VI

The linear polymers generally provide superior TGA data to the available crosslinked polymers, which typically give values as indicated in Fig. 10.5. Poor performance of the commercial crosslinking materials may be attributed to the introduction of aliphatic chain segments—these containing the reactive sites which permit crosslinking.

Thermal stability, in itself, while easily defined, is less readily measured. Under ideal conditions, with adequate polymers of known composition and high molecular weight, thermal stability could most effectively be determined by measuring the effect of time and temperature on physical strength retention, assuming, of course, that it would be possible, realistically, to ignore variables introduced by sample preparation and testing.

However, many of the new polymers are not available in sufficient quantities and in the higher-molecular-weight ranges required to obtain

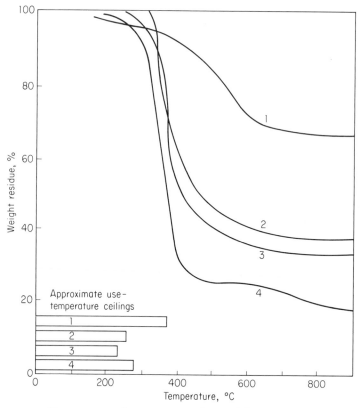

FIG 10.5 *Thermograms and use-temperature limits of thermosets* [17].
(1) *Silicon resin;* (2) *phenolic;* (3) *epoxy;* (4) *polyester.*

satisfactory physical properties in the form of laminate, coating, and adhesive data. In these cases, the thermal stability is often estimated from small samples by means of TGA data. This is accomplished by heating the sample of a controlled rate and measuring the weight loss vs. temperature. Materials showing lowest weight loss and/or maximum weight retention to high temperatures are potential candidates for more intensive research. Further general information can be obtained by observing isothermal thermogravimetric data, in which weight loss, at a constant temperature, is determined as a function of time. Thus, a material may decompose and evaporate completely within hours at a temperature far lower than would be indicated by standard TGA curves.

Further information on the stability of the new polymers is obtained by conducting the pyrolysis in vacuum and inert atmospheres as well as in air. On the basis of these relatively simple tests, then, polymers may be selected for more intensive evaluation.

In this chapter, preponderance of data will involve thermograms as relative indications of expected thermal stability. These data, while not so meaningful as strength data vs. time and temperature, have validity in their simplicity. The molecular weight of the polymer is less significant in TGA work than it is in measurements involving physical strength properties (e.g., laminate and adhesive data). Thus, a low-molecular-weight polymer, quite promising in terms of thermal stability, might well be screened out in high-temperature testing because of poor physical properties, these being more a function of molecular weight than of inherent thermal stability. (Early weight loss in TGA tests is characteristic of thermal degradation of end groups in low-molecular-weight polymers present in the specimen and is frequently disregarded when estimating thermal stability.)

The thermograms provided in this chapter may be compared with curves for the new commercial polymers described in earlier chapters. Additionally, thermograms for six of the older commercial thermoplastic materials are shown in Fig. 10.6 for reference.

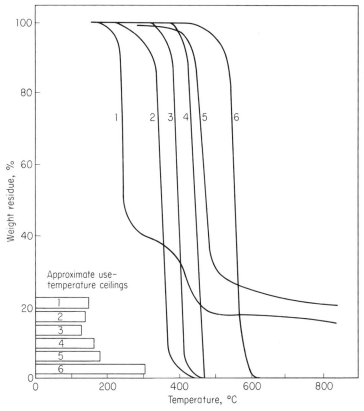

FIG 10.6   *Thermograms and use-temperature limits for commercial thermoplastics* [17]. (1) *Polyvinyl chloride;* (2) *polymethyl methacrylate;* (3) *polystyrene;* (4) *polyethylene;* (5) *polycarbonate;* (6) *polytetrafluoroethylene.*

While greatest possible thermal stability is a major present goal of organic polymer synthesis, processing characteristics are a very important consideration. A finely divided powder, incapable of further processing, is only of academic interest, irrespective of its thermal stability.

From the standpoint of processability, what is ideally required is a material that can conveniently be formed, pressed, or made into its final shape while in the liquid state, by some heat and/or pressure technique. Such materials can be applied as an adhesive, molding powder, laminating matrix, coating, etc. Subsequently, through the use of heat or other means, this soluble, formable material could be converted to a completely insoluble, inert, and thermally stable polymer.

Unfortunately, the conversion of condensation polymers to their final form involves the elimination of small molecules, which must escape from the system along with any solvents used in processing.

With molding compounds, the problem of volatiles becomes increasingly difficult, since there are no ready pathways for the escape of volatiles. Thus, the best that can be hoped for is the development of molding powders which are virtually infusible, but which can, with heat and pressure, be converted that last little distance to the infusible form with a minimum release of volatiles, or molding powders which are sufficiently stable to permit processing at temperatures above their T_g. It would appear that the molding of such refractory materials would require a technology different from the conventional one. To date, using techniques similar to those employed with powdered metallurgy, aromatic polyimides have been molded successfully into solid tubes and blocks capable of being machined to the final form.

With coatings, adhesives, and laminates, the problem of solvent escape is less severe, although still present. Combination cure cycles, the use of pressure, and careful processing techniques must be used to create finished products of acceptable quality.

From the standpoint of synthesis, the new, higher-temperature polymers possess two points in common:

1. The inherent poor solubility of the species creates difficulties during synthesis in the attainment of high-molecular-weight species. Such data as are available suggest that a molecular weight of 20,000 or above is required for overall satisfactory strength properties. When solubility considerations operate against these weight levels, the synthesis problem is profoundly complicated.

2. The reactions of these new polymers are rather poorly understood in the present technology; thus, the attainment of optimum reaction condi-

tions and the selection of catalysts, etc., are less well developed than with the older, more thoroughly investigated species. The resultant polymers are thus less than optimum in terms of molecular-weight distribution, freedom from side reaction and chain branching, and inherent "purity."

Compounding these difficulties are the economic ones:

1. The precursors for many of the materials described in this chapter are inherently expensive by present synthesis techniques.

2. In many of the reactions, high-purity reactants are essential for the attainment of satisfactory molecular weights, thus introducing a second economic disadvantage.

It is thus evident that many of the polymers described in the next few pages will not attain any significance to the commercial technology. It is further evident that even newer polymers, designed to circumvent the specific problems involved with present species, will increasingly come to occupy the attention of chemists working in the area of high-temperature organic plastics.

LINEAR AROMATIC POLYMERS

As distinguished from the linear, heterocyclic, aromatic polymers, the linear aromatic polymers are available potentially in great variety from the reaction of acids, anhydrides, phenols, and aromatic-based chlorohydrins, with aromatic amines or aromatic hydroxyl-bearing species. The ones described below are illustrative of the research areas presently under investigation.

Aromatic Polyamines

Aromatic diamines may be reacted with xylylene dichloride to produce high-molecular-weight polysecondary amines. The reaction, in simplified form, progresses:

Aromatic polyamine

A slight excess of amine is employed to prevent the undesirable reaction of the xylylene dichloride with the formed secondary amines. This requirement tends to limit the ultimate molecular weights of the polymers, but, nonetheless, species may be developed which may be used as thermoplastic compounds, or, more generally, may be crosslinked through the secondary amine groups by the use of anhydrides, epoxy resins, etc. [56]. A TGA curve of the linear material is shown in Fig. 10.7.

Aromatic Azopolymers

Aromatic diamines are polymerized by oxygen with a cuprous chloride catalyst to give azopolymers [25, 58].

$$H_2N-\langle\bigcirc\rangle-NH_2 + O_2 \xrightarrow{\text{CuCl}} \left[-\langle\bigcirc\rangle-N{=}N-\right]_n$$

These, as can be seen from the formula, are completely conjugated. High molecular weights are prepared with many diamines: e.g., p- and m-phenylenediamine, 2,6-diaminopyridine, 4,4'-methylenedianiline, bisaminophenyl sulfone. These polymers are heat-stable, showing no weight loss when heated in nitrogen up to $325°C$ and 10 percent weight loss at $425°C$.

Aromatic Polyimines

In a reaction similar to the one shown in the preceding section, it is possible to produce a polyimine of the following structure:

$$\left[-\langle\bigcirc\rangle-N{=}CH-\langle\bigcirc\rangle-CH{=}N-\right]_n$$

Aromatic polyimine

These are prepared from the aromatic diamine and terephthaldehyde [56]. Such materials provide thermal stability as indicated in Fig. 10.8. A preliminary review of these compounds is provided by Delman et al. [42].

Polyamides

In Chap. 6, it was indicated that aromatic polyamides may be produced from the reaction of diacid chlorides with aromatic primary diamines. Such compounds contain secondary amide hydrogens.

Aromatic polyamides have also been prepared which incorporate the s-triazine structure. This ring structure has even improved stability over the benzene ring, probably because of its high-resonance stabilization energy, 82 kcal per mole as compared to 39 kcal per mole for benzene. Polymers have been prepared from terephthalic acid and melamine (I), phenylguanamine (II), and aminophenylguanamine (III) [24].

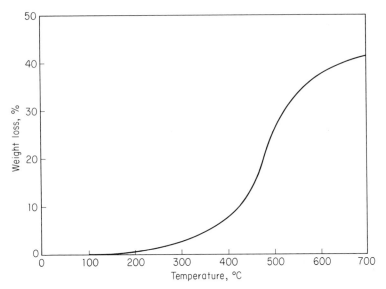

FIG 10.7 *Thermogram for aromatic polysecondary amine* (pPDA/XDA) *in nitrogen* [56]. *Powdered specimen:* 10° C *per min.*

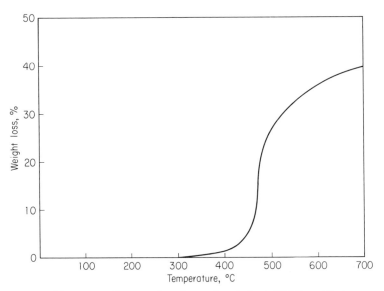

FIG 10.8 *Thermogram for aromatic polysecondary imine* (pPDA/terephthal-aldehyde) *in nitrogen* [56]. *Powdered specimen:* 10° C *per min.*

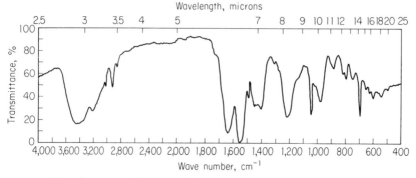

Although both melamine and aminophenylguanamine are trifunctional molecules, they form linear polymers because both are capable of tautomerizing to provide less than three primary amine groups. The possible structures range from the completely conjugated to completely nonconjugated forms:

Because of difficulties of purification, the polyamide has been obtained only in relatively pure form from aminophenylguanamine and terephthalate. An infrared structure for this polymer is shown in Fig. 10.9. Thermal stability, less than anticipated, is indicated by the thermogram in Fig. 10.10, where the initial weight loss is attributed to impurities.

FIG 10.9 *Infrared spectrum of polyaminobenzoguanamine terephthlate* [24].

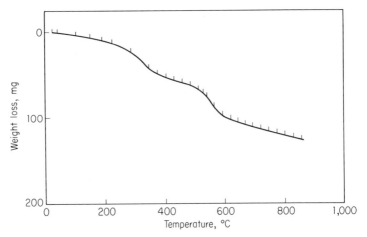

FIG 10.10 *Thermogram of aminobenzoguanamine terephthalate* [24]. *Heating rate, 6 in. per °C per min; time mark, 5 min; preset, 10 min; pressure, 0.2 mm.*

The experimental method for synthesizing the polymers of this class involved preparing a mineral oil slurry of the amine and acid and adding the slurry in small portions, under nitrogen, to hot mineral oil (170 to 180°C). After the slurry was added, the mixture was heated to 320°C. Temperature was then allowed to drop to 260°C and maintained for 2 hours. The mixture was then cooled and washed with solvent.

When *secondary* diamines are employed to produce polyamides, the product is free of secondary hydrogens. New polyamides of this type, based on *trans*-2,5-dimethylpiperazine, have been investigated. The reaction, in simplified form, is as follows:

$$\text{2,5-Dimethylpiperazine} + \text{Terephthaloyl chloride} \longrightarrow \text{Polyamide}$$

2,5-Dimethyl-
piperazine   Terephthaloyl
                   chloride   Polyamide

Compounds from both terephthaloyl and oxalyl chloride have been prepared in molecular-weight ranges of 25,000 to 35,000; both have melting points above 400°C [32]. TGA data for the systems are shown in Fig. 10.11.

The $\rangle$N—C— links, in contrast to aliphatic nylons, are quite resistant to acid-catalyzed degradation of elevated temperatures. Weight loss of

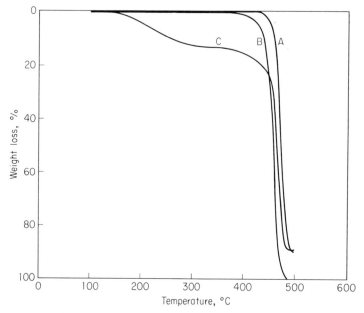

FIG 10.11   *Thermograms of polyamides in vacuum* [40]. A—*Poly(terephthaloyl-*
trans-2,5-dimethylpiperazine); B—*poly(oxaly-trans-2,5-dimethylpiperazine)*;
C—*sulfuric-acid-treated* A.

acid-treated polymers is slightly less than that of the nonacidified species,
as shown in Fig. 10.11.

Acetylated polyamides have also been prepared from the diacetyl
derivatives of aromatic diamines [56]. The derivatives were treated to
form the sodium salts from the secondary amides and then reacted with
xylylene dichloride to give

$$\left[\!\! -N\!\!-\!\!\bigcirc\!\!-\!\!N\!\!-\!\!CH_2\!\!-\!\!\bigcirc\!\!-\!\!CH_2\!\! \right]_n$$
$$\quad\; \underset{OCCH_3}{|} \qquad\quad \underset{OCCH_3}{|}$$

Acetylated poly(p-phenylenediamine p-xylylene)

Polyesters

Linear polyesters have long been known from the reaction of diacids or
anhydrides with diols. [Mylar, for example, is polyethylene terephthalate
(PET).] Improved radiation stability has been obtained by use of 2,6-
naphthalenedicarboxylic acid in place of terephthalic acid [35]. This gives
a polymer of the following structure:

$$\left[\text{(naphthalene)}\text{—CO}_2\text{CH}_2\text{CH}_2\text{O}_2\text{C} \right]_n$$

PEN-2,6

PEN-2,6, because of increased aromaticity and resonance stabilization, tends to crosslink in the presence of radiation, as opposed to Mylar, which decomposes by chain scission. The effect of radiation on intrinsic viscosities of the two polymers in o-chlorobenzene is shown in Fig. 10.12.

More highly aromatic polyesters may be prepared by the interfacial polycondensation reaction described in Chap. [5]. For example, terephthaloyl chloride may be reacted with the sodium salt of bisphenol A, as follows:

$$\text{ClOC—(C}_6\text{H}_4\text{)—COCl} + \text{NaO—(C}_6\text{H}_4\text{)—}\underset{\underset{\text{CH}_3}{|}}{\overset{\overset{\text{CH}_3}{|}}{\text{C}}}\text{—(C}_6\text{H}_4\text{)—ONa} \xrightarrow{-\text{NaCl}}$$

$$\left[\text{—O}_2\text{C—(C}_6\text{H}_4\text{)—CO}_2\text{—(C}_6\text{H}_4\text{)—}\underset{\underset{\text{CH}_3}{|}}{\overset{\overset{\text{CH}_3}{|}}{\text{C}}}\text{—(C}_6\text{H}_4\text{)—} \right]_n$$

Aromatic polyester

As with the phenoxy resins (Chap. 2), any of a large number of bisphenols and related materials (e.g., phenolphthalein) may be employed to replace bisphenol A.

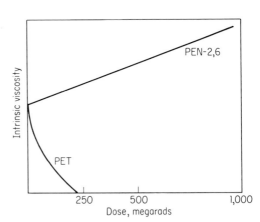

Fig 10.12   *Increase in intrinsic viscosity of solutions of PET and PEN-2,6 vs. radiation dosage* [35].

Aromatic Polysulfides

Aromatic poly-p-phenylene sulfides have been produced by the polymerization of solid cuprous bromothiophenoxide according to the following equation [12]:

$$\text{Br}-\!\!\left\langle\bigcirc\right\rangle\!\!-\text{SCu} \xrightarrow{\;200°\;} \left[\left\langle\bigcirc\right\rangle\!\!-\text{S}\right]_n$$

Aromatic polysulfide

Polymers have been obtained with molecular weights ranging from about 5,000 to 13,000. The molecular weight influences TGA performances little as shown in Figs. 10.13 and 10.14. The polymer is a white, crystalline material soluble in high-boiling solvents at elevated temperature. It melts at 285 and at 300°C in air, rapidly crosslinks to an elastomer. At 425°C, the polymer will evaporate completely in about 15 hours, as shown in Fig. 10.15.

An alternative route to the preparation of the polymers involves heating the sodium or lithium salts of 4-halothiophenols in DMF or DMSO. These polymers melt at 270 to 290°C but are heat-stable for 2 hours at 500°C in nitrogen [33].

Polyphenylene Oxides

In Chap. 3, the synthesis of substituted polyphenylene oxides was described. The 2,6-substituted materials, as indicated, are commercially available from the oxidative coupling route. Unsubstituted polyphenylene

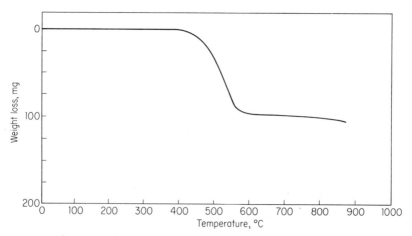

FIG 10.13 *Thermogram for poly-*p-*phenylene sulfide, mol. wt. 7,000 in helium* [12].
Weight of sample, 200 mg; weight of residue, 107.4 mg; temperature rise, 2.9°C per min.

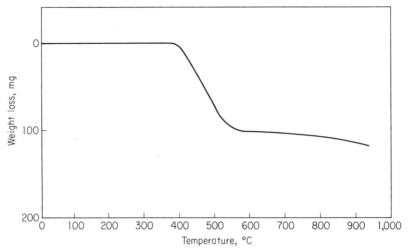

FIG 10.14   *Thermogram for poly-p-phenylene sulfide, mol. wt.* 13,000 *in helium* [12]. *Weight of sample,* 200 *mg; weight of residue,* 79.4 *mg; temperature rise,* 2.9° *C per min.*

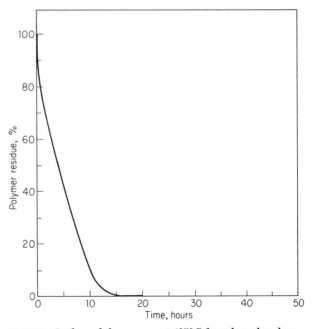

FIG 10.15   *Isothermal thermogram at* 425° *C for poly-p-phenylene sulfide, mol. wt.* 7,000 *in air* [12].   *Substrate: stainless steel; film thickness,* 3 *mil.*

oxides may be produced from the alkali metal salts of m-halophenols according to the following general equation [9]:

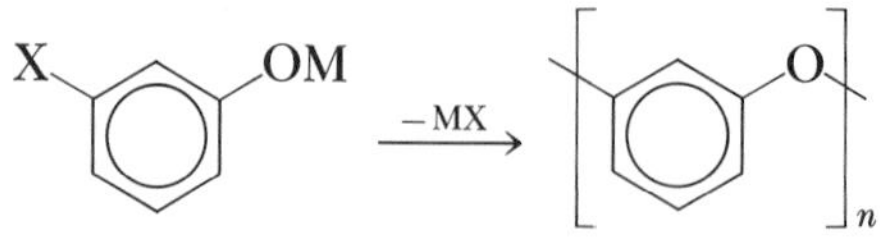

The average molecular weight of such polymers is about 9,000. They are soluble in benzene and xylene and soften at about 120 to 130°C. In air or in nitrogen, they crosslink (presumably by hydrogen abstraction to form biphenyl links) at temperatures of 300 to 350°C. A study of various copper catalysts for the reaction is in progress to obtain higher-molecular-weight species with less side branching [15].

Poly(phenyl alkylenes)

Similar to the poly-p-xylylenes (Chap. 4) are the substituted phenyl methylenes and ethylenes produced from the homopolymerization of benzyl or phenethyl chloride.

Benzyl chloride

Such polymers have been obtained as molecular-weight networks rather than the high-molecular-weight linear species. Linearity can be obtained if the 2,5-positions on the benzene ring are blocked with methyl groups to provide polymers of the following generalized form:

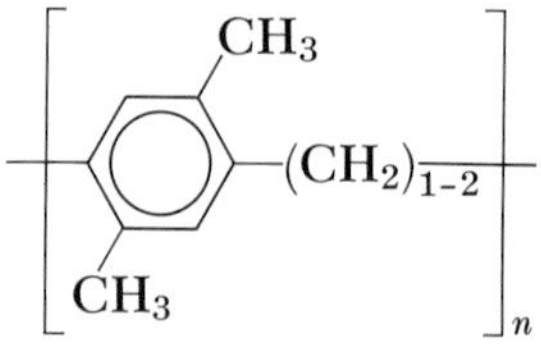

Poly(phenyl alkylenes)

The reaction is conducted in solvent, e.g., o-chlorobenzene, with a Friedel-Crafts catalyst. As catalyst, $AlCl_3$ complexed with nitrobenzene provided a yield of about 90 percent when the reaction was conducted at room temperature [30]. The products provide thermal stability as indicated in Table 10.2, but oxidative instability is encountered, as shown in Table 10.3.

TABLE 10.2 Weight Loss of Poly(2,5-dimethylbenzyl) and Poly(2,5-dimethylphenethyl) in Vacuum [30]

Aging time 1 hour, °C	Weight loss, %	
	Poly(2,5-dimethylbenzyl)	Poly(2,5-dimethylphenethyl)
300	. . . .	Negligible
350	. . . .	Negligible
400	2.8	13
425	5.9	
450	12.6	
475	19.4	

TABLE 10.3 Weight Loss of Poly(2,5-dimethylbenzyl) in Air [30]

Aging time 1 hour, °C	Weight loss, %
290	1.23
340	2.04
375	18.03

HETEROCYCLIC AROMATIC POLYMERS

The heterocyclic ring structures common to this class of polymers are, most generally, formed by heating a high-molecular-weight precursor, which is capable of being worked in solvents, to the final soluble form with the elimination of water or other small molecules during the last stages of conversion. Most systems described bear a basic similarity to one another and to the polybenzimidazoles discussed in Chap. 9, with which they share common synthesis and processing problems.

s-Triazinyl Polyethers

Melt and solution polymerization techniques for obtaining polymers from s-triazines generally provide low-molecular-weight species. High-molecular-weight s-triazinyl polyethers were produced in 1962 by the interfacial polycondensation technique, through the reaction of cyanuric chloride or 2-phenyl-4,6-dichloro-s-triazine with various dihydric aromatic compounds such as resorcinol, hydroquinone, bisphenol A, etc.

The general reaction proceeds:

| Cyanuric chloride | Hydroquinone disodium salt | s-Triazinyl polyether |

When both reactants are difunctional, linear polymers are the result. However, in tests with the aromatic diols, it was found that replacement of the chlorine atoms on the s-triazine nucleus occurs in a stepwise manner and is temperature-dependent [14]. The first chlorine is replaced at 0 to 5°C, the second at 15 to 20°C, and the third at 30 to 40°C. Thus, by the interfacial polycondensation technique, it is possible to develop linear polymers from cyanuric chloride. The polymers are withdrawn from the reaction as collapsed tubes. Thermograms of three of the better compounds, in air and in nitrogen, are given in Figs. 10.16 and 10.17.

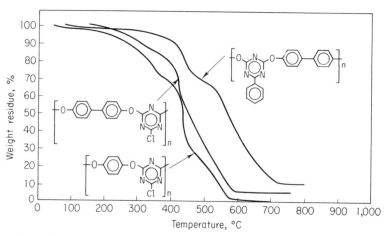

FIG 10.16 *Thermograms of* s-*triazinyl polyethers in air* [14]. *Heating rate, 90° per min.*

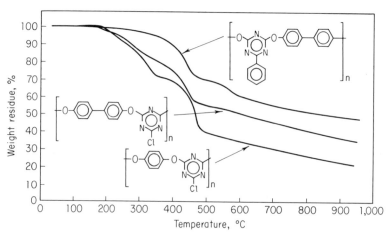

FIG 10.17 *Thermograms of* s-*triazinyl polyethers in nitrogen* [14]. *Heating rate, 90° per min.*

Polybenzothiazoles

Similar to the polybenzimidazoles are the polybenzothiazoles.   These are prepared from 3,3′-dimercaptobenzidine and the diacid, diphenyl ester, diacid chloride, etc., (e.g., diphenyl isophthalate).   The reactions are fairly complicated, and the routes somewhat uncertain.   In all cases, a soluble precursor is formed, which subsequently is converted to the final, hetero-cyclic structure by the removal of a small molecule.

Using diphenyl esters, the reaction may progress as follows [46]:

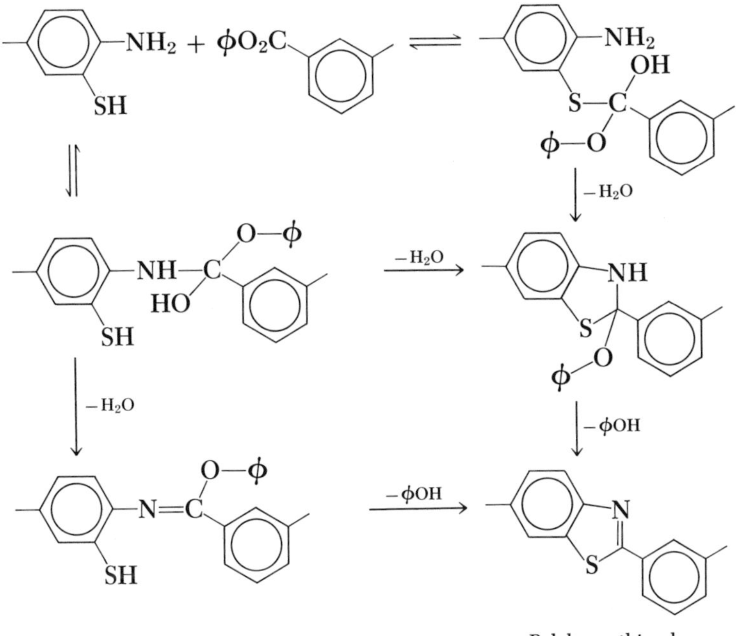

Polybenzothiazole

Typical of the structures synthesized by this procedure are the following [23]:

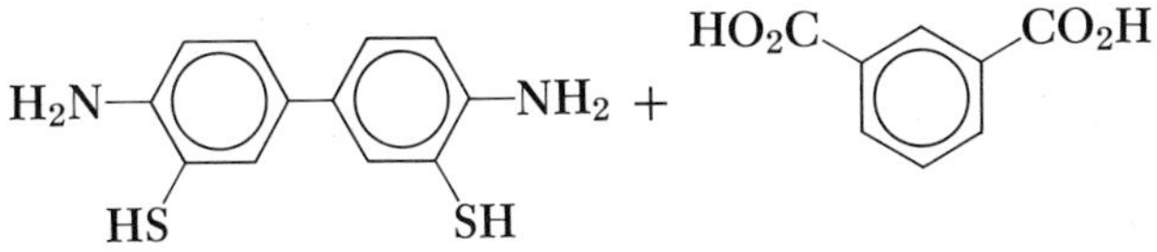

3,3′-Dimercaptobenzidine   Isophthalic acid

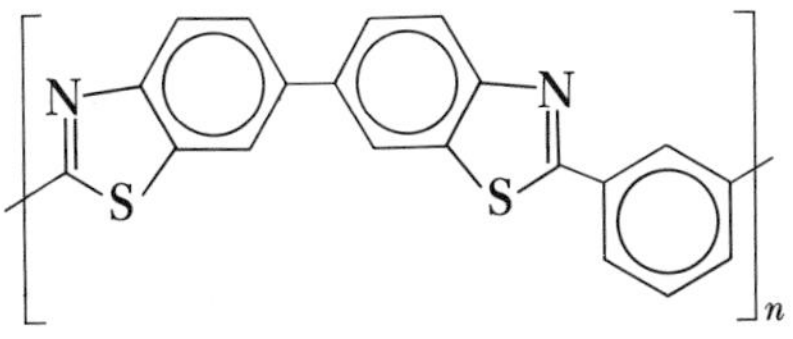

Poly-2,2′-(m-phenylene)-6,6′-bibenzothiazole

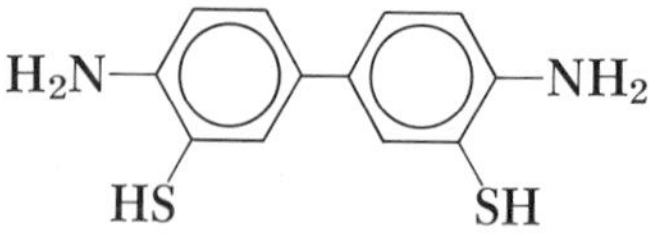

3,3'-Dimercaptobenzidine

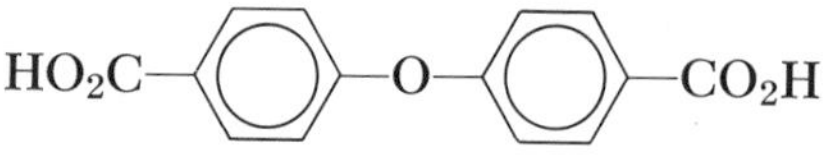

p-Oxydibenzoic acid

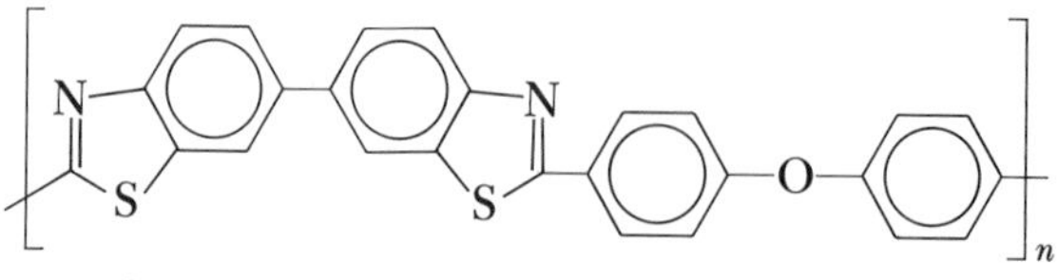

Poly-2,2'-[*p,p*'-oxybis(phenylene)]-6,6'-bibenzothiazole

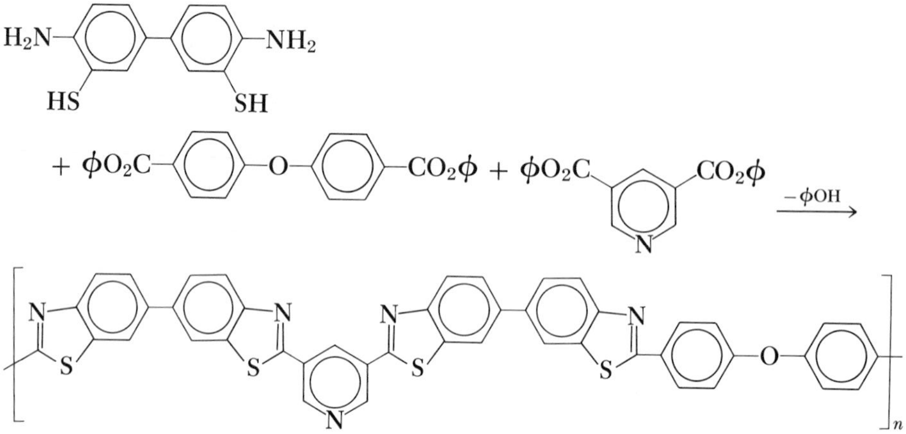

Poly-2,2'-[*p,p*'-oxybis(phenylene)-6,6'-bibenzothiazolyl]-2,2'-(3,5-pyridinediyl)-
6,6'-bibenzothiazole

The hydrochloric acid salt of 3,3'-dimercaptobenzidine may be used along with the diacid chloride [46]:

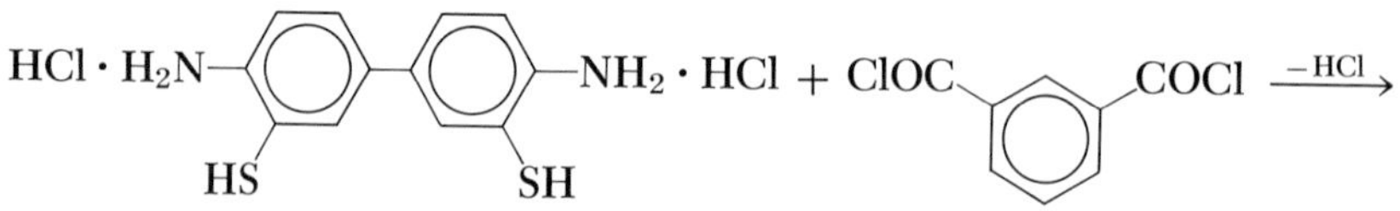

3,3-Dimercaptobenzidine dihydrochloride

Isophthaloyl chloride

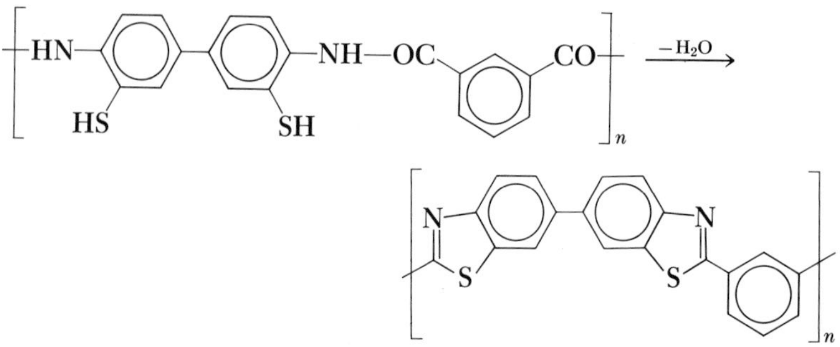

Use of the hydrochloric acid salt overcomes the problem of sensitivity to air oxidation of the parent mercaptoamine. The above reaction is conducted in N,N-diethylaniline or polyphosphoric acid [46]. Alternatively, the following route may be used [45]:

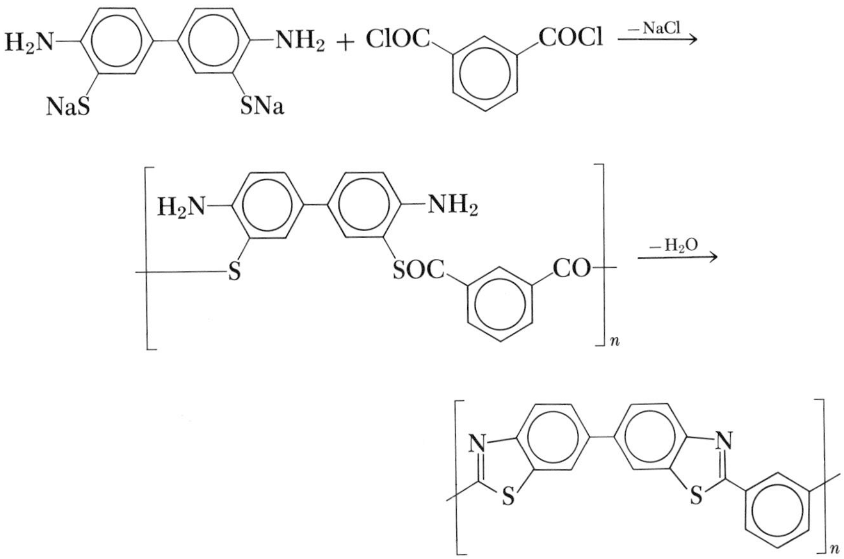

$$H_2N- \text{(structure)} -NH_2 + ClOC- \text{(structure)} -COCl \xrightarrow{-NaCl}$$

with NaS and SNa substituents

$$\left[H_2N- \text{(structure)} -NH_2 \atop -S \text{(structure)} SOC- \text{(structure)} -CO- \right]_n \xrightarrow{-H_2O}$$

$$\left[\text{(benzothiazole structure)} \right]_n$$

In this case, the thioester prepolymer, under alkaline conditions, partially rearranges to the polyamide according to the following [45]:

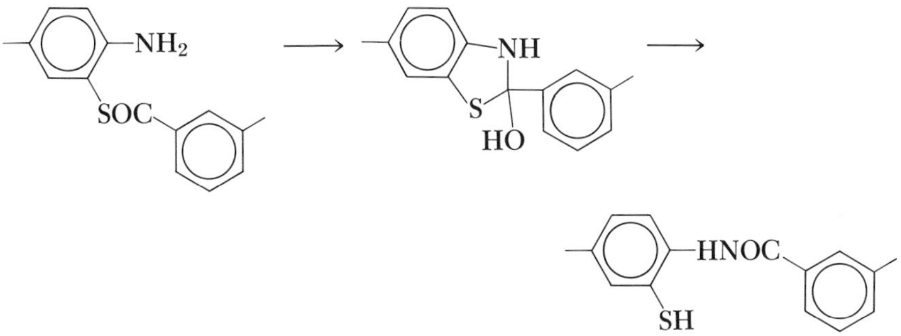

$$\text{(structure with } -NH_2, SOC) \longrightarrow \text{(structure with } -NH, S, HO) \longrightarrow$$

$$\text{(structure with } -HNOC, SH)$$

Other techniques involve condensation of 3-mercapto-4-aminobenzoic acid using polyphosphoric acid (PPA) as a catalyst [45]:

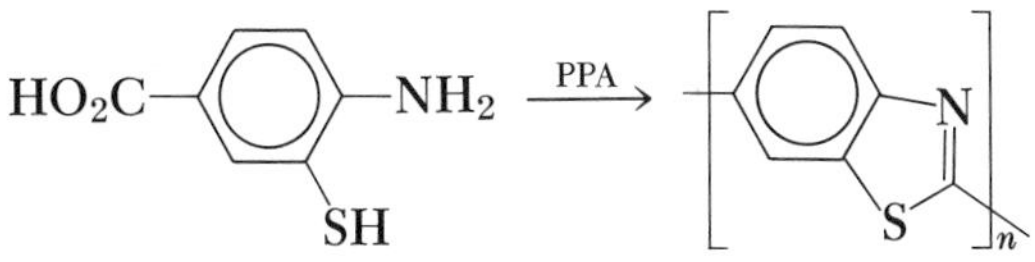

$$HO_2C- \text{(structure)} -NH_2 \xrightarrow{PPA} \left[\text{(benzothiazole structure)} \right]_n$$

with SH substituent

or using diamides, such as the following:

$$HCl \cdot H_2N-\text{⬡}-\text{⬡}-NH_2 \cdot HCl + H_2NOC-CONH_2 \xrightarrow{PPA}$$

3,3'-Dimercaptobenzidine   Oxamide

Polybibenzothiazole

Other aromatic polymers containing thiazole rings have been suggested. For example [8]:

$$\text{Dithio-1,4-benzenedicarboxamide} + BrCH_2C-\text{⬡}-CCH_2Br \xrightarrow{-H_2O}$$

Dithio-1,4-benzenedicarboxamide   p-Bis(bromoacetyl)-benzene

Poly(2,5-thiazolyl-p-phenylene)

The material gives clear, brown, tough films, with a modulus of 220,000 psi, tensile strengths of 10,000 psi, elongations of 7 percent, volume resistivity of 8×10^{15} ohm-cm, and dielectric constant of 3.6. In air, the weight loss is 2 percent at 400°C, and in helium 2 percent at 500°C [41]. The aromatic rings may be hydrogenated to provide alicyclic species with 2 percent weight loss in air at 320°C [41]. Attempts to synthesize the following polythiazole (a polythiazolothiazole) did not result in clean-cut reactions or a satisfactory product [23]:

$$H_2NSC-CSNH_2 + OHC-\text{⬡}-CHO \xrightarrow{-H_2O}$$

Dithiooxamide   Terephthalaldehyde

Typical reaction conditions for polybenzothiazoles are indicated in Table 10.4. As can be appreciated, many of the problems associated with the synthesis of the polybenzimidazoles are common to the synthesis of the polybenzothiazoles. Typical TGA data for representative polymers are given in Fig. 10.18.

Polybenzoxazoles

Similar to the polybenzothiazoles are the polybenzoxazoles. In these, oxygen replaces the sulfur atom of the previous polymers. The materials are synthesized from 4,4'-dihydroxy-*m*-benzidine and isophthaloyl chloride (or isophthalamide) as follows, in simplified form:

Polybenzoxazole

The amine is dissolved in dimethyl acetamide/pyridine and the acid chloride in cyclohexanone. The acid chloride is added dropwise to produce the polyamide (Fig. 10.19), which is soluble in *N*-methyl-2-pyrrolidone and dimethyl acetamide. Heating the polyamide produces the converted product (Fig. 10.20). If conversion is conducted in air at temperatures above 220°C, oxidative degradation occurs, as shown in Fig. 10.21. In the same figure, TGA data for the converted polymer are given.

Similar compounds, by both solution and melt polymerization, have been synthesized from 2-amino-4-cyanophenol [60]. Polyphosphoric acid may be used as a catalyst [65]:

TABLE 10.4 Benzothiazole Polymers from 3,3'-Dimercaptobenzidine [54]

Carboxylic reactant	Reaction conditions			Postreaction polymerization conditions in vacuo	Color	Maximum inherent viscosity	TGA,° % weight loss to:	
	Medium	Temperature, °C	Time, hours				538°C	593°C
ϕO_2C—⬡—$CO_2\phi$	$Et_2N\text{-}\phi$	215	5	2 hours at 400°C	Yellowish brown	0.48	2.0	4.0
NC—⬡—CN	$Et_2N\text{-}\phi$	215	17	1 hour at 400°C	Yellow	0.30	2.4	7.3
ϕO_2C—⬡—O—⬡—$CO_2\phi$	$Et_2N\text{-}\phi$	215	25	1 hour at 400°C	Green	0.50	2.1	4.8
ϕO_2C—⬡—O—⬡—$CO_2\phi$	$Et_2N\text{-}\phi$	215	5	1 hour at 400°C	Brown	Insoluble	3.1	6.9
ϕO_2C—⬡(N)—$CO_2\phi$	PPA	200	1	.....	Yellow	1.51†	0	0

Structure					Color			
HO$_2$C–⬡–CO$_2$H	PPA	240	3.3	· · · ·	Yellow	0.47	2.9	8.3
H$_2$NOC–⬡–CONH$_2$	PPA	250	18	· · · ·	Yellow	0.49	0	1.0
HO$_2$C–⬡(N)–CO$_2$H	PPA	250	21	1 hour at 400°C	Brown	0.41	3.2	6.4
HO$_2$C–⬡–O–⬡–CO$_2$H	PPA	250	21	· · · ·	Light green	0.62	1.8	3.6
MeO$_2$C–⬡–CO–⬡–CO$_2$Me	PPA	160	2	1 hour at 400°C	Orange	0.36	3.9	8.8

° $\Delta T = 3.2°\mathrm{C/min}$.

† Highly pure dimercaptobenzidine employed, 0.30% H$_2$SO$_4$ solution.

337

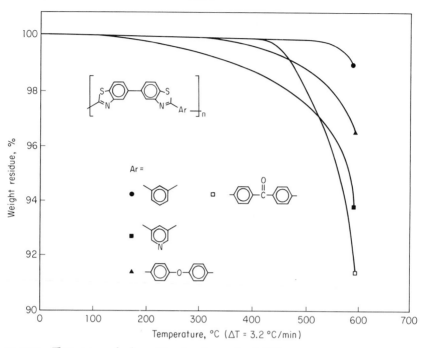

FIG 10.18 *Thermograms for benzothiazole polymers in air* [23].

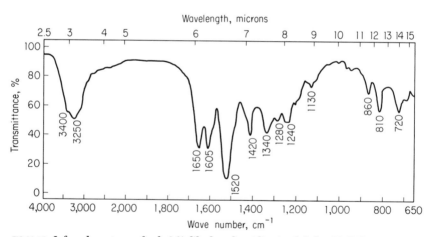

FIG 10.19 *Infrared spectrum of poly-3,3'-dihydroxybenzidine isophthalamide* [26].

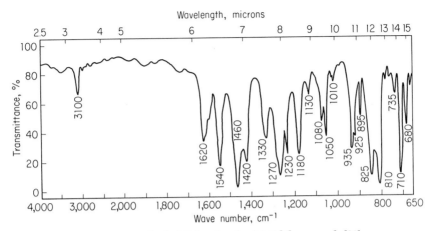

FIG 10.20   *Infrared spectrum of poly-2,2'-(m-phenylene)-6,6'-bibenzoxazole* [26].

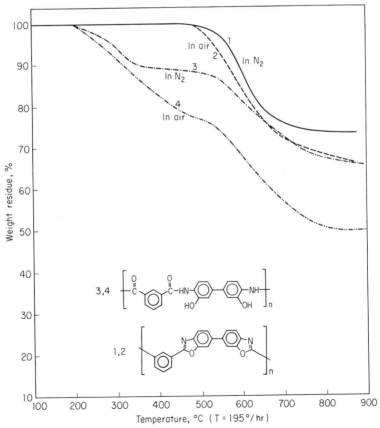

FIG 10.21   *Thermograms for polyamide and polybenzoxazole in nitrogen and air* [26].

Polyoxadiazoles

Similar to the polybenzoxazoles are the polyoxadiazoles. The generalized reaction for their synthesis is as follows:

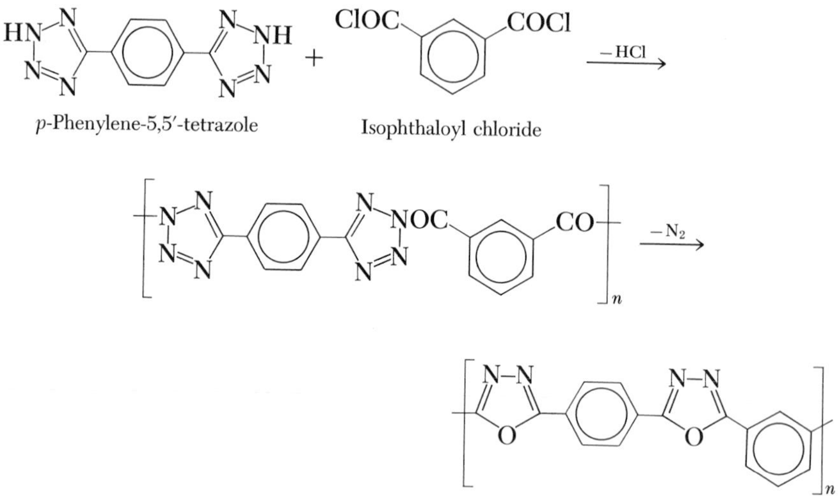

p-Phenylene-5,5'-tetrazole   Isophthaloyl chloride

Poly(m,p-phenylene-3,5-oxadiazolylene)

Preparations for a number of these polymers are shown in Table 10.5. TGA data are given in Fig. 10.22. Only minor weight loss was observed below 450°C in air, and an abrupt weight loss occurred above that temperature for poly(m-phenylene-1,3-4-oxadiazole) [49].

Polyoxadiazoles may also be obtained by heating polyhydrazides (see the section Triazole Polymers). The reaction can be represented as follows:

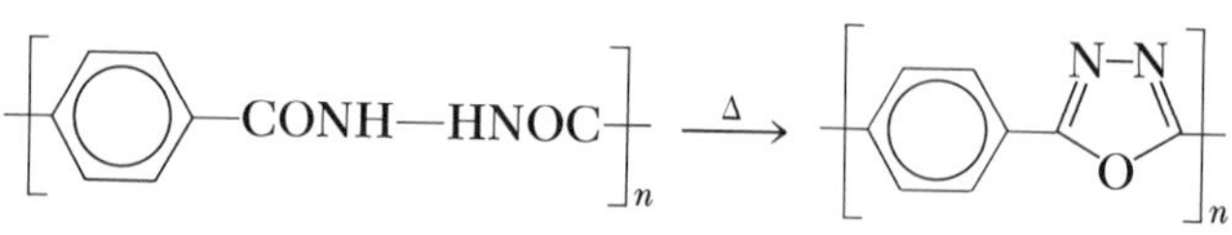

Fibers prepared from the polyhydrazides have been converted to the polyoxadiazoles [61]. These show essentially no change in properties up to about 200°C and retain 60 percent or better of room-temperature properties even at 300°C [20]. Properties of these fibers are given in Tables 10.6 and 10.7. Thermograms indicate little variation in thermal stability with increasing molecular weight of the polymer, as indicated in Fig. 10.23. Thermal stabilities of the parent polyhydrazide and the oxidiazole are compared in Fig. 10.24.

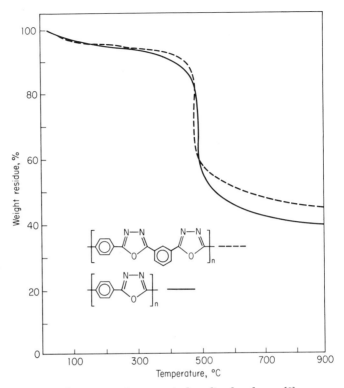

FIG 10.22   *Thermograms for two typical oxadiazole polymers* [6].

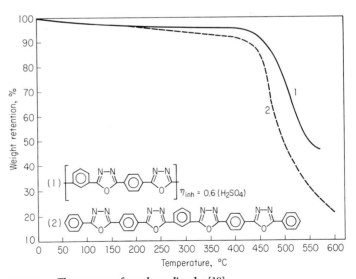

FIG 10.23   *Thermograms for polyoxadiazoles* [19].

TABLE 10.5 Preparation of Polyoxadiazoles [6]

	Polymer	Monomers
I	(structure: N–N oxadiazole)	4 g p-phenylenebistetrazole 3.7944 g terephthaloyl chloride
II	(structure: N–N oxadiazole)	4 g p-phenylenebistetrazole 3.7944 g isophthaloyl chloride 4 g m-phenylenebistetrazole 3.7944 g terephthaloyl chloride
III	(structure: N–N oxadiazole)	4 g m-phenylenebistetrazole 3.7944 g isophthaloyl chloride
IV	(structure: N–N oxadiazole)	2.7304 g p-phenylenebistetrazole 3.5597 g p,p'-biphenyldicarboxylic acid chloride
V	(structure: N–N oxadiazole)	3.8351 g p-phenylenebistetrazole 5.0000 g 2,2'-biphenyldicarboxylic acid chloride
VI	(structure: N–N oxadiazole)	3.0118 g p-phenylenebistetrazole 1.7860 g oxaloyl chloride
VII	(structure: N–N oxadiazole)	3.0118 g m-phenylenebistetrazole 1.7860 g oxaloyl chloride
VIII	(structure: N–N oxadiazole $(CH_2)_7$)	5.0277 g p-phenylenebistetrazole 5.2861 g azelaoyl chloride
IX	(structure: N–N oxadiazole)	4 g p-phenylenebistetrazole 3.8131 g pyridine-2,6-dicarboxylic acid chloride
X	(structure: N–N oxadiazole)	4 g m-phenylenebistetrazole 3.8131 g pyridine-2,6-dicarboxylic acid chloride

TABLE 10.5   (Continued)

Amount of pyridine, ml	Reflux time, hours	Dilution solvent	Yield, grams	Inherent viscosity, % H_2SO_4			
				0.2	0.1	0.05	0.025
130	72	3 liters CH_2Cl_2	4.0	0.129	0.125	0.063	0.042
110	72	2 liters CH_2Cl_2	3.00	0.148	0.191	0.215	0.322
100	120	3 liters CH_2Cl_2	3.90	0.157	0.213	0.214	0.258
100	120	3 liters CH_2Cl_2	3.50	0.134	0.171	0.257	0.172
23	96	3 liters CH_2Cl_2	4.00	0.054	0.030		
25	96	3 liters H_2O	4.97	0.086	0.078		
120	96	2 liters CH_2Cl_2	1.20	Partially insoluble			
120	96	2 liters CH_2Cl_2	0.70	Partially insoluble			
100	72	3 liters CH_3OH	4.00	0.148	0.170	0.210	0.342
100	72	3 liters H_2O	3.00	0.104	0.156	0.209	0.376
100	72	3 liters H_2O	2.00	0.099	0.146	0.188	0.293

TABLE 10.6 Initial Poly-1,3,4-oxadiazole Fiber Properties [20]

Straight:	
T/E/M°	2.6/3.1/124
Denier	3.0
Loop:	
T/E°	1.8/2.8
Denier	3.9
Knot:	
T/E/M°	2.3/2.8/79
Denier	3.0
X-ray crystallinity, amount/perfection.............	Low/low
X-ray orientation, degrees........................	31–38
Oxygen analysis (theoretical 11.10%), %	12.10

° T = tensile strength. E = elongation. M = modulus of elasticity.

TABLE 10.7 Retention of Fiber Properties of Poly-1,3,4-oxadiazole Fiber after Exposure at Elevated Temperatures [20]

Thermal treatment				
Temperature, °C	Medium	Time, hours	T/E/M/denier°	% retention, T/E/M°
300	Air	6	2.6/3.2/103/3.0	100/100/81.2
		96	1.2/1.2/87/2.7	46.2/38.1/70.0
		168†	1.2/1.2/112/2.7	46.2/38.1/90.3
350	Air	24	2.1/2.2/103/2.7	80.8/71.0/83.1
		48	2.1/2.2/93/2.9	80.8/67.7/91.1
		96‡	1.1/1.1/102/3.3	42.3/32.3/82.3
375	Air§	4	1.9/2.2/72/2.8	73.1/71.0/58.1
		6	1.7/1.7/66/2.7	64.4/54.8/53.2
		48‡	1.6/1.3/100/2.7	61.5/41.9/80.6
400	Air	4	2.1/1.9/81/2.5	80.8/61.3/65.3
		24	2.5/2.6/67/2.6	96.2/83.9/54.0
		40‡	1.8/1.8/84/2.8	69.2/58.0/67.7
450	Air	>1	Disintegration of fiber	
300	N₂	2	2.7/4.2/104/3.3	>100/>100/84.0
		24	2.3/2.4/107/2.9	92.5/77.5/86.5
		150‡	1.7/1.6/87/2.9	65.4/51.6/70.0
350	N₂	24	2.3/2.2/132/2.9	88.5/71.0/>100
		48	2.8/2.6/128/2.8	96.2/83.9/>100
		96‡	1.2/1.2/83/2.7	46.2/38.7/66.9
375	N₂	6	1.2/1.2/97/3.3	46.2/38.7/78.2
		24	1.6/1.4/112/2.7	61.5/45.2/90.3
		48‡	1.3/1.1/92/3.0	50.0/35.5/74.2
400	N₂	4	1.7/1.8/100/3.0	65.8/58.1/80.6
		6	1.6/1.5/89/2.9	59.6/48.4/71.8
		24‡	1.3/1.2/102/2.8	50.4/38.7/82.3
450	N₂	>1	Disintegration of fiber	

° T = tensile strength. E = elongation. M = modulus of elasticity. Retention of properties expressed as percent of initial properties (Table 10.6) for straight fiber: T/E/M = 2.6/3.1/124.
† Fiber was too brittle to test in duplicate experiment.
‡ Longer exposure produced fiber which was too brittle to test.
§ Fiber samples degraded partially in duplicate runs owing to uneven heating.

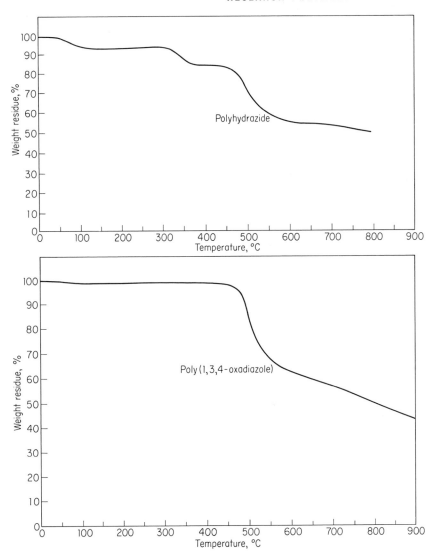

FIG 10.24 *Thermograms of polyhydrazide and poly(1,3,4-oxadiazole) in nitrogen* [18].

Polythiadiazoles

Similar to the polyoxadiazoles are the polythiadiazoles. The aromatic materials have been produced in fiber form by cyclizing an aromatic poly-oxathiahydrazide at 200 to 250°C:

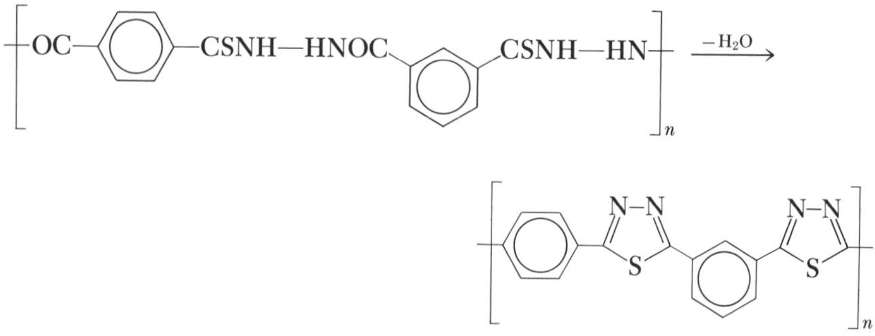

$$\left[\text{OC}-\bigcirc-\text{CSNH}-\text{HNOC}-\bigcirc-\text{CSNH}-\text{HN}\right]_n \quad \xrightarrow{-\text{H}_2\text{O}}$$

Polythiadiazole

These fibers retain 92 percent of original tenacity after aging 144 hours at 300°C in both air and nitrogen [60].

Polyoxadiazolyls

Polyoxadiazolyls are produced from the reaction of terephthalonitrile oxide

$$\text{O}\leftarrow\text{N}\equiv\text{C}-\bigcirc-\text{C}\equiv\text{N}\rightarrow\text{O}$$

Terephthalonitrile oxide (TNO)

with itself or with p-diethynylbenzene, benzoquinone, allylene, etc. Typical structures are as follows:

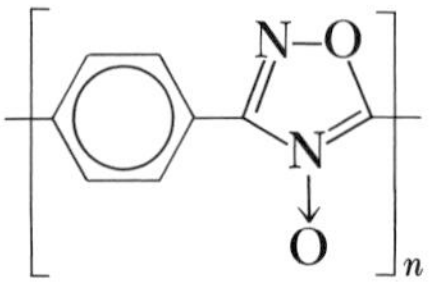

From TNO

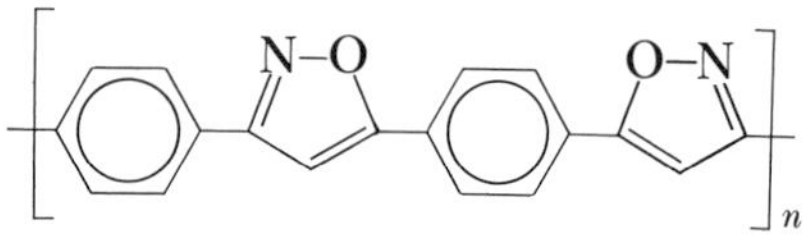

From TNO and p-diethynylbenzene

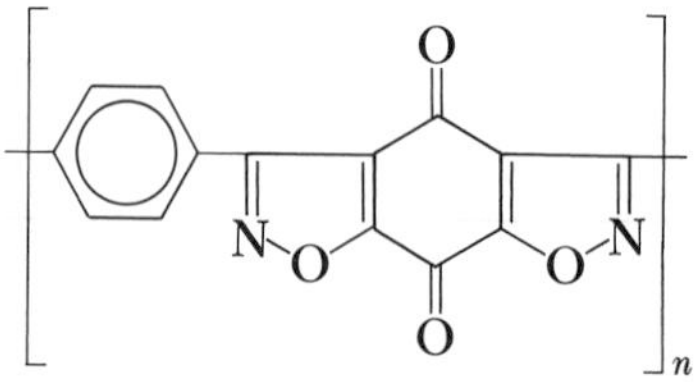

From TNO and benzoquinone

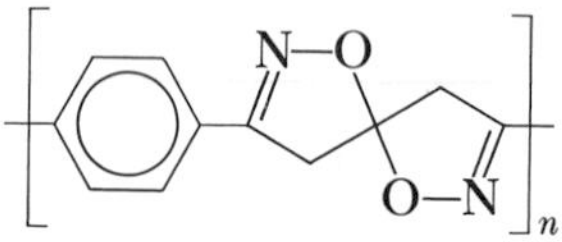

From TNO and allylene

Triazole Polymers

Similar to the previous materials are the poly(m-p-phenylene 4-phenyl-triazoles). They may be synthesized as shown in Table 10.8.

Alternatively, a linear prepolymer may be obtained as follows, using hexamethylphosphoramide (HMPA) as catalyst:

TABLE 10.8 Preparation of Polyoxatrizoles [6]

Polymer	Monomers	Amount of pyridine, ml	Reflux time, hours	Dilution solvent	Yield grams	Intrinsic viscosity, concentrated formic acid			
						0.2	0.1	0.5	0.025
$\left[\text{structure: } N\text{-}N \ /\ N\text{-}N \ \phi \right]_n$	1.7990 g p-phenylenebistetrazole 2.9676 g N,N'-diphenyl-isophthalimide chloride	80	120	H₂O	3.00	0.238	0.328	0.482	0.81 / 0.025
$\left[\text{structure: } N\text{-}N \ /\ N\text{-}N \ \phi \right]_n$	3 g m-phenylenebistetrazole 4.9486 g N,N'-diphenyl-isophthalimide chloride	100	120	3 liters H₂O	5.00	0.225	0.316	0.375	0.81

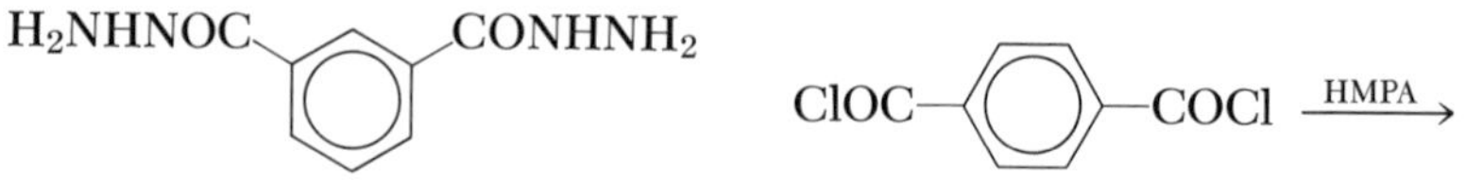

H$_2$NHNOC—[isophthaloyl ring]—CONHNH$_2$

Isophthaloyl hydrazide

ClOC—[ring]—COCl $\xrightarrow{\text{HMPA}}$

Terephthaloyl chloride

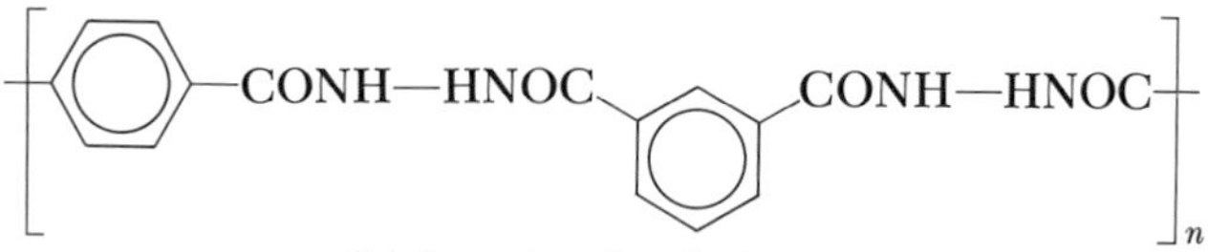

+[ring]—CONH—HNOC—[ring]—CONH—HNOC+$_n$

Poly(m,p-phenylene hydrazide)

The poly(m-p-phenylene hydrazide) is soluble and may then be reacted in solution with aniline using polyphosphoric acid as a catalyst:

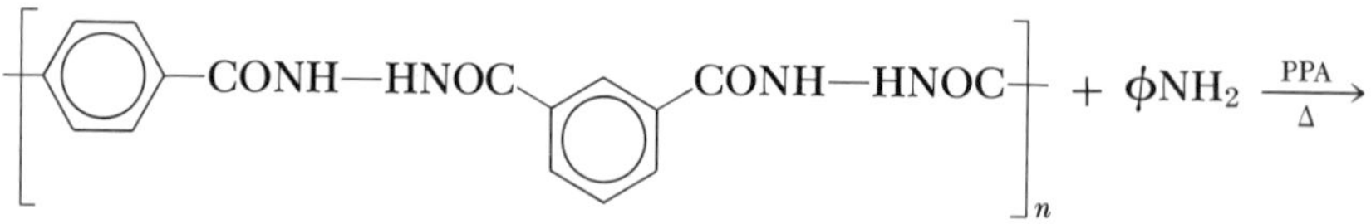

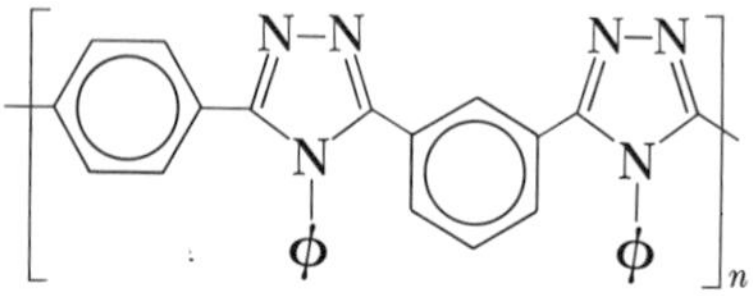

+[ring]—CONH—HNOC—[ring]—CONH—HNOC+$_n$ + ϕNH$_2$ $\xrightarrow[\Delta]{\text{PPA}}$

+[ring]—[N–N triazole ring with ϕ]—[ring]—[N–N triazole ring with ϕ]+$_n$

Poly(m,p-phenylene-4-phenyl-1,2,4-triazole)

Fibers from this compound retain 30 percent of their room-temperature strengths at 300°C [63].

1,2,4-Triazole polymers have been reported from the following reaction [13]:

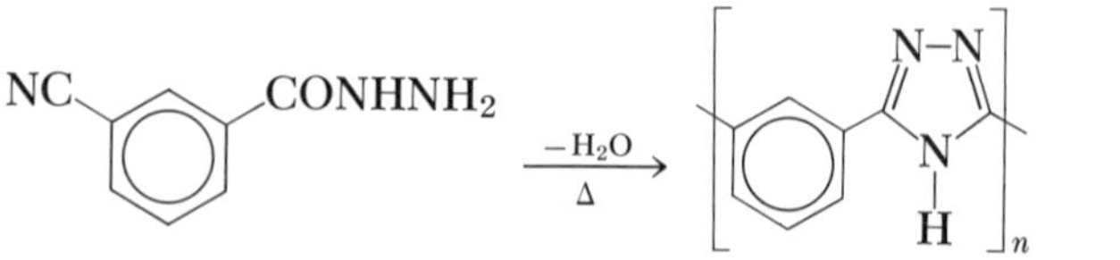

NC—[ring]—CONHNH$_2$ $\xrightarrow[\Delta]{-\text{H}_2\text{O}}$ +[ring]—[N–N triazole ring with H]+$_n$

m-Cyanobenzohydrazide   Poly(m-phenylene-3,5-triazole)

The polyaminotriazoles have melting points from 200 to 340°C and are not decomposed upon boiling with concentrated acids and bases [4].

Tetraazopyrenes

1,4,5,8-Tetraaminonaphthalene and diacid chlorides have been reacted to produce tetraazopyrenes by the following route [16]:

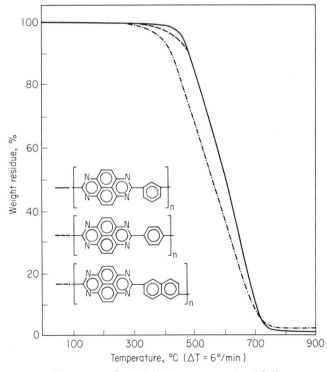

$$H_2N-\bigcirc-NH_2 \atop H_2N-\bigcirc-NH_2 + ClOC-\bigcirc-COCl \xrightarrow[-HCl]{-H_2O}$$

$$\left[\begin{array}{c} HN-\bigcirc-NH \\ N-\bigcirc-N \end{array}-\bigcirc-\right]_n \xrightarrow{[O]} \left[\begin{array}{c} N-\bigcirc-N \\ N-\bigcirc-N \end{array}-\bigcirc-\right]_n$$

TGA data, in air and in nitrogen, for several of these polymers are given in Figs. 10.25 and 10.26.

Polyquinoxalines

The polyquinoxalines are another class of high-temperature polymers and are prepared from bis-*o*-diamines and bisglyoxalyls [21, 32]:

FIG 10.25 *Thermograms for typical tetraazopyrenes in air* [16].

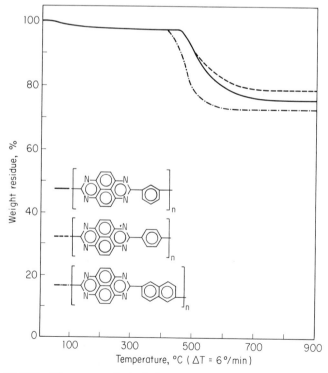

3,3′-Diaminobenzidine   p-Phenylenediglyoxal

Polyquinoxaline

As can be seen from the structures above, there are two ways in which each new ring can form; however, only the 2,2′-polyqinoxalines are isolated [32]. Other reagents used to form this type of polymer are: bis-3,4-diaminophenyl ether; bis-3,4-diaminophenyl sulfide; bis-2,3-diaminophenyl sulfone; 4,4′-diglyoxalyl phenyl ether, 4,4′-diglyoxalyl phenyl sulfide and sulfone; 1,4 and 1,3-diglyoxalylbenzene [55, 66].

FIG 10.26   *Thermograms for typical tetraazopyrenes in nitrogen* [16].

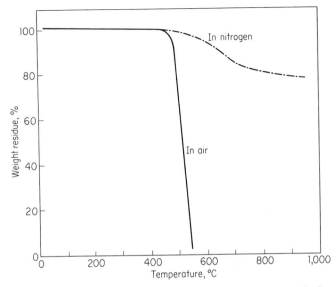

FIG 10.27   *Thermogram of poly[2,2'-(1,4-phenylene)-6,6-diquinoxaline]*
[32].   *Heating rate, 1.5° C per min.*

These polymers are formed in dioxane or DMAC solutions as prepolymers and then cured by heating at 250° C in vacuum. These infusible solids are soluble only in the strongest solvents such as sulfuric acid; however, the polymers formed from the phenyl ethers are more soluble [55].

Film can be casted using the lower-molecular-weight polymers and hexamethylphosphoramide as a solvent. The films are cured by heating to 350 to 400° C in vacuum to give tough, insoluble films [55].

These polymers are very thermally stable, losing no weight upon being heated in air or nitrogen up to 450 to 500° C [22, 31], but above 500° C in air the polyquinoxalines oxidize rapidly losing over 80 percent of their weight by 600° C. In nitrogen the polyquinoxalines can be heated to 1000° C with only 20 percent weight loss. Figure 10.27 shows a typical thermogram.

Polyquinoxalines have been prepared, using 4,4'-oxydibenzil and 4,4'-dibenzil to give polymers that have the remaining hydrogen of the heterocyclic ring replaced by a phenyl group. These polymers had TGA breaks about 20° C higher than the corresponding hydrogen-containing materials; however, the phenyl polymers were considerably more stable when tested isothermally at 370° C—isothermal testing being a better test of stability [71].

Using 3,3'-diaminobenzidine and 6,6'-bis(2,3-dihydroxyquinoxaline), a more highly ring-fused polyquinoxaline is formed [23]:

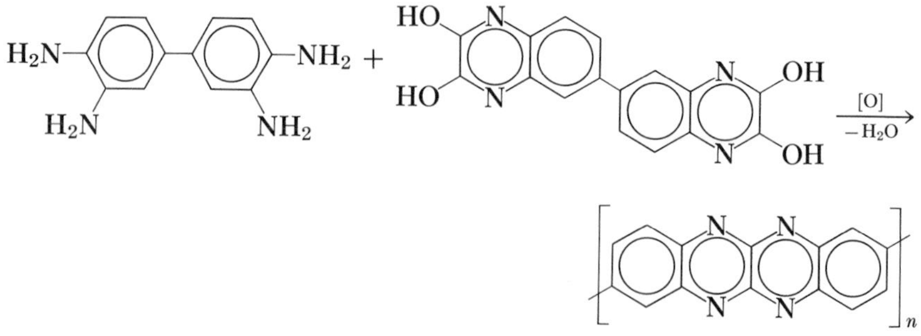

A true ladder polyquinoxaline is formed by using 1,2,4,5-tetramino-benzene and 2,5-dihydroxy-p-benzoquinone as monomer [67]:

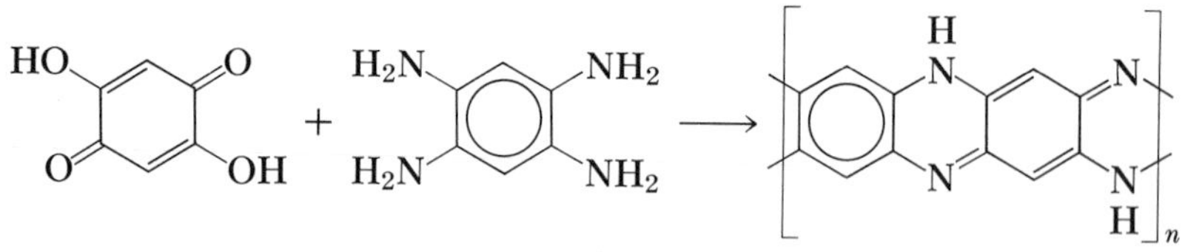

Other possible monomers are: 2,3,6,7-tetraminodibenzo-p-dioxane; 3,6-diaminoresorcinol; 2,5-dihydroxy-3,6-dichlorobenzoquinone; 2,5-dihydroxybenzoquinone diacetate; 1,2,6,7-tetraketopyrene; 1,2,5,6-anthradiquinone; and 3,3,6,6-tetramethyl-1,2,4,5-cyclohexanetetrone [74].

At elevated temperatures this type of polymer should lose hydrogen to become fully aromatic, but its stability in air is no better than that of the linear polyquinoxalines.

Mixed quinoxaline and thiazine or oxazine have also been prepared as true ladder polymers [73]:

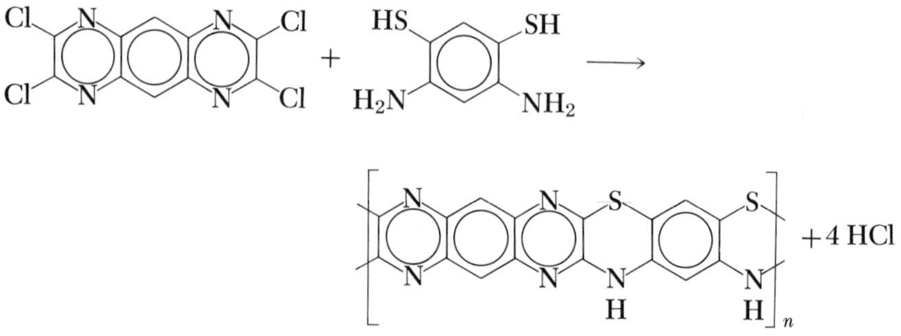

Also partial ladder polymers with blocks of four or seven fused rings were prepared. Very few physical data have been published, but the thiazine ladder polyquinoxaline seem to be stable up to 500°C.

Polyimidazopyrrolones (Pyrrones)

Polyimidazopyrrolones are produced from tetraaminodiphenyl ether, diaminobenzidine, or other aromatic tetramines and dianhydrides. Typically with PMDA, the reaction proceeds:

Polyimidazopyrrolone

Both pyromellitic dianhydride and benzophenonetetracarboxylic dianhydride have been employed in the synthesis [37].

The proposed structure (as is generally the case with these high-temperature polymers) is supported by infrared evidence, as shown in Fig. 10.28. Both the polyamic acid-amine stage and the converted stage are shown. The disappearance of secondary amide bands at 1650, 1540, and 1280 cm^{-1} is apparent as well as that of carboxyl bands at 1720, 1605, and 1225 cm^{-1}.

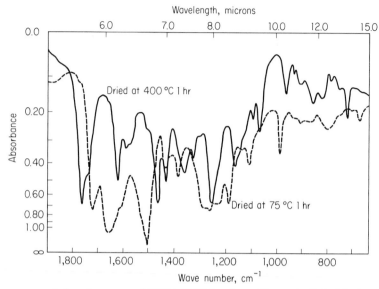

FIG 10.28   *Infrared spectrum of PMDA-TADPO polymer film, 0.15 mil thick* [37].

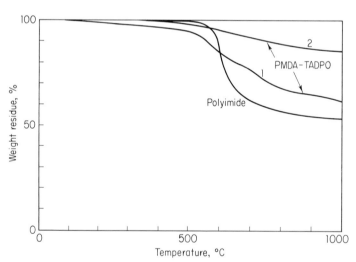

FIG 10.29   *Thermogram of PMDA-TADPO pyrrone and polyimide films in vacuum* [37].   (1) *Low state of conversion;* (2) *high state of conversion.*

The development of imide bands at 1765 and 720 cm^{-1} along with the appearance of an imidazole band at 1620 cm^{-1} further supports the proposed structure [37].

The initial polyamic acid-amine stage is soluble in dimethylformamide, dimethyl acetamide, dimethyl sulfoxide, etc.   The two consecutive cyclo-dehydrations, accomplished by heating, give the insoluble polymer.   Trouble has been experienced with solvent removal, as well as with removal of the formed water. The system appears to hold the solvent with some tenacity. The extent to which complete removal of the volatiles influences properties is indicated in Fig. 10.29, where TGA data are given in comparison with the commercial polyimide film. The T_g of the full converted polyimidaz-opyrrolone is 475°C.

Materials not containing the ether links are prepared from 3,3'-diamino-benzidine [59]. These are synthesized in a similar fashion. During synthesis, it is necessary to use precisely equimolar amounts of reagents. A small excess of amine causes low inherent viscosities, and excess anhydride causes gelation.

The deep red, flexible film of the polybenzoylenebenzimidazole has a tensile modulus of 700,000 psi, tenacity of 11,000 psi, and elongation of 2 percent. Thermogravimetric analysis in air shows very little weight loss until 550°C. Differential thermal analysis shows no exotherm below 600°C.

More recent work shows that this film can have a tangent modulus up to 1,000,000 and that the thermal stability of eight different pyrrones in air was within 50°C of one another (500 to 550°C) [70].

It has been proposed to prepare a hydrogen-free polymer using pyrazine-tetracarboxylic acid dianhydride:

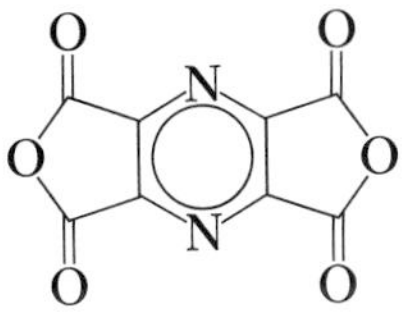

Alternatively an oxygen-free polymer may be obtained as poly(6,6'-phenyl-ene-9,9'-bibenzimidazox[1,2-c]quinazoline):

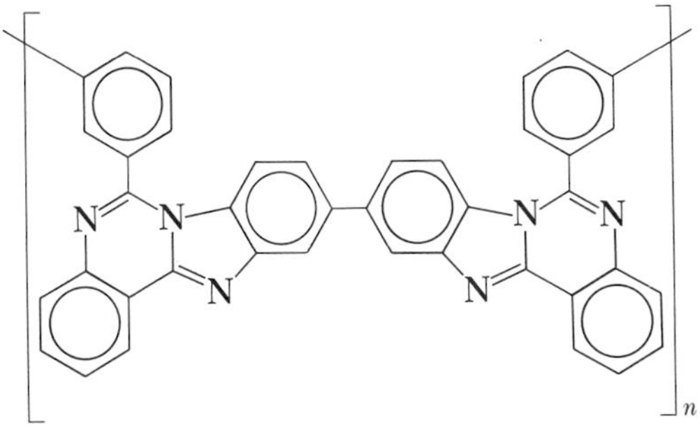

This structure is available from a 2,2'-bis-2-aminophenyl-5,5'-bibenzimid-azole (from 3,3'-diaminobenzidine and 2-aminobenzoic acid), which may be converted to the final product by addition of diphenyl isophthalate and further heating.

Materials based on napthalenetetracarboxylic acids and aromatic tetra-amines have been prepared and are structurally similar to the preceding materials [69]. These polymers lose less than 1 percent of their weight when heated up to 600°C in nitrogen and lose less than 10 percent in air up to 550°C. After heating at 315°C for 1,000 hours in air, the weight loss is less than 10 percent. The materials are soluble only in concentrated sulfuric acid, pyrophosphoric acid, methane- or benzenesulfonic acids, 85 percent phosphoric acid, and concentrated aqueous alkali, but not in DMF, DMSO, etc. Typical properties are as follows:

Tensile strength,	15,000–22,000 psi
Elongation,	3–7%
Young's modulus,	600,000–1,000,000 psi
Specific resistivity,	$3-5 \times 10^{12}$ ohm-cm
Field strength,	6×10^5 μ/cm

Unusually high resistance to ionizing radiation has been noted with no significant effect on tensile properties, even after 10,000 megarads.

The polybisbenzimidazobenzophenanthrolines have been made into fibers by wet spinning from 98 percent sulfuric acid solution [62]. Preliminary results for properties of the fibers give tenacities up to 3.4 grams per denier with 50 percent of the room-temperature strength being maintained at 550°C and a zero strength point at 700°C.

When both the tetraamine precursor and the dianhydride are mononuclear, a truly aromatic ladder polymer is produced.

From the structure it is apparent that improved thermal stability should be obtained with ladder polymers. In order for thermal chain scission to occur in these species, it is necessary to break two bonds more or less simultaneously at a given chain segment. This requirement indicates a statistical improvement in stability well out of proportion to what has, to date, been realized in practice from such compounds.

REFERENCES

1958

1. C. S. Marvel and J. Hartzell, Preparation and Aromatization of Poly-1,3-cyclohexadiene, *J. Am. Chem. Soc.*, **81**:448.
2. W. Postelnek, Search for High Temperature Elastomer, *Ind. Eng. Chem.* **50**:1602.
3. W. Postelnek, L. T. Coleman, and A. M. Lovelace, Fluorine-containing Polymers, I: Fluorinated Vinyl Polymers with Functional Groups, Condensation Polymers, and Styrene Polymers, *Fortschr. Hochpolymer. Forsch.*, vol. 1, no. 1.

1959

4. V. V. Korshak, G. N. Chelnokova, and M. A. Shkolina, Synthesis of Poly(4-amino-1,2,4-triazoles), *Isv. Akad. Nauk SSSR, Otd. Khim. Nauk* 1959:925–926.
5. P. W. Morgan and S. L. Kwolek, Interfacial Polycondensation, II., *J. Polymer Sci.* 40:299–327.

1961

6. C. J. Abshire and C. S. Marvel, Some Oxadiazole and Triazole Polymers, *Makromol. Chem.* 44–46:388–397.
7. J. E. Mulvaney and C. S. Marvel, Disiloxane Benzimidazole Polymers, *J. Polymer Sci.* 50:541–547.
8. J. E. Mulvaney and C. S. Marvel, Synthesis of Polymers Containing Reoccurring Thiazole Rings, *J. Org. Chem.* 26:95–97.

1962

9. G. P. Brown et al., Synthesis and Evaluation of Thermally Stable Polymers, WADD TR-61-255, part II, May.
10. L. Gilman et al., Heat Resistant Laminating Resins, WADC TR-59-328, part III, June.
11. J. E. Mulvaney et al., Polybenzborimidazolines, *J. Polymer Sci.* 62:59–72.
12. H. A. Smith and C. E. Handlovits, Phenylene Sulfide Polymers, ASD-TDR-62-322, part II, December.

1963

13. Belg. 628,618, Feb. 2.
14. L. G. Picklesimer and T. F. Saunders, Synthesis of *s*-Triazinyl Polyethers by Interfacial Condensation, AD 454 903.

1964

15. G. P. Brown and A. Goldman, Poly-*m*-phenoxylene, II: Catalyst Studies, ACS Symposium, Philadelphia, April.
16. F. Dawans et al., 2,7-Disubstituted 1,3,6,8-Tetrazopyrene and Related Polymers, *J. Polymer Sci.*, part A, vol. 2, pp. 5005–5016.
17. W. R. Dunnavant and S. Palinchak, Trends in the Development of Thermally Stable Polymers, *Battelle Tech. Rev.*, September, pp. 15–21.
18. A. H. Frazer and I. M. Sarasohn, Thermal Behavior of Polyhydrazides and Poly(1,3,4-oxadiazoles), ACS Symposium, Philadelphia, April.
19. A. H. Frazer, W. Sweeny, and F. T. Wallenberger, Poly(1,3,4-oxadiazoles): a New Class of Polymers by Cyclodehydration of Polyhydrazides, *J. Polymer Sci.*, part A, vol. 2, pp. 1157–1169.
20. A. H. Frazer and F. T. Wallenberger, Poly(1,3,4-oxadiazole) Fibers: New Fibers with Superior High Temperature Resistance, *J. Polymer Sci.*, part A, vol. 2, pp. 1171–1179.
21. G. P. de Gaudemaris and B. J. Sillion, New Polymers Obtained by Polyheterocyclization: Polyquinoxalines, *J. Polymer Sci.*, part B, vol. 2, pp. 203–207.
22. G. de Gaudemaris, B. J. Sillion, and J. Preve, Heat-stable Polymers, I; Polyquinoxalines, *Bull. Soc. Chim. France* 1964:1793.
23. P. M. Hergenrother et al., High Temperature Structural Adhesives, AD 602 679.
24. E. A. Hoess and E. L. O'Brien, Synthesis of Polyamides Containing *s*-Triazine Rings, AD 433 664.

25. I. L. Kotyarevskii, M. P. Terpugova, and E. K. Andrievskaya, Highly Unsaturated Polymers, X: Polymers with Azo Groups in the Chain, *Izv. Akad. Nauk SSSR Ser. Khim.* **1964**(10): 1854–60.

26. T. Kubota and R. Nakanishi, Preparation of Fully Aromatic Polybenzoxazoles, *J. Polymer Sci.*, part B, vol. 2, pp. 655–659.

27. V. C. R. McLoughlin and J. Thrower, Fluoroaromatic Polymers, Royal Aircraft Establishment, London, Report CPM 11, AD 449 455.

28. H. F. Marks and S. H. Atlas, Principles of Polymer Stability, SPE Symposium on Stability of Plastics, Washington, D.C., June.

29. C. S. Marvel, Thermally Stable Polymers with Aromatic Recurring Units, *SPE J.*, March, pp. 219–226.

30. J. E. Moore, Polybenzyls and Polyphenethyls from the Friedel-Crafts Reaction, ACS Symposium, Philadelphia, April.

31. J. K. Stille and J. R. Williamson, Polyquinoxalines, *J. Polymer Sci.*, part A, vol. 2, p. 3867.

32. J. K. Stille and J. R. Williamson, Polyquinoxalines, *J. Polymer Sci.*, part B, vol. 2, p. 209.

33. S. Tsunawaka and C. C. Price, Preparation of Polyarylenesulfides, *J. Polymer Sci.*, part A, vol. 2, p. 1511.

1965

34. H. R. Allock and R. L. Kugel, Synthesis of High Polymeric Alkoxy- and Aryloxyphosphoni-triles, *J. Am. Chem. Soc.* **18**:4216–4217.

35. Aromatic Polymers Resist Space Environments, *C&E News*, May 17, pp. 38–39.

36. T. F. Banigan, New Approaches to High-heat Stable Resins from Trimeric and Tetrameric Phosphonitrilic Chlorides, Preprint of Contributed Papers on Polymer Chemistry, Western Regional Meeting of ACS, Los Angeles, November.

37. V. L. Bell and G. F. Pezdirtz, Poly(imidazopyrrolones): a New Route to Ladder Polymers, *J. Polymer Sci.*, part B, vol. 3, p. 977; also, NASA TN D = 3148.

38. N. Bilow and L. J. Miller, Synthesis of Fusible Branched Polyphenylenes, Proceedings of the Symposium on High Temperature Polymers: Synthesis and Degradation, Western Regional Meeting of ACS, Los Angeles, November.

39. B. P. Block et al., Recent Developments in the Study of Poly(metal phosphenates), ACS Symposium, Atlantic City, N.J., September.

40. S. D. Bruck, Thermal Degradation of Piperazine Polyamides, I, ACS Symposium, Atlantic City, N.J., September.

41. J. M. Craven and T. M. Fischer, Film-forming Polythiazoles, *J. Polymer Sci.*, part B, vol. 3, no. 1, pp. 35–37.

42. A. D. Delman, A. A. Stein, and B. B. Simms, Synthesis and Thermal Stability of Structurally Related Aromatic Schiff Bases and Acid Amides, Proceedings of the Symposium on High Temperature Polymers: Synthesis and Degradation, Western Regional Meeting of ACS, Los Angeles, November.

43. H. K. Garner et al., Phosphinitrile Polymers Stable at High Temperatures, AD 612 217.

44. J. Green, Thermal Stability of Carborane-containing Polymers, Proceedings of the Symposium on High Temperature Polymers: Synthesis and Degradation, Western Regional Meeting of ACS, Los Angeles, November.

45. P. M. Hergenrother and H. H. Levine, Polybenzothiazoles, II: a New Synthetic Approach and Preliminary Stability Evaluation, Proceedings of the Symposium on High Temperature Polymers: Synthesis and Degradation, Western Regional Meeting of ACS, Los Angeles, November.

46. P. M. Hergenrother, W. Wrasidlo, and H. H. Levine, Polybenzothiazoles, I: Synthesis and Preliminary Stability Evaluation, *J. Polymer Sci.*, part A, vol. 3, pp. 1665–1674.

47. Heterofluoropolymers Aim for Commercial Use, *C&E News*, Oct. 11, pp. 80–81.

48. "Inorganic Benzene" Makes Its Bid, *Chem. Week*, Feb. 20, pp. 97, 98, 100.

49. Y. Iwakura, K. Uno, and S. Hara, Poly-1,3,4-oxadiazoles, I: Polyphenylene-1,3,4-oxadiazoles, *J. Polymer Sci.*, part A, vol. 3, p. 45.

50. F. X. Maggio and C. O. Wilson, Jr., Preparation and Properties of Some Polyborphosphane Resins, Proceedings of the Symposium on High Temperature Polymers: Synthesis and Degradation, Western Regional Meeting of ACS, Los Angeles, November.

51. C. S. Marvel, Thermally Stable Polymers, Proceedings of the Symposium on High Temperature Polymers: Synthesis and Degradation, Western Regional Meeting of ACS, Los Angeles, November.

52. C. G. Overberger and S. Fujimoto, Polycycloaddition of Terephthalonitrile Oxide, Proceedings of the Symposium on High Temperature Polymers: Synthesis and Degradation, Western Regional Meeting of ACS, Los Angeles, November.

53. S. Popetti et al., The Preparation of Poly-*m*-carboranylene-siloxanes, ACS Symposium, Atlantic City, N.J., September.

54. J. Preston and W. B. Black, New High Temperature Polymers: Ordered Heterocyclic Copolymers, ACS Symposium, Atlantic City, N.J., September.

55. J. K. Stille, J. R. Williamson, and F. E. Arnold, Polyquinoxalines, *J. Polymer Sci.*, part A, vol. 3, p. 1013.

56. R. L. Taylor, High Temperature Polyamine Resins, AD 461 106.

57. L. A. Wall et al., Polymerization and Pyrolysis of Poly-1,2-dihydronaphthalene, ACS Symposium, Atlantic City, N.J., September.

1966

58. H. C. Bach, Oxidative Coupling of Primary Aromatic Diamines: Aromatic Azopolymers, ACS Meeting, New York, September.

59. J. G. Colson, R. J. Michal, and R. M. Paufler, Poly(benzoylenebenzimidazoles), *J. Polymer Sci.*, part A, vol. 1, pp. 4, 59.

60. A. H. Frazer and W. P. Fitzgerald, Aromatic Poly-1,3,4-thiadiazole Fibers, ACS Winter Meeting, Phoenix, Ariz., January.

61. A. H. Frazer and T. A. Reed, Aromatic Poly-1,3,4-oxadiazole Fibers, ACS Winter Meeting, Phoenix, Ariz., January.

62. W. P. Gloor, Fiber Formation and Drawing of Polybisbenzimidazobenzophenanthroline, ACS Meeting, New York, September.

63. J. R. Holsten and M. R. Lilyquist, Poly(phenylene)triazoles: New Thermally Stable Fibers, ACS Winter Meeting, Phoenix, Ariz., January.

64. W. J. Pummer and J. M. Antonucci, Aromatic Fluorocarbon Polymers, ACS Meeting, New York, September.

65. R. D. Stacy, N. P. Loire, and H. H. Levine, Polybenzoxazoles, I: Homocondensation of 3-Amino-4-hydroxybenzonitrile and Cocondensation of 3,3'-Dihydroxybenzidine with Isophthalamide, ACS Winter Meeting, Phoenix, Ariz., January.

66. J. K. Stille and F. E. Arnold, Polyquinoxalines, III, *J. Polymer Sci.*, part A, vol. 4, p. 551.

67. J. K. Stille and E. Mainen, Ladder Polyquinoxalines, *Polymer Letters* 4:39.

68. J. Thrower and M. A. White, Perfluoro-meta-polyphenylenes, ACS Meeting, New York, September.

69. R. L. Van Deusen, O. K. Goins, and A. J. Sicree, Some Properties of Polybenzimidazobenzophenanthrolines, ACS Meeting, New York, September.

1967

70. V. L. Bell and R. A. Jewell, Properties of Polyimidazopyrrolones, ACS Spring Meeting, Miami Beach, Fla., April.

71. P. M. Hergenrother and H. H. Levine, Phenyl Substituted Polyquinoxalines, ACS Spring Meeting, Miami Beach, Fla., April.

72. H. Muramol, F. W. Harris, R. O. Rakutis, J. K. Stille, Diels-Alder Polymerizations: Polymers Containing Controlled Aromatic Segments, ACS Spring Meeting, Miami Beach, Fla., April.

73. M. Okada and C. S. Marvel, Ladder and Partial Ladder Heterocyclic Aromatic Polymers with Quinoxaline and Thiazine or Oxazine Recurring Units, ACS Spring Meeting, Miami Beach, Fla., April.

74. J. K. Stille, E. L. Mainen, M. E. Freeburger, and F. W. Harris, Ladder Polymers: Simultaneous and Two-step Condensation Polymerization, ACS Spring Meeting, Miami Beach, Fla., April.

Index